Centre for Innovation in Mathematics Teaching
University of Exeter

FURTHER STATISTICS

| **Writers** | John White |
| | Roger Williamson |

| **Editor** | David Burghes |

Assistant	Ann Ault
Editors	Nigel Price
	Paul White

Heinemann Educational

Heinemann Educational
a division of Heinemann Educational Books Ltd.
Halley Court, Jordan Hill, Oxford OX2 8EJ

OXFORD LONDON EDINBURGH
MADRID ATHENS BOLOGNA PARIS
MELBOURNE SYDNEY AUCKLAND SINGAPORE
TOKYO IBADAN NAIROBI HARARE
GABORONE PORTSMOUTH NH (USA)

ISBN 0 435 51607 8

First Published 1994

© CIMT, 1994

Typseset by ISCA Press, CIMT, University of Exeter

Printed in Great Britain by The Bath Press, Avon

FURTHER STATISTICS

This is one of the texts which has been written to support the AEB Mathematics syllabus for A and AS level awards first available in Summer 1996.

The development of these texts has been coordinated at the

Centre for Innovation in Mathematics Teaching

at Exeter University in association with Heinemann and AEB.

The overall development of these texts has been directed by David Burghes and coordinated by Nigel Price.

Enquiries regarding this project and further details of the work of the Centre should be addressed to

Margaret Roddick
CIMT
School of Education
University of Exeter
Heavitree Road
EXETER EX1 2LU.

CONTENTS

PREFACE

Statistical techniques are now used throughout modern industrial societies for analysis of data, to explain observations, and to help make rational decisions. Modern communication techniques have also meant a widespread use of statistical ideas and techniques in presenting and analysing data for public consumption. For example, the way election night results are presented has been revolutionised over the past few decades with all sorts of technical props at the fingertips of the presenters. But it should be remembered that statistics alone does not solve problems and indeed can come up with the wrong conclusions. This was borne out by the failure of political pollsters to correctly predict the result of the 1992 election in the U.K.

Nevertheless this is just one instance of where statistical analysis did not provide correct answers; there are many instances when it does, and perhaps more importantly, instances where statistical analysis helps decision making. We live in a stochastic world, that is, one that is not predetermined. Governments and local authorities use statistical techniques for planning, developments, allocating resources, controlling the economy and indeed gauging public opinion on topical isues. The range and scope of the techniques available has increased considerably over the past few decades, and most importantly the technology is now available to cope, relatively cheaply, with large amounts of data. Even the smallest business can afford its own computing power which can be used to monitor and predict future trading patterns.

This text has been written with the aim of giving readers a thorough understanding of statistical ideas and concepts, beyond those met in the *Statistics* text. It is not a recipe of what to do - there are plenty of good texts that fit that bill already - but attempts to show why a particular technique is used as well as explaining how to use it. We want readers to get a feel for statistics - both its potential and its limitations. There are many worthy techniques not included in this text, but readers gaining a sound understanding of probability and statistics should have little difficulty in coping with these techniques if they are needed later.

This text has been produced for students and includes examples, activities and exercises. It should be noted that the activities are **not** optional but are an important part of the learning philosophy in which you are expected to take a very active part. The text integrates

- **Exposition**   in which the concept is explained;
- **Examples**   which show how the techniques are used;
- **Activities**   which either introduce new concepts or reinforce techniques;
- **Discussion Points**   which are essentially 'stop and think' points, where discussion with other students and teachers will be helpful;
- **Exercises**   at the end of most sections in order to provide further practice;
- **Miscellaneous Exercises**   at the end of most chapters , providing opportunities for reinforcement of the main points of the chapter.

Discussion points are written in a special typeface as illustrated here.

Note that answers to the exercises are given at the back of the book. You are expected to have a calculator available throughout your study of this text and occasionally to have access to a computer.

This text is one of a series of texts written specially for the new AEB Mathematics syllabus for A and AS level coursework. The framework is shown opposite. Essentially each module corresponds to an AS level syllabus and two suitable modules provide the syllabus for an A level award. Optional coursework is available for students taking any of the three applied modules

Mechanics, Statistics and Discrete Mathematics.

Full details of the scheme are available from AEB, Stag Hill House, Guildford GU2 5XJ.

We hope that you enjoy working through the book. We would be very grateful for comments, criticisms and notification of any errors. These should be sent to

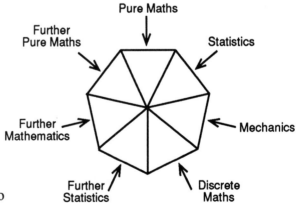

Margaret Roddick
CIMT
School of Education
University of Exeter
EXETER EX1 2LU.

ACKNOWLEDGEMENTS

This text has been written for the new AEB Mathematics syllabus
and assessment, which will be examined for the first time in
Summer 1996. I am grateful for the continued support from AEB
through its mathematics officer, Jackie Bawden, and to the staff at
Heinemann, particularly Philip Ellaway.

I am grateful to John White and Roger Williamson for writing
the text, to Nigel Price for help with editing, and to Ann Ault and
Paul White for checking the calculations. Finally, I am indebted
to the staff at CIMT who work with dedication and good humour
despite the pressure which I continually put them under; in
particular, to Liz Holland, Margaret Roddick and Ann Tylisczuk
for producing camera ready copy.

David Burghes

(Project Director)

1 CONTINUOUS PROBABILITY DISTRIBUTIONS

Objectives

After studying this chapter you should

- know the definition of $E(X)$ and $E(g(X))$ for both discrete and continuous distributions;

- know the definition of mean and variance in terms of expectations;

- be able to do calculations involving linear combinations of independent normal random variables;

- be able to calculate probabilities using the exponential distribution.

1.0   Introduction

In the text *Statistics*, continuous probability distributions were introduced in Chapter 7. Probability was represented by the area under a curve, known as the probability density function.
A probability density function of a random variable, X, must be non-negative for all values of X and the total area under the curve must be 1.

If the **probability density function** is denoted $f(x)$ then the probability that an observed value of X lies between a and b is given by

$$\boxed{P(a < x < b) = \int_a^b f(x)dx}$$

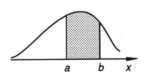

Also note that

$$\int_{-\infty}^{\infty} f(x)dx = 1.$$

The most important continuous distribution and indeed the most important distribution of any kind in statistics is the normal distribution. This was introduced in *Statistics*, Chapter 8.
A familiarity with the normal distribution is essential for an understanding of what follows.

This chapter starts by drawing together definitions and laws of expectations and variances for discrete and continuous distributions. Many of the ideas have already been met in *Statistics*. Some well known results are proved. Students may prefer to omit the proofs, particularly at first reading. It is possible to leave sections of this chapter, which deal with some of the more mathematical ideas in Statistics, until later in the course if preferred.

1.1 Expectation

For a discrete probability distribution

$$E(X) = \sum_x xP(X = x)$$

If $g(x)$ is a function of x then

$$E(g(x)) = \sum_x g(x)P(X = x)$$

If, for example, the random variable X can take the values 1, 2 or 3 with probabilities 0.2, 0.3 and 0.5 respectively, then

$$E(X) = 0.2 \times 1 + 0.3 \times 2 + 0.5 \times 3 = 2.3$$

$$E(\sqrt{X}) = 0.2 \times \sqrt{1} + 0.3 \times \sqrt{2} + 0.5 \times \sqrt{3} = 1.49.$$

For a continuous distribution

$$E(X) = \int_{-\infty}^{\infty} xf(x)dx$$

and

$$E(g(X)) = \int_{-\infty}^{\infty} g(x)f(x)dx$$

Example

The random variable X has probability density function $\frac{3}{4}x(2-x)$

for $0 < x < 2$ Find $E(X)$ and $E\left(\frac{1}{X}\right)$.

Solution

$$E(X) = \int_0^2 \frac{3}{4}x^2(2-x)dx$$

$$= \frac{3}{4}\int_0^2 (2x^2 - x^3)dx$$

$$= \frac{3}{4}\left[\frac{2}{3}x^3 - \frac{x^4}{4}\right]_0^2$$

$$= \frac{3}{4}\left(\frac{16}{3} - 4\right)$$

$$= 1$$

and
$$E\left(\frac{1}{X}\right) = \int_0^2 \frac{1}{x}\cdot\frac{3}{4}x(2-x)dx$$

$$= \int_0^2 \frac{3}{4}(2-x)dx$$

$$= \frac{3}{4}\left[2x - \frac{x^2}{2}\right]_0^2$$

$$= 1.5$$

1.2 Mean and variance

For any random variable whether continuous or discrete, the mean is defined to be $E(X)$ and this is usually denoted by μ. The variance is defined to be

$$E(X - E(X))^2$$

and this is usually denoted σ^2

$$\boxed{\sigma^2 = E\left([X-\mu]^2\right)}$$

An equivalent formula is

$$\boxed{\sigma^2 = E(X^2) - \mu^2} \quad \text{(see section 1.4)}$$

Why is the second formula for σ^2 preferred for calculations?

The next example is to revise some of the ideas introduced in the text *Statistics*, Chapter 7.

Example

A charity group raises funds by collecting waste paper. A skip-full will contain an amount, X, of other materials such as plastic bags and rubber bands. X may be regarded as a random variable with probability density function

$$f(x) = k(x-1)(4-x) \qquad 1 < x < 4$$

$$= 0 \qquad\qquad \text{otherwise.}$$

(All numerical values in this question are in units of 100 kg.)

(a) Show that $k = \dfrac{2}{9}$.

(b) Find the mean and standard deviation of X.

(c) Find the probability that X exceeds 3.5.

A skip-full may normally be sold for £250 but if X exceeds 3.5 only £125 will be paid. Find the expected value of a skip-full.

Alternatively the paper may be sorted before being placed in the skip. This will ensure a very low value of X and a skip-full may then be sold for £310. However the effort put into sorting means that 25per cent fewer skips-full will be sold. Advise the charity whether or not to sort the paper.   (AEB)

Solution

(a) $\displaystyle\int_1^4 k(x-1)(4-x)dx = 1$

$\displaystyle k\int_1^4 \left(-x^2 + 5x - 4\right)dx = 1$

$\displaystyle k\left[\frac{-x^3}{3} + \frac{5x^2}{2} - 4x\right]_1^4 = 1$

$\displaystyle k\left[\frac{8}{3} - \left(-\frac{11}{6}\right)\right] = 1$

$\qquad 4.5k = 1$

$\qquad \dfrac{9}{2}k = 1 \;\Rightarrow\; k = \dfrac{2}{9}$

(b) Mean, $\displaystyle E(X) = \int_1^4 \frac{2}{9}x(x-1)(4-x)dx$

$\displaystyle = \frac{2}{9}\left(\int_1^4 -x^3 + 5x^2 - 4x\right)dx$

$\displaystyle = \frac{2}{9}\left[\frac{-x^4}{4} + \frac{5x^3}{3} - \frac{4x^2}{2}\right]_1^4$

$\displaystyle = \frac{2}{9}\left(\frac{32}{3} - \left(-\frac{7}{12}\right)\right)$

$\displaystyle = 2.5$

$$E\left(X^2\right) = \int_1^4 \frac{2}{9}x^2(x-1)(4-x)dx$$

$$= \frac{2}{9}\int_1^4 \left(-x^4 + 5x^3 - 4x^2\right)dx$$

$$= \frac{2}{9}\left[-\frac{x^5}{5} + \frac{5x^4}{4} - \frac{4x^3}{3}\right]_1^4$$

$$= \frac{2}{9}\left(\frac{448}{15} - \left(-\frac{17}{60}\right)\right)$$

$$= 6.7$$

Hence

$$\text{variance} = E\left(X^2\right) - \mu^2 = 6.7 - 2.5^2 = 0.45$$

and

$$\text{standard deviation} = \sqrt{\text{variance}} = 0.671.$$

(c) Probability that X exceeds 3.5 is given by

$$P(X > 3.5) = \int_{3.5}^4 \frac{2}{9}(x-1)(4-x)dx$$

$$= \frac{2}{9}\left[-\frac{x^3}{3} + \frac{5x^2}{2} - 4x\right]_{3.5}^4$$

$$= \frac{2}{9}\left(\frac{8}{3} - \frac{7}{3}\right)$$

$$= 0.0741$$

(d) Expected value of a skip-full

$$= £125 \times 0.0741 + £250 \times (1 - 0.0741)$$
$$= £241$$

For each skip-full of unsorted material only 0.75 skips-full of paper would be obtained after sorting. This would be worth
$$0.75 \times £310 = £232.5$$

Thus the charity will make more money in the long run if the paper is not sorted.

Exercise 1A

1. A temporary roundabout is installed at a crossroads. The time, X minutes, which vehicles have to wait before entering the crossroads has probability density function

$$f(x) = 0.8 - 0.32x \qquad 0 < x < 2.5$$
$$= 0 \qquad \text{otherwise}$$

Find the mean and standard deviation of X.

(AEB)

2. The random variable, Y, has probability density function

$$f(y) = k(8 - 2y) \qquad 0 < x < 4$$
$$= 0 \qquad \text{otherwise}$$

(a) Verify that $k = 0.0625$ and that the median is 1.172.

(b) Find the mean and standard deviation of Y.

(c) What is the probability that the mean of a random sample of size 50 from this distribution will lie between the mean and the median? (AEB)

3. A technique for measuring the density of a silicon compound is a random variable, X, with probability density function

$$f(x) = k \qquad 0.04 < x < 0.04$$
$$= 0 \qquad \text{otherwise}$$

(a) Find the value of k.

(b) Find the mean and standard deviation of X.

(c) Find the probability that the error is between -0.03 and 0.01.

(d) Find the probability that the magnitude of the error is greater than 0.035.

1.3 Laws of expectation

The following laws apply to expectations of both discrete and continuous random variables.

(i)

$$\boxed{E(a + bX) = a + bE(X)}$$

where a and b are constants and X is a random variable.

(ii)

$$\boxed{E(X + Y) = E(X) + E(Y)}$$

where X and Y are any random variables.

Laws (i) and (ii) may be extended to a more general form

(iii)

$$\boxed{\begin{aligned} E(a_1X_1 + a_2X_2 + \ \dots + a_nX_n) \\ = a_1E(X_1) + a_2E(X_2) + \ \dots + a_nE(X_n) \end{aligned}}$$

when $X_1, X_2 \dots, X_n$ are random variables and $a_1, a_2 \dots, a_n$ are constants.

(iv)

$$\boxed{E(XY) = E(X)E(Y)}$$

when X and Y are independent random variables .

Note that (iv) is only true if X and Y are independent.

1.4 Some results for variances

The laws of expectation together with the definition of variance can be used to derive some interesting and useful results. In the following $V(X)$ is used to denote the variance of X and $E(X) = \mu$ and $V(X) = \sigma^2$.

Note: Brief proofs are included but will not be tested in the AEB examination and may be omitted.

(i)
$$\boxed{V(X) = E\left([X - \mu]^2\right)}$$

$$= E\left(X^2\right) - 2\mu E(X) + \mu^2$$

$$= E\left(X^2\right) - 2\mu^2 + \mu^2$$

$$= E\left(X^2\right) - \mu^2$$

This result has been used in *Statistics* and in Section 1.2 above.

(ii)
$$\boxed{V(a + bX) = b^2 V(X)}$$

where a and b are constants.

Since

$$E(a + bX) = a + bE(X)$$

$$= a + b\mu,$$

then

$$V(a + bX) = E\left([a + bX - a - b\mu]^2\right)$$

$$= E\left(b^2[X - \mu]^2\right)$$

$$= b^2 E\left([X - \mu]^2\right)$$

$$= b^2 V(X)$$

(iii) If X and Y are **independent** random variables

$$\boxed{V(X \pm Y) = V(X) + V(Y)}$$

Note: (a) this is only true if X and Y are independent;

(b) the left hand side has a sign but the variances are always added. Clearly it would not make sense to take one variance from another as this could lead to a negative result. A negative variance is impossible.

The proof follows from

$$E(X+Y) = E(X)+E(Y)$$

$$= \mu_x + \mu_y, \text{ say}$$

$$V(X \pm Y) = E\left(\left[X \pm Y - \{\mu_x \pm \mu_y\}\right]^2\right)$$

$$= E\left(\left[\{X - \mu_x\} \pm \{Y - \mu_y\}\right]^2\right)$$

$$= E\left(\left[X - \mu_x\right]^2\right) + E\left(\left[X - \mu_y\right]^2 \pm 2E\left(\left[X - \mu_x\right]\left[Y - \mu_y\right]\right)\right)$$

$$= V(X) + V(Y) \pm 2E(X - \mu_x)E(Y - \mu_x)$$

since X and Y are independent.

Now

$$E(X - \mu_x) = E(X) - \mu_x$$

$$= \mu_x - \mu_x$$

$$= 0$$

Hence

$$V(X \pm Y) = V(X) + V(Y).$$

(iv)   The results above can be extended to

$$\boxed{\begin{array}{l} V(a_1 X_1 + a_2 X_2 + ... + a_n X_n) \\ = a_1{}^2 V(X_1) + a_2{}^2 V(X_2) + ... + a_n{}^2 V(X_n) \end{array}}$$

where $a_1, a_2, ... a_n$ are constants and $X_1, X_2, ... X_n$ are **independent** random variables.

1.5   Distribution of the sample mean

The results above can be used to derive the mean and variance of a sample mean.

(a)   If $\overline{X}$ is the mean of a random sample of n observations of the random variable X, then

$$E(\overline{X}) = E\left(\frac{[X_1 + X_2 + ... + X_n]}{n}\right)$$

where X_i denotes the ith observation in the sample, giving

$$E(\overline{X}) = \frac{1}{n}\left(E[X_1] + E[X_2] + \dots + E[X_n]\right)$$

$$= \frac{1}{n}(\mu + \mu + \dots + \mu)$$

$$= \frac{1}{n}(n\mu)$$

$$= \mu$$

(b) $V(\overline{X}) = E(\overline{X} - \mu)^2$ since the mean of $\overline{X}$ has just been shown to be μ.

$$V(\overline{X}) = V\left(\frac{1}{n}(X_1 + X_2 + \dots + X_n)\right)$$

$$= \frac{1}{n^2}\left(V(X_1) + V(X_2) + \dots + V(X_n)\right)$$

$$= \frac{1}{n^2}\left(\sigma^2 + \sigma^2 + \dots + \sigma^2\right)$$

$$= \frac{1}{n^2}\left(n\sigma^2\right)$$

$$= \frac{\sigma^2}{n}$$

You have now shown that the sample mean $\overline{X}$ is distributed with mean μ and variance $\dfrac{\sigma^2}{n}$, a result which has been used frequently in *Statistics*.

1.6 Unbiased estimate of variance

The results above can be used to find an unbiased estimate of the variance.

First consider

$$\Sigma(X_i - \mu)^2 = \Sigma\left([X_i - \overline{X}] + [\overline{X} - \mu]\right)^2$$

$$= \Sigma(X_i - \overline{X})^2 + \Sigma(\overline{X} - \mu)^2 + 2\Sigma(X_i - \overline{X})(\overline{X} - \mu)$$

Now $\quad \Sigma(X_i - \overline{X})(\overline{X} - \mu) = (\overline{X} - \mu)\Sigma(X_i - \overline{X})$

$$= (\overline{X} - \mu)([\Sigma X_i] - n\overline{X})$$

$$= (\overline{X} - \mu)(\Sigma X_i - \Sigma X_i)$$

$$= 0$$

Hence

$$\Sigma(X_i - \mu)^2 = \Sigma(X_i - \overline{X})^2 + \Sigma(\overline{X} - \mu)^2$$

$$= \Sigma(X_i - \overline{X})^2 + n(\overline{X} - \mu)^2.$$

Taking expectations of both sides gives

$$\Sigma E\left([X_i - \mu]^2\right) = E\left(\Sigma[X_i - \overline{X}]^2\right) + nE\left([\overline{X} - \mu]^2\right)$$

$$\Rightarrow \qquad n\sigma^2 = E\left(\Sigma[X_i - \overline{X}]^2\right) + \frac{n\sigma^2}{n}.$$

Hence

$$E\left(\Sigma[X_i - \overline{X}]^2\right) = (n-1)\sigma^2$$

or $\qquad \dfrac{E\left(\Sigma[X_i - \overline{X}]^2\right)}{(n-1)} = \sigma^2.$

The expression on the left hand side was met in *Statistics* and is denoted $\hat{\sigma}^2$. You have just shown that $E(\hat{\sigma}^2) = \sigma^2$. $\hat{\sigma}^2$ is said to be an unbiased estimator of σ^2 and this is why it is generally used to estimate σ^2. Note however that $\hat{\sigma}$ is not an unbiased estimator of σ.

Why is $\hat{\sigma}$ not an unbiased estimator of σ?

1.7   Distribution of a linear combination of independent normal random variables

The results in Sections 1.3 and 1.4 cover the mean and variance of linear combinations of independent random variables. If the variables are all normally distributed then a linear combination of them will also be normally distributed. The proof of this is beyond the scope of this book.

To take a simple example, in the mass production of jars of jam the weight of jam put in each jar is a normally distributed random variable, X, with mean 456 g and standard deviation 4 g. The weight of the jar (including the lid) is an independent normally distributed random variable, Y, with mean 35 g and standard deviation 3 g.

The total weight of the jam plus the jar is $X + Y$.

The mean of $X + Y = E(X + Y) = E(X) + E(Y) = 456 + 35 = 491$ g

The variance of $X + Y = V(X) + V(Y) = 4^2 + 3^2 = 25$.

The standard deviation will be $\sqrt{25} = 5$ g.

Since the two variables are independently normally distributed the distribution of the total weight will also be normal.

A child opens a new jar of jam and takes a spoonful out. The weight of jam in the spoon is a random variable, Z, with mean 22 g standard deviation 2 g. Z is independent of X.

The weight of jam remaining in the jar is $X - Z$.

The mean is $E(X) - E(Z) = 456 - 22 = 434$ g.

The variance of $X - Z$ is $V(X) + V(Z) = 4^2 + 2^2 = 20$.

The standard deviation is $\sqrt{20} = 4.47$ g.

Since X and Z are independently normally distributed the distribution of $X - Z$ is also normal.

Example

A machine produces rubber balls whose diameters are normally distributed with mean 5.50 cm and standard deviation 0.08 cm.

(a) What proportion of balls will have diameters
 (i)   less than 5.60 cm,
 (ii) between 5.34 and 5.44 cm?

(b) The balls are packed in cylindrical tubes whose internal diameters are normally distributed with mean 5.70 cm and standard deviation 0.12 cm. If a ball, selected at random, is placed in a tube, selected at random, what is the distribution of the clearance? (The clearance is the internal diameter of the tube minus the diameter of the ball.) What is the probability that the clearance is between 0.05 cm and 0.25 cm?

(AEB)

Solution

(a) (i) $z = \dfrac{(5.60 - 5.50)}{0.08} = 1.25$.

Using Normal tables, the probability of being less than 5.60 cm is 0.894.

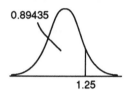

(ii) $z_1 = \dfrac{(5.34 - 5.50)}{0.08} = -2.0$

$z_2 = \dfrac{(5.44 - 5.50)}{0.08} = -0.75$.

Hence the probability of being between 5.34 cm and 5.44 cm is given by

$0.97725 - 0.77337 = 0.204$.

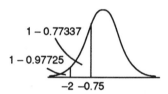

(b) If X is the diameter of the ball and Y is the diameter of the tube the clearance is $Y - X$. This will be normally distributed with

$$\text{mean} = 5.70 - 5.50 = 0.20$$

$$\text{variance} = 0.08^2 + 0.12^2 = 0.0208$$

$$\text{standard deviation} = 0.1442.$$

To calculate the probability that the clearance is between 0.05 cm and 0.25 cm you first find

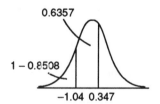

$$z_1 = \dfrac{(0.05 - 0.20)}{0.1442} = -1.040$$

$$z_2 = \dfrac{(0.25 - 0.20)}{0.1442} = -0.347$$

so that probability of the clearance between 0.05 cm and 0.25 cm is given by

$$0.6357 - (1 - 0.8508) = 0.4865.$$

Note: Interpolation has been used in reading the normal tables, but the effect on the final answer is small.

Example

A baker makes digestive biscuits whose masses are normally distributed with mean 24.0 g and standard deviation 1.9 g. The biscuits are packed by hand into packets of 25.

(i)   Assuming the biscuits included in each packet are a random sample from the population, what is the distribution of the total mass of biscuit in a packet and what is the probability that it lies between 598 g and 606 g?

(ii) Ten packets of biscuits are placed in a box. What is the probability that the total mass of biscuit in the box lies between 6010 g and 6060 g?

(iii) A new packer was including 26 biscuits in each packet. What is the probability that a packet selected at random from those containing 25 biscuits would contain a greater mass of biscuits than a packet selected at random from those containing 26 biscuits?   (AEB)

Solution

(i)   Since the sample is random the masses of the 25 biscuits included in the packet will be independent of each other. The distribution of the total mass will therefore be normal.

The mean mass of the biscuits in the packet will be
$24 + 24 + \ldots + 24 = 25 \times 24 = 600\,\text{g}$.

The variance of the total mass will be
$1.9^2 + 1.9^2 + \ldots + 1.9^2 = 25 \times 1.9^2 = 90.25$,

giving a standard deviation $= 9.5$ g.

The distribution is $N\left(600,\ 9.5^2\right)$.

To find the probability the total mass lies between 598 g and 606 g, note that

$$z_1 = \frac{(598 - 600)}{9.5} = -0.211$$

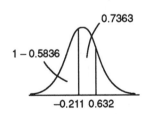

$$z_2 = \frac{(606 - 600)}{9.5} = 0.632.$$

Probability between 598 g and 606 g

$$= 0.7363 - (1 - 0.5836) = 0.320.$$

(ii) Ten packets of biscuits are placed in a box. Provided their masses are independent the total mass will be normally distributed with mean $10 \times 600 = 6000$ g.

The variance will be $10 \times 90.25 = 902.5$ and the standard deviation $\sqrt{902.5} = 30.04$ g. To calculate the probability between 6010 g and 6060 g,

$$z_1 = \frac{(6010 - 6000)}{30.04} = 0.333$$

$$z_2 = \frac{(6060 - 6000)}{30.04} = 1.997 \, .$$

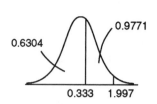

Probability of being between 6010 g and 6060 g

$$= 0.9771 - 0.6304 = 0.347 \, .$$

(iii) If X is the mass of biscuit in a packet containing 25 biscuits then we already know that X is N(600, 90.25). If Y is the mass of biscuit in a packet containing 26 biscuits then Y is normally distributed with mean $26 \times 24 = 624$ g and variance $26 \times 1.9^2 = 93.86$.

The difference $Y - X$ is normally distributed with

mean $= 624 - 600 = 24$ g,

variance $= 90.25 + 93.86 = 184.11$,

standard deviation $= \sqrt{184.11} = 13.57$.

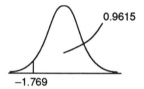

A packet containing 25 biscuits will weigh more than a packet containing 26 biscuits if $Y - X$ is negative, i.e. $Y - X < 0$.

Thus

$$z = \frac{(0 - 24)}{13.57} = -1.769 \, .$$

This gives the probability of this occurring as

$$1 - 0.9615 = 0.0385 \, .$$

Exercise 1B

1. A dispenser discharges an amount of soft drink which is normally distributed with mean 475 ml and standard deviation 20 ml.

   (a) What is the distribution of the total amount in two independent drinks?

   (b) If the capacity of the cups into which the drink is dispensed is normally distributed with mean 500 ml and standard deviation 30 ml, what is the distribution of the difference between the capacity of a cup and the amount dispensed?
   Assume the two are independent.

2. The weights of pieces of home made fudge are normally distributed with mean 34 g and standard deviation 5 g.

   (a) A bag contains 15 pieces of fudge chosen at random. What is the distribution of the total weight of fudge in the bag? What is the probability that the total weight is between 490 g and 540 g?

   (b) What is the probability that the total weight of fudge in a bag containing 15 pieces exceeds that in another bag containing 16 pieces? (AEB)

3. Audrey is a regular customer of Toto's taxis. When she rings from home the time, X, a taxi takes to arrive is normally distributed with mean 19 minutes and standard deviation 3 minutes.

   (a) (i) What is the probability of her having to wait less than 15 minutes for a taxi?

   (ii) What waiting time will be exceeded with probability 0.1?

   Audrey decides to try Blue Star taxis. The standard deviation of her waiting time, Y, is 7 minutes and the probability of Y exceeding 8 minutes is 0.97725.

   (b) Find the mean of Y, assuming a normal distribution.

   (c) What is the distribution of T where $T = X - Y$? (X and Y may be assumed independent.) If both firms were rung at the same time, what is the probability that Toto would arrive first?

   (d) In order to catch a train Audrey needs a taxi within 10 minutes. Which firm would you advise her to ring? Explain your answer.

   (AEB)

1.8   The exponential distribution

If cars passing a point on a motorway follow a Poisson distribution, the interval of time between successive cars passing follows an exponential distribution.

The exponential distribution has probability density function

$$f(x) = \begin{cases} me^{-mx} & x > 0, \text{ where } m \text{ is constant} \\ 0 & \text{otherwise} \end{cases}$$

The mean of this exponential distribution is

$$\int_0^\infty mxe^{-mx}\,dx = \left[-xe^{-mx}\right]_0^\infty - \int_0^\infty -e^{-mx}\,dx = \left[-\frac{e^{-mx}}{m}\right]_0^\infty = \frac{1}{m}$$

$$E(X^2) = \int_0^\infty mx^2 e^{-mx}\,dx = \left[-x^2 e^{-mx}\right]_0^\infty - \int_0^\infty -2xe^{-mx}\,dx = \frac{2}{m^2}$$

since we have already shown that

$$\int_0^\infty mxe^{-mx}\,dx = \frac{1}{m}\ .$$

Thus

$$V(X) = \frac{2}{m^2} - \frac{1}{m^2} = \frac{1}{m^2}.$$

Hence the standard deviation is $\dfrac{1}{m}$.

Note: the AEB syllabus requires polynomial integration only and these proofs will not be tested.

1.9 Cumulative distribution function

The probability that an observed value from the negative exponential distribution is less than x is given by

$$P(X < x) = \int_0^x me^{-mx}\,dx = \left[-e^{-mx}\right]_0^x = 1 - e^{-mx}$$

This expression is known as the **cumulative distribution function**.

It is denoted $F(x)$.

For this distribution

$$\boxed{F(x) = 1 - e^{-mx}}$$

The cumulative distribution function may be used as an alternative to integration for evaluating probabilities. If a and b are two constants and $a > b$, the probability that X takes a value between a and b is

$$\boxed{P(X < a) - P(X < b) = F(a) - F(b)}$$

For example, the interval, X seconds, between cars passing a point on a motorway follows an exponential distribution with probability density function

$$f(x) = \begin{cases} 2e^{-2x} & 0 < x \\ 0 & \text{otherwise} \end{cases}$$

(This distribution may alternatively be described as an exponential distribution with parameter 2.)

The probability that the next interval is between 1 and 2 seconds is

$$F(2) - F(1) = 1 - e^{-4} - \left(1 - e^{-2}\right) = 0.9817 - 0.8647 = 0.117.$$

You may check this result by evaluating

$$\int_1^2 2e^{-2x}\,dx.$$

The probability that the next interval is longer than 3 seconds is

$$F(\infty) - F(3) = 1 - \left(1 - e^{-6}\right) = 0.0025.$$

The probability that the next interval is less than 1.5 seconds is

$$F(1.5) - F(0) = \left(1 - e^{-3}\right) - \left(1 - e^0\right) = 0.9502.$$

This exponential distribution will have a mean of $\frac{1}{2} = 0.5$

seconds. Therefore the average number of cars passing the point

per second is $\frac{1}{0.5} = 2$.

In general the intervals between successive events from a Poisson distribution with mean m are distributed according to the exponential distribution with parameter m.

1.10 Conditional probability and the exponential distribution

Perhaps the most interesting feature of the exponential distribution is that it is 'memory less'. Using the cumulative distribution for the exponential distribution with parameter m, the probability that the next interval will last longer than a seconds is

$$F(\infty) - F(a) = 1 - \left(1 - e^{-ma}\right) = e^{-ma}.$$

The probability that the interval lasts longer than $a + b$ seconds is similarly $e^{-m(a+b)}$.

The probability that an interval lasts longer than $a + b$, given that it has already lasted a seconds, may be written

$$P(X > a + b \mid X > a).$$

Using the laws of probability
$$P\left[(X > a + b) \cap (X > a)\right] = P(X > a) \times P(X > a + b \mid X > a).$$

If an interval lasts longer than $a + b$ seconds it must have lasted longer than a seconds. Therefore

$$P\left[(X > a + b) \cap (X > a)\right] = P(X > a + b) = e^{-m(a+b)}$$

Therefore $\quad e^{-m(a+b)} = e^{-ma} P(X > a + b \mid X > a).$

i.e. $\quad P(X > a + b \mid X > a) = e^{-mb} = P(X > b).$

That is, the probability of the next event occuring within b seconds is the same whether an event has just occurred or whether the last event occurred a seconds ago.

Why is a distribution with this probability described as 'memory less'?

In the earlier example the probability that the interval between cars passing a point on a motorway would be longer than 3 seconds was calculated. The calculation would have been identical if the probability required had been that no car will pass in the next 3 seconds.

Exercise 1C

1. The interval, T minutes, between successive telephone calls to a school office follows an exponential distribution with parameter 0.2. Find the probability that the interval between the next two telephone calls will be

   (a) between 3 and 6 minutes,

   (b) between 2 and 7 muinutes,

   (c) longer than 8 minutes,

   (d) less than 10 minutes.

2. A factory worker is employed to watch a monitor and give a warning when the monitor signals that action is needed to adjust the process. The interval, X hours, between successive signals follows an exponential distribution with parameter 0.08.

   What is the probability that the interval between the next two signals is

   (a) between 10 and 20 hours,

   (b) between 6 and 16 hours

   (c) longer than 50 hours,

   (d) less than 2 hours?

   The factory worker decides to read a newspaper for a few minutes instead of watching the monitor. How long can she read for if the probability of missing a signal is to be less than 0.01?

3. The lives of electric light bulbs, T hours, follows an exponential distribution with probability distribution function

$$f(t) = \begin{cases} 0.004e^{-0.004t} & 0 < t \\ 0 & \text{otherwise} \end{cases}$$

   What is the probability that a bulb will last

   (a) between 200 and 300 hours,

   (b) between 250 and 350 hours,

   (c) more than 400 hours

   (d) less than 100 hours?

   What is the mean and standard deviation of T?

   What is the mean and standard deviation of the mean life of 225 bulbs?

   Find, approximately, the probability that the mean life of 225 bulbs will be less than 240 hours.

1.11 Miscellaneous Exercises

1. A clothing factory uses rolls of cloth for making suits. The length, in cm, of cloth wasted (because it is too short to use) at the end of each roll may be regarded as a random variable, X, with probability density function

$$f(x) = \begin{cases} \dfrac{1}{a} & 0 < x < a \\ 0 & \text{otherwise} \end{cases}$$

   (a) Derive the mean, μ ,and variance, σ^2, in terms of a.

   (b) Write down the mean and variance of $\overline{X}$, the mean of a sample of size n from the distribution.

   (c) The median, Y, of a random sample of size 3 from the distribution has a probability density function

$$g(y) = \begin{cases} \dfrac{6y}{a^2} - \dfrac{6y^2}{a^3} & 0 < y < a \\ 0 & \text{otherwise} \end{cases}$$

   Find the mean and variance of Y.   (AEB)

2. The Sunset Times has an average of 1 typing error per 500 words. The distribution of X, the number of words between successive typing errors, has probability density function

$$f(x) = \begin{cases} 0.002e^{-0.002x} & 0 < x \\ 0 & \text{otherwise} \end{cases}$$

Find the probability that the number of words between successive errors is

(a) between 400 and 600,

(b) between 200 and 800,

(c) greater than 1000,

(d) less than 100.

What is the probability that a reader starting at a random point in the paper will read more than 750 words before reaching an error?

The editor, Mr B. Pad, always reads the first paragraph before the paper is published. How many words can the first paragraph contain if the probability of it containing an error is to be not more than 0.05?

3. The thickness of a certain grade of hardboard stocked by a DIY shop is normally distributed with mean 7.3 mm and standard deviation 0.5 mm.

(a) What proportion of sheets will be between 7 mm and 8 mm thick?

(b) Sheets of the same grade bought from a second shop contain 9.1% over 8 mm thick and 2.3% less than 7 mm thick. Assuming that the thickness is normally distributed, find its mean and standard deviation correct to the nearest tenth of a mm.

(c) What is the distribution of $Y - X$ where X and Y are the thickness of pieces of hardboard selected at random from the first and second shops respectively? Find the probability that X exceeds Y.

(d) It is possible to buy batches of hardboard from the first shop with any required mean and with the standard deviation remaining 0.5 mm. What value of the mean should be chosen

   (i) to minimise the proportion of sheets outside the range 7 mm to 8 mm (no proof required),

   (ii) so that 0.1% of sheets are less than 7 mm thick?

4. A certain brand of beans is sold in tins, the tins being filled and sealed by a machine. The mass of beans in each tin is normally distributed with mean 425 g and standard deviation 25 g and the mass of the tin is normally distributed with mean 90 g and standard deviation 10 g.

(a) Find the probability that the total mass of the sealed tin and its beans

   (i) exceeds 550 g,

   (ii) lies between 466 g and 575 g.

(b) Calculate an interval within which approximately 90% of the masses of the filled tins will lie.

The tins are packed in boxes of 24, the mass of the box being normally distributed with mean 500 g and standard deviation 30 g.

(c) Find the probability that a full box weighs less than 12.75 kg.

5. Lin Ying belongs to an athletic club. In 800 m races her times are normally distributed with mean 128 seconds and standard deviation 4 seconds.

(a) What is the probability of her time in an 800 being between 120 and 130 seconds?

(b) What time will she beat in 70% of her races?

Julie belongs to the same club. In 800 m races 85% of her times are less than 140 seconds and 70% are less than 135 seconds. Her times are normally distributed.

(c) Find the mean and standard deviation of Julie's times, each correct to two significant figures.

(d) What is the probability that in an 800 m race Lin Ying will beat Julie?

(e) The club has to choose one of these two athletes to enter a major competition. In order to qualify for the final rounds it is necessary to achieve a time of 114 seconds or less in the heats. Which athlete should be chosen and why?

6. The contents of bags of oats are normally distributed with mean 3.05 kg, standard deviation 0.08 kg.

(a) What proportion of bags contain less than 3.11 kg?

(b) What proportion of bags contain between 3.00 and 3.15 kg?

(c) What weight is exceeded by the contents of 99.9% of the bags?

(d) If 6 bags are selected at random, what is the probability that the mean weight of the contents will be between 3.00 and 3.15 kg?

The weight of the bags when empty is normally distributed with mean 0.12 kg, standard deviation 0.02 kg. Full bags are packed into boxes each of which holds 6 bags.

(e) What is the distribution of the weight in a box, i.e. 6 bags together with their contents? Assume that the weight of all bags and contents in a box are independent of each other.

(f) Within what limits will the weight in a box lie with probability 0.9?

7. Fertilizer is packed, by a machine, into bags of nominal mass 12 kg. The random mass of each bag may be regarded as a normally distributed random variable with mean 12.05 kg, standard deviation 0.20 kg.

(a) What is the probability that the mass of a bag exceeds 12 kg?

(b) What mass is exceeded by exactly 95% of the bags?

A farmer buys 20 bags at a time.

(c) What is the probability that their mean mass will exceed 12 kg?

(d) What is the distribution of the total mass of the 20 bags and what is the probability that it lies between 239.5 kg and 240.5 kg?

The mass of the bags packed by a second machine may be regarded as a normally distributed random variable with mean 12.05 kg, standard deviation 0.05 kg. If the farmer's 20 bags are made up of n from the first machine and the rest from the second machine, what is the largest possible value of n which gives a probability of at least 0.95 of the total mass of the bags exceeding 240 kg?

(AEB)

2 ESTIMATION

Objectives

After studying this chapter you should

- be able to calculate confidence intervals for the mean of a normal distribution with unknown variance;
- be able to calculate confidence intervals for the variance and standard deviation of a normal distribution;
- be able to calculate approximate confidence intervals for a proportion;
- be able to calculate approximate confidence intervals for the mean of a Poisson distribution.

2.0   Introduction

In Chapter 9 of the text *Statistics* the idea of a confidence interval was introduced. Confidence intervals are used when we want to estimate a population parameter from a sample. The parameter may be estimated by a single value (a point estimate) but it is usually preferable to estimate it by an interval which will give some indication of the amount of uncertainty attached to the estimate. In *Statistics*, estimation of the mean of a normal population with known standard deviation was considered.

If $\bar{x}$ is the mean of a random sample of size n from a normal distribution with mean μ and standard deviation σ there is a

probability of 0.95 that x lies within $1.96\dfrac{\sigma}{\sqrt{n}}$ of μ. If this is the

case the interval

$$\bar{x} \pm 1.96\frac{\sigma}{\sqrt{n}}$$

will contain μ. This interval is called a **95% confidence interval** for μ.

If further samples of size n were taken and the calculation repeated, different intervals would be calculated. 95% of these intervals would contain μ, but 5% would not.

Note: although μ is unknown, it does not vary, it is the intervals that vary. It is possible to calculate 99% or even 99.9% confidence intervals which would be wider than the 95% interval but it is not possible to calculate 100% confidence intervals.

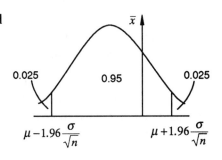

Example

The length of time a bus takes to travel from Chorlton to All Saints in the morning rush hour is normally distributed with standard deviation 4 minutes. A random sample of 6 journeys took 23, 19, 25, 34, 24 and 28 minutes. Find

(i) a 95% confidence interval for the mean journey time,

(ii) a 99% confidence interval for the mean journey time.

Solution

The sample mean is $\dfrac{153}{6} = 25.5$

(i) 95% confidence interval is

$$25.5 \pm 1.96 \times \frac{4}{\sqrt{6}} \quad \text{i.e } 25.5 \pm 3.20 \text{ or } (22.3,\ 28.7)$$

(ii) 99% confidence interval is
$$25.5 \pm 2.576 \times \frac{4}{\sqrt{6}} \quad \text{i.e. } 25.5 \pm 4.21 \text{ or } (21.3,\ 29.7)$$

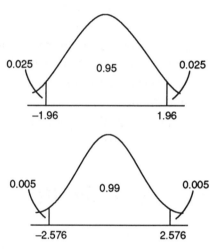

2.1 Confidence interval for mean: standard deviation unknown

The example above of the bus journey times is somewhat unrealistic. How was it known that the bus journey times were normally distributed with a standard deviation of 4 minutes? If so much was known about the distribution how was it that the mean was unknown?

Probably the journey times for similar journeys had been studied and the standard deviation found to be about four minutes. The statement that the standard deviation was 'known' was probably something of an exaggeration. The same argument applies to the normal distribution. However, as you are dealing with the sample mean, no great error will result from assuming a normal distribution unless the distribution is extremely unusual.

If the standard deviation is completely unknown or if you do not wish to accept a rough estimate, there is still a way forward. Provided the sample has more than one member, an estimate of the standard deviation may be made from the sample.

In the case of the bus journey times $\hat{\sigma} = 5.09$, this is most easily found by using the σ_{n-1} or s_{n-1} button on a calculator. Alternatively the formula

$$\hat{\sigma}^2 = \sum \frac{(x-\bar{x})^2}{(n-1)}$$

or equivalent can be used.

For a 95% confidence interval, σ known, the formula

$\bar{x} \pm 1.96 \dfrac{\sigma}{\sqrt{n}}$ was used. Now the known standard deviation σ will

be replaced by an estimate $\hat{\sigma}$. There will be some uncertainty in this estimate since, if you started again and took a different sample of the same size, the estimate of $\hat{\sigma}$ would almost certainly be different. It therefore seems reasonable that to allow for this extra uncertainty, the interval should be widened by increasing the figure of 1.96 which came from tables of the normal distribution. How much you need to increase it by has fortunately been calculated for you and is tabulated in tables of the *t* **distribution**.

The required value of *t* will, however, depend on the sample size. If you had a random sample of 1000 bus journeys then you would be able to make a very accurate estimate of the population standard deviation and there would be no real need to change the figure 1.96. However, in this case with a sample of 6 there is quite a lot of uncertainty in the estimate and you may need to make quite a large change. If the sample had been of size 2 there would have been a huge amount of uncertainty and a very large change may have been necessary.

The amount of uncertainty is measured by the **degrees of freedom**. Degrees of freedom are a concept related to the mathematical definition of the **chi-squared distribution**. For your purposes they may be thought of as a measure of the number of pieces of information you have to estimate the standard deviation. It is impossible to use a sample of size one to make an estimate of the standard deviation. The standard deviation is a measure of spread and one item can tell nothing about how spread out a distribution is. A sample of size two gives one piece of information about the spread and a sample of size three gives two pieces. In general, a sample of size n gives $n-1$ pieces of information and an estimate made from such a sample is said to be based on $n-1$ degrees of freedom.

In the example there were 6 bus journey times and so the estimate of 5.09 for the standard deviation is based on 5 degrees of freedom. To find a 95% confidence interval you therefore require the upper and lower 0.025 tails of the *t* distribution with 5 degrees of freedom, denoted t_s. As with the standard normal distribution, the *t* distribution is symmetrical about zero and the required values are ± 2.571 (see table in the Appendix).

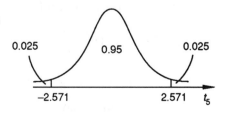

A 95% confidence interval for the mean, making no assumption about the standard deviation, is given by

$$25.5 \pm 2.571 \times \frac{5.09}{\sqrt{6}} \quad \text{i.e. } 25.5 \pm 5.34 \text{ or } (20.2, \ 30.8)$$

Note: For the use of the t distribution to be valid the data must be normally distributed. However, small deviations from normality will not seriously affect the results.

In general, the formula is

$$\boxed{\bar{x} \pm t_{n-1} \frac{\hat{\sigma}}{\sqrt{n}}}$$

Example

The resistances (in ohms) of a random sample from a batch of resistors were

      2314 2456 2389 2361 2360 2332 2402

Assuming that the sample is from a normal distribution calculate

(i)   a 95% confidence interval for the mean,

(ii)   a 90% confidence interval for the mean.

Solution

The data gives $\bar{x} = 2373.4$ and $\hat{\sigma} = 47.4$.

(i) $t_{6, \ 0.025} = 2.447$, so the

    95% confidence interval for the mean is given by

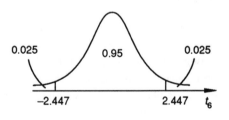

    $2373.4 \pm 2.447 \times \dfrac{47.4}{\sqrt{7}}$

    $\Rightarrow$ 2373.4 ± 43.8

    $\Rightarrow$ $(2330, \ 2417)$.

(ii) $t_{6, \ 0.025} = 1.943$, giving

    90% confidence interval for the mean as

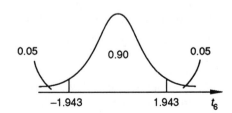

    $2373.4 \pm 1.943 \times \dfrac{47.4}{\sqrt{7}}$

    $\Rightarrow$ 2373.4 ± 34.8

    $\Rightarrow$ $(2339, \ 2408)$.

Activity 1

The following data are random observations from a normal distribution with mean 10.

6.86	11.53	12.41	12.08	12.80	10.42	8.99	9.55	8.23	5.84
7.59	5.96	10.14	10.12	10.22	10.42	11.83	8.73	11.57	11.83
10.76	9.93	10.63	7.94	12.44	12.49	9.63	9.45	13.40	10.78
13.44	11.85	13.62	13.24	12.56	10.56	10.77	8.51	11.65	9.36
8.12	11.88	11.68	7.36	7.07	10.04	9.55	12.97	10.85	8.58
8.27	9.22	11.36	9.43	8.80	9.07	7.66	13.16	8.34	7.12
3.49	13.04	13.16	11.48	8.30	10.01	10.29	11.78	13.18	8.18
10.00	12.27	14.18	9.91	9.62	7.48	8.50	10.53	13.06	6.74
6.05	9.96	7.51	10.19	9.07	9.29	6.01	12.02	10.04	10.64
9.74	8.23	9.45	5.41	9.68	10.64	6.77	10.76	8.10	10.33
8.34	11.61	9.72	11.24	12.84	6.10	10.78	8.27	8.52	7.42
8.91	8.52	10.66	14.06	9.37	10.44	11.81	9.87	9.78	10.44
10.82	10.10	7.68	11.87	7.49	9.99	8.54	4.65	5.37	8.83
15.00	10.02	9.41	8.16	9.54	9.32	6.15	12.59	12.24	13.02
9.80	8.61	8.92	8.86	11.92	13.01	14.11	11.57	10.46	11.27
8.35	8.95	9.12	7.20	11.20	13.42	13.46	12.80	10.99	10.33
14.31	7.72	9.88	10.57	13.20	11.90	8.48	9.41	7.76	10.35
8.78	9.45	11.48	10.96	7.68	9.26	14.29	8.35	6.80	8.29
8.83	10.72	10.02	11.80	13.56	13.00	10.79	7.51	8.15	10.14
11.02	8.49	9.82	8.97	9.86	7.74	11.81	9.87	10.77	9.18

Starting at any point in the table take a sample of size 3 and calculate $\hat{\sigma}$. Calculate an 80% confidence interval for the mean using the t-distribution.

Now take the next sample of 3 and repeat the calculation. Carry on until you have calculated at least 20, and preferably more, intervals. If possible work with a group so that the labour of calculation may be divided up between you.

What proportion of your intervals contain 10, the population mean? Is this approximately the proportion you would have expected?

Recalculate the intervals using z-values, i.e. calculate, for each sample

$$\bar{x} \pm 1.282 \frac{\hat{\sigma}}{\sqrt{3}}.$$

What proportion of these intervals contain 10? Which set of intervals gave results more in line with your expectations?

Exercise 2A

1. Samples of a high temperature lubricant were tested and the temperature (°C) at which they ceased to be effective were as follows:

   235 242 235 240 237 234 239 237

   Calculate a 95% confidence for the mean.

2. In a study aimed at improving the design of bus cabs the functional arm reach of a random sample of bus drivers was measured. The results, in mm, were as follows:

   701, 642, 651, 700, 672, 674, 656, 649

   Calculate a 95% confidence interval for the mean.

3. As part of a research study on pattern recognition a random sample of students on a design course were asked to examine a picture and see if they could recognise a word. The picture contained the word 'technology' written backwards. The times, in seconds, taken to recognise the word were as follows:

   55, 28, 79, 54, 87, 61, 62, 68, 38

   Calculate

   (a) a 95% confidence interval for the mean,

   (b) a 99% confidence interval for the mean.

2.2 Confidence interval for the standard deviation and the variance

In Section 2.1 the standard deviation of a population of bus journey times was estimated from a sample of bus journey times. As was stated, the estimate is subject to uncertainty as, if another sample of the same size were taken, a different estimate would almost certainly result. Provided the data comes from a normal distribution it is possible to estimate the population standard deviation with a confidence interval rather than using a single figure (or point estimate).

To do this you need to use the fact that for a sample of size n from a normal distribution

$$\sum \frac{(x - \bar{x})^2}{\sigma^2}$$

is distributed as

$$\chi^2_{n-1} \quad \text{(chi-squared with } n-1 \text{ degrees of freedom)}.$$

$\sum(x-\bar{x})^2$ is equal to $(n-1)\hat{\sigma}^2$ and this is usually the easiest way of calculating it.

In the case of the bus journey times a sample of size 6 gave
$$\hat{\sigma}^2 = 5.09^2 = 25.9.$$

If you find the upper and lower 0.025 tails of χ^2, there will be a

probability of 0.95 that $\sum \dfrac{(x-\bar{x})^2}{\sigma^2}$ will lie between them.

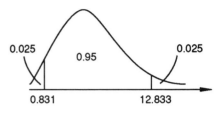

A 95% confidence interval for the variance is defined by

$$0.831 < 5 \times \frac{25.9}{\sigma^2} < 12.833$$

$$\Rightarrow \quad 0.006415 < \frac{1}{\sigma^2} < 0.0990965$$

$$\Rightarrow \quad 10.09 < \sigma^2 < 155.9$$

and this is a 95% confidence interval for the variance.

Although the variance has a very important role to play in the mathematical theory of statistics, for practical applications the standard deviation is a much more useful statistic. A 95% confidence interval for the standard deviation is found simply by taking the square root of the two limits,

i.e. $\quad 3.2 < \sigma < 12.5$

Note that the interval is not symmetrical about the point estimate which was 5.09. Clearly the interval would not make sense unless it contained the point estimate and this is a useful check on the calculation. However, as the standard deviation cannot be negative but has no upper limit, it would not be expected that the point would lie exactly in the middle.

Is it possible to calculate 100% confidence interval for the standard deviation?

Example

In processing grain in the brewing industry, the percentage extract recovered is measured. A particular brewery introduces a new source of grain and the percentage extract on eleven separate days is as follows:

95.2, 93.1, 93.5, 95.9, 94.0, 92.0, 94.4, 93.2, 95.5, 92.3, 95.4

(a) Regarding the sample as a random sample from a normal population, calculate

   (i) a 90% confidence interval for the population variance,

   (ii) a 90% confidence interval for the population mean.

(b) The previous source of grain gave daily percentage extract figures which were normally distributed with mean 94.2 and standard deviation 2.5. A high percentage extract is desirable but the brewery manager also requires as little day to day variation as possible. Without further calculation, compare the two sources of grain.   (AEB)

Solution

For this data

$$n = 11 \qquad \bar{x} = 94.045 \qquad \hat{\sigma} = 1.34117$$

(a)

   (i) 90% confidence interval for variance is given by

$$3.94 < 10 \times \frac{1.34117^2}{\sigma^2} < 18.307$$

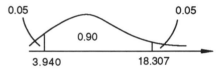

$$\Rightarrow \quad 0.2190 < \frac{1}{\sigma^2} < 1.0178$$

$$\Rightarrow \quad 0.98 < \sigma^2 < 4.57$$

   (ii) 90% confidence interval for mean is given by

$$94.045 \pm 1.812 \times \frac{1.34117}{\sqrt{11}}$$

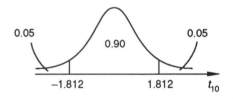

$$\Rightarrow \quad 94.045 \pm 0.733$$

$$\Rightarrow \quad (93.31, \ 94.78)$$

(b) The mean of the previous source of grain was 94.2. This lies in the middle of the confidence interval calculated for the mean of the new source of grain. There is therefore no evidence that the means differ.

The standard deviation of the previous source of grain was 2.5 and hence the variance was $2.5^2 = 6.25$.

This is above the upper limit of the confidence interval for the variance of the new source of grain. This suggests that the new source gives less variability.

Combining these two conclusions suggests that the new source is preferable to the previous source.

Activity 2

Take a sample of size 6 from the data in Activity 1. Calculate an 80% confidence interval for the standard deviation.

Take further samples of size 6 and repeat the calculation at least 20 times. Work in a group, if possible, so that the calculations may be shared.

The data in Activity 1 came from a normal distribution with standard deviation 2. What proportion of your intervals contain the value 2? Is this proportion similar to the proportion you would expect?

Exercise 2B

1. Using the data in Questions 1, 2 and 3 of Exercise 2A, calculate 95% confidence intervals for the population standard deviations.

2. The external diameter, in cm, of a random sample of piston rings produced on a particular machine were

   9.91, 9.89, 10.12, 9.98, 10.09,
   9.81, 10.01, 9.99, 9.86

   Calculate a 95% confidence interval for the standard deviation . Assume normal distribution.

   Do your results support the manufacturer's claim that the standard deviation is 0.06 cm?

3. The vitamin C content of a random sample of 5 lemons was measured. The results in 'mg per 10 g' were

   1.04, 0.95, 0.63, 1.62, 1.11

   Assuming a normal distribution calculate a 95% confidence interval for the standard deviation.

   A greengrocer claimed that the method of determining the vitamin C content was extremely unreliable and that the observed variability was more due to errors in the determination rather than to actual differences between lemons. To check this 7 independent determinations were made of the vitamin C content of the same lemon. The results were as follows

   1.21, 1.22, 1.21, 1.23, 1.24, 1.23, 1.22

   Assuming a normal distribution, calculate a 90% confidence interval for the standard deviation of the determinations. Does your result support the greengrocer's claim?

2.3 Confidence intervals for proportions

An insurance company receives a large number of claims for storm damage. A manager wished to estimate the proportion of these claims which were for less than £500. He examined a random sample of 120 claims and found that 18 of them were for less than £500.

Obviously the best estimate of the proportion of all claims which are for less than £500 is $\frac{18}{120} = 0.15$.

To calculate a confidence interval for the proportion we must observe that, r, the number of claims for less than £500 in a sample of size n, will be an observation from a binomial distribution. This will have mean np and variance $np(1-p)$. From *Statistics* you know that a binomial distribution can be approximated by a normal distribution if n is large and np is reasonably large.

In this case $n = 120$ and p is estimated by 0.15. Hence r can be approximated by a normal distribution with variance

$120 \times 0.15 \times 0.85 = 15.3$ and standard deviation $\sqrt{15.3} = 3.912$.

The proportion of claims for less than £500 is estimated by $\dfrac{r}{n}$.

This has variance

$$\frac{np(1-p)}{n^2} = \frac{p(1-p)}{n} \quad .$$

In this case the proportion can be estimated by a normal distribution with variance

$$\frac{0.15 \times 0.85}{120} = 0.0010625$$

and standard deviation 0.03260.

Hence an approximate 95% confidence interval for the proportion is given by

$$0.15 \pm 1.96 \times 0.0326$$

$\Rightarrow \quad 0.15 \pm 0.064$

$\Rightarrow \quad (0.086, \ 0.214).$

In general, the formula for an approximate confidence interval for a proportion is

$$\boxed{\hat{p} \pm z \sqrt{\frac{\hat{p}(1-\hat{p})}{n}}}$$

where $\hat{p}$ is an estimate of p and z is the appropriate value from normal tables to give the required percentage confidence interval.

Note this formula is valid only if the parameters of the binomial distribution make it reasonable to use the normal approximation.

Example

Employees of a firm carrying out motorway maintenance are issued with brightly coloured waterproof jackets. These come in five different sizes numbered 1 to 5. The last 40 jackets issued were of the following sizes

2 3 3 1 3 3 2 4 3 2 5 4 1 2 3 3 2 4 5 3

2 4 4 1 5 3 3 2 3 3 1 3 4 3 3 2 5 1 4 4

(a) (i) Find the proportion in the sample requiring size 3. Assuming the 40 employees can be regarded as a random sample of all employees, calculate an approximate 95% confidence interval for the proportion, p, of all employees requiring size 3.

(ii) Give two reasons why the confidence interval calculated in (i) is approximate rather than exact.

(b) Your estimate of p is $\hat{p}$.

(i) What percentage is associated with the approximate confidence interval $\hat{p} \pm 0.1$?

(ii) How large a sample would be needed to obtain an approximate 95% confidence interval of the form $\hat{p} \pm 0.1$?   (AEB)

Solution

(a) (i) There are 15 out of 40 requiring size 3, a proportion of $\frac{15}{40} = 0.375$. An approximate 95% confidence interval is given by

$$0.375 \pm 1.96 \times \sqrt{\frac{0.375 \times 0.625}{40}}$$

$$\Rightarrow \quad 0.375 \pm 0.150$$

$$\Rightarrow \quad (0.225,\ 0.525).$$

(ii) The confidence interval is approximate because an estimate of p is used (the true value is unknown) and because the normal distribution is used as an approximation to the binomial distribution.

(b) (i) Confidence interval is given by

$$\hat{p} \pm z \sqrt{\frac{\hat{p}(1-\hat{p})}{n}}.$$

Hence if interval is $\hat{p} \pm 0.1$,

$$0.1 = z \sqrt{\frac{0.375 \times 625}{40}}$$

i.e. $z = 1.306$;

this is $(1 - 2 \times 0.096) \times 100 = 81$ per cent confidence interval.

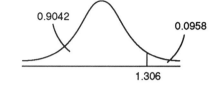

(ii) 95% confidence interval

$$\hat{p} \pm 1.96 \sqrt{\frac{0.375 \times .625}{n}} \, .$$

If this is $\hat{p} \pm 0.1$,

$$0.1 = 1.96 \sqrt{\frac{0.375 \times .625}{n}}$$

$\Rightarrow \qquad \sqrt{n} = 9.4888$

$\Rightarrow \qquad n = 90.04$

Sample of size 90 needed.

Exercise 2C

1. When a random sample of 80 climbing ropes were subjected to a strain equivalent to the weight of ten climbers 12 of them broke. Calculate a 95% confidence interval for the proportion of ropes which would break under this strain.

2. Data from a completed questionnaire were entered into a computer as a series of binary digits (i.e. each digit was 0 or 1). A check on 1000 digits revealed errors in 19 of them. Assuming the probability of an error is the same for each digit entered, calculate a 90% confidence interval for the proportion of digits where an error will be made.

3. A large civil engineering firm issues every new employee with a safety helmet. Five different sizes are available numbered 1 to 5. A random sample of 90 employees required the following sizes

2	4	2	2	2	5	4	5	4	4
4	2	4	3	4	2	3	1	5	4
3	2	3	3	3	4	3	2	4	4
3	4	4	5	3	3	3	2	4	4
2	2	3	2	3	2	3	3	5	4
2	3	4	2	4	3	2	2	3	2
3	4	2	3	4	5	2	3	3	2
4	3	2	2	3	3	3	2	3	4
2	3	2	4	2	3	3	2	2	3

Calculate an approximate 90% confidence interval for the proportion of employees requiring size 2.   (AEB)

2.4 Confidence intervals for the mean of a Poisson distribution

In an area of moorland, plants of a certain variety are known to be distributed at random at a constant average rate; that is, they are distributed according to the Poisson distribution. A biologist counts the number of plants in a randomly chosen square of area 10 m² and finds 142 plants. An approximate confidence interval for the average number of plants in a square of area 10 m² can be found by approximating the Poisson distribution by a normal distribution with mean 142 and standard deviation $\sqrt{142}$. This approximation is valid since the mean is large.

In this case a 95% approximate confidence interval is given by

$$142 \pm 1.96\sqrt{142}$$

$$\Rightarrow \quad 142 \pm 23.4$$

$$\Rightarrow \quad (118.6,\ 165.4).$$

In general the formula is

$$\boxed{m \pm z\sqrt{m}}$$

where m is the observed value and z is the appropriate value from normal tables to give the required percentage confidence interval. Remember this is only valid if the mean is reasonably large so that the normal distribution gives a good approximation.

If a confidence interval for the mean number of plants per m² was required, the interval calculated for 10 m² would be divided by 10. The result would be 14.2 ± 2.34 or $(118.6,\ 165.4)$.

The calculation could have been carried out by finding the mean number of plants observed in 10 areas of 1m² and basing the calculation on this. However, there would be no advantage in this as it would give the identical answer.

For example in this case, if 10 separate m² had been observed, the mean number of plants in each square would be 14.2 and the distribution would be approximated by normal mean 14.2 standard deviation $\sqrt{14.2}$. Since you now have the mean of 10 observations the calculation for a 95% interval would be

$$14.2 \pm 1.96 \frac{\sqrt{14.2}}{\sqrt{10}}$$

$$\Rightarrow \quad 14.2 \pm 2.34,\ \text{as before.}$$

It is probably always easiest to work in terms of the total number of events observed and then scale the final answer as required.

Why is a confidence interval calculated for the mean of a Poisson distribution only an approximation?

Exercise 2D

1. Cars pass a point on a motorway during the morning rush hour at random at a constant average rate. An observer counts 212 cars passing during a 5 minute interval. Calculate

   (a) a 95% confidence interval for the mean number of cars passing in a 5 minute interval,

   (b) a 95% confidence interval for the mean number of cars passing in a one minute interval,

   (c) a 90% confidence interval for the mean number of cars passing in a two minute interval,

   (d) a 99% confidence interval for the mean number of cars passing in an hour.

2. The number of times a machine needs resetting on a night shift follows a Poisson distribution. On three randomly selected nights it was reset 9, 5 and 11 times. Calculate a 95% confidence interval for the average number of times it needs resetting per night.

3. The number of a certain type of organism suspended in a liquid follows a Poisson distribution. 10 cc of the liquid are found to contain 35 of the organisms. Calculate

   (a) a 90% confidence interval for the mean number of organisms per 10 cc,

   (b) a 95% confidence interval for the mean number of organisms per cc,

   (c) a 99% confidence interval for the mean number of organisms per 100 cc.

   A further 10 cc of the liquid were examined and found to contain 26 of the organisms. Modify your answers to (a), (b) and (c) to take account of this additional data.

2.5   Miscellaneous Exercises

1. The development engineer of a company making razors records the time it takes him to shave, on seven mornings, using a standard razor made by the company. The times, in seconds, were

   217, 210, 254, 237, 232, 228, 243

   Assuming that this may be regarded as a random sample from a normal distribution, calculate a 95% confidence interval for the mean.

   (AEB)

2. A car insurance company found that the average amount it was paying on bodywork claims was 435 with a standard deviation of 141. The next eight bodywork claims were subjected to extra investigation before payment was agreed. The payments, in pounds, on these claims were

   48, 109, 237, 192, 403, 98, 264, 68.

   (a) Assuming the data can be regarded as a random sample from a normal distribution, calculate a 90% confidence interval for

   (i) the mean payment after extra investigation,

   (ii) the standard deviation of the payments after extra investigation.

   (b) Explain to the manager whether or not your results suggest that the distribution of payments has changed after special investigation and comment on her suggestion that in future all claims over £900 should be subject to special investigation. (AEB)

3. A car manufacturer purchases large quantities of a particular component. Tests have shown that 3% fail to function and that, of those that do function, the mean working life is 2400 hours with a standard deviation of 650 hours. The manufacturer is particularly concerned with the large variability and the supplier undertakes to improve the design so that the standard deviation is reduced to 300 hours.

   (a) A random sample of 310 of the new components contained 12 which failed to function. Calculate an approximate 95% confidence interval for the proportion which fail to function.

   (b) A random sample of 3 new components tested had working lives of 2730, 3120 and 2300 hours.

Assuming that the claim of a standard deviation of 300 hours is correct and that the lives of the new components follow a normal distribution, calculate

(i) a 90% confidence interval for the mean working life of the components,

(ii) how many components it would be necessary to test to make the width of a 90% confidence interval for the mean just less than 100 hours.

(c) Lives of components commonly follow a distribution that is not normal. If the assumption of normality is invalid in this case, comment briefly on the amount of uncertainty in your answers to (b)(i) and (b)(ii).

(d) Using all the information available, compare the two designs and recommend which one should be used. (AEB)

4. The resistances (in ohms) of a sample from a batch of resistors were

2314, 2456, 2389, 2361, 2360, 2332, 2402.

Assuming that the sample is from a normal distribution,

(a) Calculate a 90% confidence interval for the standard deviation of the batch.

Past experience suggests that the standard deviation, σ, is 35 ohms.

(b) Calculate a 95% confidence interval for the mean resistance of the batch

(i) assuming $\sigma = 35$,

(ii) making no assumption about the standard deviation.

(c) Compare the merits of the confidence intervals calculated in (b). (AEB)

5. Packets of baking powder have a nominal weight of 200 g. The distribution of weights is normal and the standard deviation is 7 g. Average quantity system legislation states that, if the nominal weight is 200 g,

(i) the average weight must be at least 200 g,

(ii) not more than 2.5% of packages may weigh less than 191 g,

(iii) not more than 1 in 1000 packages may weigh less than 182 g.

A random sample of 30 packages had the following weights:

218 207 214 189 211 206 203 217 183 186
219 213 207 214 203 204 195 197 213 212
188 221 217 184 186 216 198 211 216 200

(a) Calculate a 95% confidence interval for the mean weight.

(b) Find the proportion of packets in the sample weighing less than 191 g and use your result to calculate an approximate 95% confidence interval for the proportion of all packets weighing less than 191 g.

(c) Assuming that the mean weight is at the lower limit of the interval calculated in (a), what proportion of packets would weigh less than 182 g?

(d) Discuss the suitability of the packets from the point of view of the average quantity system. A simple adjustment will change the mean weight of future packages. Changing the standard deviation is possible but very expensive. Without carrying out any further calculations, discuss any adjustments you might recommend. (AEB)

6. A car manufacturer introduces a new method of assembling a new component. The old method had a mean assembly time of 42 minutes with a standard deviation of 4 minutes. The manufacturer would like the assembly time to be as short as possible and to have as little variation as possible. He expects the new method to have a smaller mean but to leave the variability unchanged. A random sample of assembly times, in minutes, taken after the new method had become established was

27, 19, 68, 41, 17, 52, 35, 72, 38.

A statistician glanced at the data and said she thought the variability had increased.

(a) Suggest why she said this.

(b) Assuming the data may be regarded as a random sample from a normal distribution, calculate a 95% confidence interval for the standard deviation. Does this confirm the statistician's claim or not?

(c) Calculate a 90% confidence interval for the mean using a method which is appropriate in the light of your answer to (b).

(d) Comment on the suitability of the new process. (AEB)

7. Stud anchors are used in the construction industry. Samples are tested by embedding them in concrete and applying a steadily increasing load until the stud fails.

(a) A sample of 6 tests gave the following maximum loads in kN

27.0, 30.5, 28.0, 23.0, 27.5, 26.5

Assuming a normal distribution for maximum loads, find 95% confidence intervals for

(i) the mean,

(ii) the standard deviation.

(b) If the mean was at the lower end and the standard deviation at the upper end of the confidence intervals calculated in (a), find the value of k which the maximum load would exceed with probability 0.99.

Safety regulations state that the greatest load that may be applied under working conditions

is $\dfrac{(\bar{x} - 2\hat{\sigma})}{3}$ where $\bar{x}$ is the mean and $\hat{\sigma}^2$ is

the unbiased estimate of variance calculated from a sample of 6 tests. Calculate this figure for the data above and comment on the adequacy of this regulation in these circumstances.

(AEB)

8. A campaign to combat the economic devastation caused to coalfield communities by pit closures employed a researcher. The campaign organisers wished to know the proportion of redundant miners who were able to find alternative employment within a year of becoming redundant.

(a) The researcher found that the probability of a redundant miner visited at home refusing to answer a questionnaire is 0.2.

What is the probability that on a day when he visits twelve redundant miners at home

(i)   3 or fewer will refuse to answer the questionnaire,

(ii) exactly 3 will refuse to answer the questionnaire,

(iii) at least 10 will agree to answer the questionnaire?

(b) The researcher decided to try a postal survey and as a pilot scheme sent out 70 questionnaires to randomly selected redundant miners. There were 26 completed questionnaires returned. Calculate an approximate 95% confidence interval for the proportion of redundant miners who would return a completed questionnaire.

(c) Of the 26 who replied, 10 had obtained employment. Of all redundant miners who would reply to a questionnaire, a proportion p have obtained emplyment. Approximately how many replies would be necessary to obtain 95% confidence interval of width 0.1 for p?

(d) Using the results of (b) and (c) estimate approximately how many letters should be sent out to give a high probability of obtaining sufficient replies to calculate the confidence interval in (c). Explain your answer.   (AEB)

9. It is known that repeated weighings of the same object on a particular chemical balance give readings which are normally distributed with mean equal to the mass of the object. Past esperience suggests that the standard deviation, σ, is 0.25 mg. Seven repeated weighings gave the following readings (mg).

19.3, 19.5, 19.1, 19.0, 19.8, 19.7, 19.4

(a) Use the data to calculate a 95% confidence interval for σ.

(b) Calculate a 95% confidence interval for the mass of the object assuming $\sigma = 25$ mg.

(c) Calculate 95% confidence interval for the mass of the object, making no assumption about σ, and using only data from the sample.

(d) Give two reasons for preferring the confidence interval calculated in (b) to that calculated in (c).

3 HYPOTHESIS TESTING: ONE SAMPLE TESTS

Objectives

After studying this chapter you should

- understand when, and be able, to carry out a one sample *t*-test;
- be able to carry out a test for a normal population variance;
- be able to test hypotheses for a binomial population proportion, either by calculating exact probabilities or by using an appropriate approximation;
- be able to test hypotheses for the mean of a Poisson population parameter, either by calculating exact probabilities or by using a normal approximation;
- be able to carry out a sign test for a population median, either by using a binomial distribution or an approximation.

3.0   Introduction

In Chapter 10 of *Statistics* you were introduced to some important basic concepts of hypothesis testing:

Null hypothesis (H_0): an assertion that a parameter in a statistical model takes a particular value, and is assumed true until experimental evidence suggests otherwise.

Alternative hypothesis (H_1): expresses the way in which the value of a parameter may deviate from that specified in the null hypothesis, and is assumed true when the experimental evidence suggests that the null hypothesis is false.

Type 1 error: rejecting the null hypothesis when it is, in fact, true.

Type 2 error: accepting the null hypothesis when it is, in fact, false.

Test statistic: a function of a sample of observations which provides a basis for testing the validity of the null hypothesis.

Critical region: the null hypothesis is rejected when a calculated value of the test statistic lies within this region.

Critical value: the value which determines the boundary of the critical region.

Significance level (α): the size of the critical region; the probability of a Type 1 error.

One-tailed test: the critical region is located wholly at one end of the sampling distribution of the test statistic; H_1 involves < or > but not both.

Two-tailed test: the critical region comprises areas at both ends of the sampling distribution of the test statistic; H_1 involves $\neq$.

Example

A consumer group, concerned about the mean fat content of a certain grade of steakburger submits to an independent laboratory a random sample of 12 steakburgers for analysis. The percentage of fat in each of the steakburgers is as follows.

21 18 19 16 18 24 22 19 24 14 18 15

The manufacturer claims that the mean fat content of this grade of steakburger is less than 20%. Assuming percentage fat content to be normally distributed with a standard deviation of 3, carry out an appropriate hypothesis test in order to advise the consumer group as to the validity of the manufacturer's claim.

Solution

For this problem, denoting the percentage fat content by X, then $X \sim N(\mu, 3^2)$ and it is required to test

H_0: $\mu = 20\%$

H_1: $\mu < 20\%$ (one-tailed)

Significance level, $\alpha = 0.05$ (say)

Critical region, $z < -1.645$

Under H_0, $\bar{X} \sim N\left(20, \dfrac{3^2}{12}\right)$

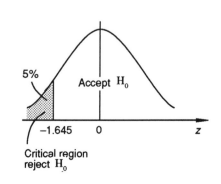

5%

Accept H_0

−1.645   0   z

Critical region
reject H_0

Now the test statistic is

$$z = \frac{\bar{x} - \mu}{\frac{\sigma}{\sqrt{n}}}$$

Calculation gives

$$\bar{x} = \frac{\sum x}{n} = \frac{228}{12} = 19$$

and thus

$$z = \frac{19 - 20}{\frac{3}{\sqrt{12}}} = -1.15$$

This value does not lie in the critical region. Thus there is no evidence, at the 5% level of significance, to support the manufacturer's claim.

3.1 Normal population mean (n small, σ unknown)

Consider again the previous example on steakburgers and now suppose that it can be assumed that the percentage fat content is normally distributed but with an **unknown standard deviation**.

Now from Section 2.1 you have seen that if $X \sim N(\mu, \sigma^2)$ then

$$\frac{\bar{x} - \mu}{\frac{\hat{\sigma}}{\sqrt{n}}}$$

is a t statistic with degrees of freedom $v = n - 1$, where

$$\hat{\sigma}^2 = \frac{1}{n-1}\sum(x - \bar{x})^2 = \frac{1}{n-1}\left[\sum x^2 - \frac{(\sum x)^2}{n}\right].$$

So a z-test, used when σ is known, is replaced by a t-test when σ is unknown.

What is meant by the term 'degrees of freedom' and why is its value important?

A re-working of the steakburger problem, assuming that σ is now unknown, is thus as follows.

H_0: $\mu = 20\%$

H_1: $\mu < 20\%$ (one-tailed)

Significance level, $\alpha = 0.05$ (say)

Degrees of freedom, $v = n - 1 = 11$

Critical region, $t < -1.796$

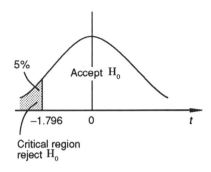

5%

Accept H_0

−1.796   0 t

Critical region
reject H_0

Under H_0, $\bar{X} \sim N\left(20, \dfrac{\sigma^2}{12}\right)$

Now the test statistic is

$$t = \frac{\bar{x} - \mu}{\dfrac{\hat{\sigma}}{\sqrt{n}}}$$

with $\bar{x} = 19$ and $\hat{\sigma}^2 = \dfrac{1}{11}\left(4448 - \dfrac{228^2}{12}\right) = 10.545$ and so $\hat{\sigma} = 3.25$.

Hence $t = \dfrac{19 - 20}{\dfrac{3.25}{\sqrt{12}}} = -1.07$

This value does not lie in the critical region. Thus there is no evidence, at the 5% level of significance, to support the manufacturer's claim.

Activity 1   Weights and measures

Collect a random sample of between 5 and 10 'identical' items on which is stated the contents.

For example, boxes of matches, boxes of paper clips, packets of drawing pins, packets of crisps, chocolate biscuits, etc.

Count or measure, as appropriate, the contents of each item.

Investigate the hypothesis that your sample mean differs significantly from the value stated.

Exercise 3A

1. During a particular week, 13 babies were born in a maternity unit. Part of the standard procedure is to measure the length of the baby. Given below is a list of the lengths, in centimetres, of the babies born in this particular week.

   49 50 45 51 47 49 48 54 53 55 45 50 48

   Assuming that this sample came from an underlying normal population, test, at the 5% significance level, the hypothesis that the population mean length is 50 cm. (AEB)

2. A random sample of 12 steel ingots was taken from a production line. The masses, in kilograms, of these ingots are given below.

   24.8 30.8 28.1 24.8 27.4 22.1
   24.7 27.3 27.5 27.8 23.9 23.2

   Assuming that this sample came from an underlying normal population, investigate the claim that its mean exceeds 25.0 kg. (AEB)

3. A random sample of 14 cows was selected from a large dairy herd at Brookfield Farm. The milk yield in one week was recorded, in kilograms, for each cow. The results are given below.

   169.6 142.0 103.3 111.6 123.4 143.5 155.1
   101.7 170.7 113.2 130.9 146.1 169.3 155.5

   Stating clearly any distributional assumptions that you make, investigate the claim that the mean weekly milk yield for the herd is greater than 120 kg. (AEB)

4. A random sample of 15 workers from a vacuum flask assembly line was selected from a large number of such workers. Ivor Stopwatch, a work-study engineer, asked each of these workers to assemble a one-litre vacuum flask at their normal working speed. The times taken, in seconds, to complete these tasks are given below.

109.2	146.2	127.9	92.0	108.5
91.1	109.8	114.9	115.3	99.0
112.8	130.7	141.7	122.6	119.9

   Assuming that this sample came from an underlying normal population, investigate the claim that the population mean assembly time is less than 2 minutes. (AEB)

5. In processing grain in the brewing industry, the percentage extract recovered is measured. A particular brewing introduces a new source of grain and the percentage extract on 11 separate days is as follows.

   95.2 93.1 93.5 95.9 94.0 92.0
   94.4 93.2 95.5 92.3 95.4

   Test the hypothesis that the true mean percentage extract recovered is 95.0. What assumptions have you made in carrying out your test? (AEB)

6. A car manufacturer introduces a new method of assembling a particular component. The old method had a mean assembly time of 42 minutes. The manufacturer would like the assembly time to be as short as possible, and so he expects the new method to have a smaller mean. A random sample of assembly times (minutes) taken after the new method had become established was

   27 39 28 41 47 42 35 32 38

   Stating any necessary distributional assumptions, investigate the manufacturer's expectation. (AEB)

3.2 Normal population variance

In Section 2.2 it was stated that if $\hat{\sigma}^2$ denotes the variance [divisor $(n-1)$] of a random sample of size n from a normal population with variance σ^2, then

$$\frac{(n-1)\hat{\sigma}^2}{\sigma^2} \sim \chi^2$$

with degrees of freedom, $v = n-1$.

The statistic $\dfrac{(n-1)\hat{\sigma}^2}{\sigma^2}$ may thus be used to test hypotheses concerning a normal population variance or, by implication, a normal population standard deviation.

How does the χ^2 distribution differ in shape from the t-distribution and how does this affect the percentage points of the χ^2 distribution?

Example

A user of a certain gauge of steel wire suspects that the standard deviation of its breaking strength, in newtons (N), is different from the value of 0.75 as specified by the manufacturer.

Consequently the user tests the breaking strength of each of a random sample of nine lengths of wire and obtains the following results.

72.1 74.5 72.8 75.0 73.4 75.4 76.1 73.5 74.1

Assuming breaking strength to be normally distributed, test, at the 10% level of significance, the manufacturer's specification.

Solution

H_0: $\sigma = 0.75\,\text{N}$ or H_0: $\sigma^2 = 0.5625\,\text{N}^2$

H_1: $\sigma \neq 0.75\,\text{N}$ or H_1: $\sigma^2 \neq 0.5625\,\text{N}^2$ (two-tailed)

Significance level, $\alpha = 0.10$

Degrees of freedom, $v = 8$

Critical region, $\chi^2 < 2.733$ or $\chi^2 > 15.507$

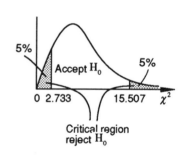

Calculation gives

$$(n-1)\hat{\sigma}^2 = \Sigma x^2 - \frac{(\Sigma x)^2}{n}$$

$$= 49430.49 - \frac{666.9^2}{9} = 13.2$$

Under H_0, $\chi^2 = \dfrac{(n-1)\hat{\sigma}^2}{\sigma^2} = \dfrac{13.2}{0.5625} = 23.47$

This value does lie in the critical region. Thus there is evidence, at the 10% level of significance, to dispute the manufacturer's specification as regards variability of breaking strength.

Activity 2	Random standardised normal deviates

Obtain from tables, calculator, or computer a random sample of between 10 and 15 values of the standardised normal random variable.

Investigate the hypothesis that your sample provides significant evidence that the variance differs from unity.

Exercise 3B

1. Given the data in Question 1 of Exercise 3A, test, at the 5% level of significance, the hypothesis that the population standard deviation of length is 2.5 cm.   (AEB)

2. Referring to Question 2 of Exercise 3A, investigate the claim that the population standard deviation is greater than 2 kg.   (AEB)

3. Using the data given in Question 3 of Exercise 3A, test the hypothesis that the standard deviation of yield for the herd at Brookfield Farm is 20 kg.

    (AEB)

4. The variability in unit mass is very critical in the pharmaceutical industry. The mass, in grams, of each of 15 randomly selected units of a specific drug is as follows.

    3.48 3.52 3.50 3.47 3.49 3.54 3.51 3.52

    3.46 3.45 3.55 3.48 3.51 3.52 3.50

    Assuming that this sample comes from an underlying normal population, test the hypothesis that the variance of the population exceeds 0.002 gm^2.   (AEB)

5. With reference to Question 5 of Exercise 3A, the variance of percentage extract recovered was 6.0 prior to introducing the new source of grain. Does the new source of grain result in a decrease in the variability of percentage extract recovered?   (AEB)

6. Referring to Question 6 of Exercise 3A, the manufacturer assumes that the new method of assembly will reduce the variability of assembly times. Given that the old assembly method had a standard deviation of 8 minutes, investigate the manufacturer's assumption.   (AEB)

3.3   Binomial population proportion

In situations where the population parameter of interest in a hypothesis test is a proportion, or percentage, rather than a mean or variance, then a binomial distribution, or an appropriate approximation, provides the basis for the test.

Remember from Chapter 9 of *Statistics*, that if X denotes the number of successes in n repeated trials, each of which may result in a success with probability p, then $\quad\quad X \sim B(n, p)$

and $\quad\quad P(X = x) = \binom{n}{x} p^x (1-p)^{n-x} \quad\quad x = 0, 1, 2, ..., n$

where $\quad\quad \binom{n}{x} = \dfrac{n!}{x!(n-x)!}$

Example

Until recently, an average of 60 out of every 100 patients have survived a particularly severe infection. When a new drug was administered to a random sample of 15 patients with the infection, 12 survived. Does this provide evidence that the new drug is effective?

Solution

Let X denote the number of patients who survive.

Then $X \sim B(15, p)$, and it is required to test

$\quad\quad$ H_0: $p = 0.6$ $\quad\quad$ (not effective)

$\quad\quad$ H_1: $p > 0.6$ $\quad\quad$ (effective; one-tailed)

Now assuming H_0 is true, $X \sim B(15, 0.6)$, and so

$$P(X = 12) = \binom{15}{12} 0.6^{12} \, 0.4^3 = 0.06339$$

$$P(X = 13) = \binom{15}{13} 0.6^{13} \, 0.4^2 = 0.02194$$

$$P(X = 14) = \binom{15}{14} 0.6^{14} \, 0.4^1 = 0.00470$$

$$P(X = 15) = \binom{15}{15} 0.6^{15} \, 0.4^0 = 0.00047$$

For a 5% level of significance, what is the critical region?

Hence, under H_0, the probability of

15 patients surviving	$= 0.00047$
14 or 15 patients surviving	$= 0.00517$
13, 14 or 15 patients surviving	$= 0.02711$
12, 13, 14 or 15 patients surviving	$= 0.09050$

Note that if 14 surviving is adopted as a 'significant' result, the probability of 15 must be included as well (because 15 is actually a 'better' result than 14). Similarly with 13, the probabilities for 14 or 15 must be included, and so on.

From the above (cumulative) probabilities it can be seen that the critical region for say a 5% test is $X \geq 13$

since $\qquad P(X \geq 13) = 0.02711 < 0.05$

but $\qquad P(X \geq 12) = 0.09050 > 0.05$

The number of patients who actually survived was 12. This value does not lie in the critical region. Thus there is no evidence, at the 5% level of significance, to suggest that the drug is effective.

Note that rather than actually determine the critical region, it is equally valid to simply argue that since

$P(X \geq 12) = 0.09050 > 0.05$, then H_0 cannot be rejected.

Remember also that tables of the Cumulative Binomial Distribution Functions (see Appendix) may often provide an easier and quicker alternative for calculating probabilities or finding critical regions.

Activity 3   Can you tell the difference?

Can you tell HP Baked Beans from a supermarket brand? Can you tell Coca Cola from a supermarket brand? Can you tell Stork from butter?

You are going to set up an experiment to determine whether people really can tell the difference between two similar foods or drinks.

Each person taking part in the test is given 3 samples; 2 of one product and 1 of another (so they may have 2 beakers containing Coca Cola (say) and 1 beaker containing a supermarket brand or vice-versa).

Ask each person to try to identify the sample which is different from the other two.

Note that there are 6 possible groupings of the 3 samples,

ABB   BAB   BBA   BAA   ABA   AAB

and a die may be used to decide which grouping to give each individual person taking part.

Plan the experiment carefully before you start. Write out a list showing the groupings for each of your participants (about 12, say).

Ensure that your participants take the test individually in quiet surroundings, free from odours. All 3 samples must be of the same size and temperature. If there are any differences in colour then you can blindfold your participants. Record each person's answer. Count the number of persons giving the correct answer. Participants who are unable to detect any difference at all in the 3 samples must be left out of the analysis.

Use your results to test the hypotheses

$$H_0: p = \frac{1}{3} \qquad \text{(participants are simply guessing)}$$

$$H_1: p > \frac{1}{3} \qquad \text{(participants can distinguish)}$$

Under what conditions does a Poisson distribution provide a suitable approximation to a binomial distribution?

Example

A machine which manufactures black polythene dustbin bags, is known to produce 3% defective bags. Following a major breakdown of the machine, extensive repair work is carried out which may result in a change in the percentage of defective bags produced. To investigate this possibility, a random sample of 200 bags is taken from the machine's production and a count reveals 12 defective bags. What may be concluded?

Solution

Here $n = 200$, $p =$ population proportion of defective bags produced, and it is required to test

$$H_0: p = 0.03 \qquad \text{(no change)}$$

$$H_1: p \neq 0.03 \qquad \text{(change; two-tailed)}$$

$$\text{Significance level, } \alpha = 0.05 \text{(say)}$$

Again from Chapter 6 of *Statistics*, a Poisson distribution with $\lambda = np$ provides an approximation to a binomial distribution when $n \geq 50$ and $p \leq 0.1$ (or $p \geq 0.9$).

Thus if X denotes the number of defective bags in the sample, then under H_0

$$X \sim Po(\lambda = 200 \times 0.03 = 6.0)$$

Using tables of the Cumulative Poisson Distribution Functions (see Appendix),

$$P(X \geq 12) = 1 - P(X \leq 11)$$
$$= 1 - 0.9799 = 0.0201$$

Since the test is two-tailed, this probability is compared with $\frac{\alpha}{2} = 0.025$, because a small number of defective bags could also lead to the rejection of the null hypothesis.

Here, $0.0201 < 0.025$ so H_0 is rejected. There is evidence, at the 5% level of significance, that the percentage of defective bags produced has changed following the repair work.

Under what conditions does a normal distribution provide a suitable approximation to a binomial distribution?

Example

Company A proposes the take-over of Company B. The latter's Chief Executive claims that her Company's shareholders are equally divided for and against the take-over on the basis of the terms offered. However, the Chairman of Company A claims that more than half of Company B's shareholders are in favour of accepting his Company's offer.

To investigate these two rival claims, the view of each of 400 randomly selected shareholders of Company B is sought. A subsequent count reveals that 219 are in favour of the offer; the remainder are against.

Does this provide evidence, at the 1% significance level, that the claim made by Company B's Chairman is valid?

Solution

Let p denote the actual proportion of Company B's shareholders who are in favour of the offer. Then

H_0: $p = 0.50$ (claim of Company B's Chief Executive)

H_1: $p > 0.50$ (claim of Company A's Chairman; one-tailed)

Significance level, $\alpha = 0.01$

If X denotes the number of Company B's shareholders in the sample who are in favour of the offer, then under H_0

$$X \sim B(400, 0.50) \quad \text{with mean, } np = 200 \text{ and}$$
$$\text{variance, } np(1-p) = 100$$

47

From Chapter 8 of *Statistics*, a normal distribution provides an approximation to a binomial distribution when $n \geq 50$ and $0.1 \leq p \leq 0.9$.

Thus under H_0, $X \sim N(200,100)$, or denoting the sample proportion by $\hat{P} = \dfrac{X}{n}$ then

$$\hat{P} \sim N\left(\frac{200}{400}, \frac{100}{400^2}\right)$$

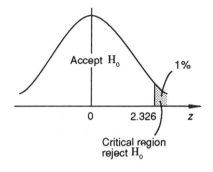

i.e. $\qquad \hat{P} \sim N(0.50, 0.000625)$

So $\qquad$ Critical region is $z > 2.326$

Now value of sample proportion,

$$\hat{p} = \frac{219}{400} = 0.5475$$

so test statistic,

$$z = \frac{0.5475 - 0.50}{\sqrt{0.000625}} = 1.90$$

This value does not lie in the critical region. Thus there is no evidence, at the 1% level of significance, to support the claim of Company A's Chairman.

Exercise 3C

1. A pharmacist claims that more than 60% of all customers simply collect a prescription. One of her assistants notes that, in a random sample of 12 customers, 10 simply collected a prescription. Does this provide sufficient evidence, at the 5% level, to support the pharmacist's claim?

2. In a survey carried out in Funville, 14 children out of a random sample of 30 said that they bought the Bopper comic regularly. Test, at the 10% level of significance, the hypothesis that the true proportion of all children who buy this comic regularly is 0.35. (AEB)

3. A random sample of 30 coffee drinkers were each asked to taste-test a new brand of coffee. The responses are listed below with L representing 'like', I representing 'indifferent', and D representing 'dislike'.

    L D L L D L L L L I
    L L L I L D L I L L
    I L L L D L L L L I

    Do these data support the claim that more than half of all coffee drinkers like this new brand of coffee?

4. Tins of baked beans are packed in boxes of 24. Results from a random sample of 25 boxes delivered to supermarkets show that a total of 8 tins were damaged. Assess the claim that less than 2% of tins are damaged during delivery.

    (AEB)

5. A survey of Aldervale revealed that 223 houses out of a random sample of 500 were fitted with some form of double glazing. Test the hypothesis that 40% of all houses in Aldervale have some form of double glazing. (AEB)

6. Prior to joining a coaching course, a netball player has scored with 45% of her shots at the basket, and so is considered to have a scoring ability of 0.45. In games following the course, she scores with 72 of her 135 shots at the basket. Stating clearly any assumptions made, investigate whether or not the course has improved her shooting ability.

3.4   Poisson population mean

In the previous Section it was seen how a Poisson distribution may be used as an approximation to a binomial situation when testing hypotheses concerning a population proportion. However, there are situations for which a Poisson distribution is appropriate in its own right when testing hypotheses concerning a population mean value.

Under what conditions would you expect a Poisson distribution to provide a suitable model for a random variable?

Recall from Chapter 6 of *Statistics*, that if $X \sim Po(\lambda)$ then

$$P(X = x) = \frac{\lambda^x e^{-\lambda}}{x!} \quad x = 0, 1, 2, 3, \ldots,$$

with mean $= \lambda$ and variance $= \lambda$.

What do you know about the sum of two independent Poisson variables?

Example

The number of faults in one metre of a particular type of thread is known to have a Poisson distribution. It is claimed that the average number of faults is 0.02 per metre. A random sample of 100 one metre lengths of the thread reveals a total of 6 faults. Does this information support the claim?

Solution

Remembering that if $A \sim Po(a)$ independent of $B \sim Po(b)$ then $C = A + B \sim Po(a+b)$, and denoting the total number of faults in the 100 one metre lengths by X, then if the claim is valid

$$X \sim Po(100 \times 0.02 = 2)$$

It is thus required to test

$\quad$ H_0: $\lambda = 2$

$\quad$ H_1: $\lambda \neq 2$ $\quad$ (two-tailed)

$\quad$ Significance level, $\alpha = 0.05$ (say)

The observed number of faults is 6, and using tables of the Cumulative Poisson Distribution Functions with $\lambda = 2$ (see Appendix)

$\quad$ $P(X \geq 6) = 1 - P(X \leq 5)$

$\qquad\qquad\quad = 1 - 0.9834 = 0.0166 < 0.025$ (two-tailed)

There is evidence, at the 5% level of significance, that the claim is not valid.

Activity 4   Simulated traffic flow

The random variable X denotes the number of vehicles in a 30 second interval passing a traffic check point on a country road.

Use a three-digit random number, y, to generate an 'observed' value, x, of X using the following rules.

$000 \leq y \leq 548$	$x = 0$
$549 \leq y \leq 877$	$x = 1$
$878 \leq y \leq 976$	$x = 2$
$977 \leq y \leq 996$	$x = 3$
$997 \leq y \leq 999$	$x = 4$

Using the above rules, obtain 5 'observed' values of X.

Use the total of these values to test the hypothesis that the average number of vehicles passing the traffic check point in 30 seconds is 0.60.

Repeat the test for 10, 15 and 20 simulated 'observed' values of X.

Consider the conclusions of your four tests.

For a Poisson distribution with a mean greater than 15, a normal distribution with $\mu = \sigma^2 = \lambda$ provides a good approximation (see Chapter 8 of *Statistics*).

Example

Prior to extensive modernisation of its forecourt, the average number of vehicles calling for fuel at a small garage has been 5 per hour. Following the modernisation, a total of 543 vehicles called for fuel in a random sample of 100 one-hour intervals. Has the modernisation of the garage's forecourt significantly increased the average number of vehicles calling for fuel?

Solution

If X denotes the total number of vehicles calling for fuel in the 100 one-hour intervals, then under the null hypothesis of no increase

$$X \sim Po(100 \times 5 = 500) \quad \approx \quad N(500, 500)$$

The test is thus as follows.

$H_0: \lambda = 500$

$H_1: \lambda > 500$ (one-tailed)

Significance level, $\alpha = 0.05$ (say)

Critical region is $z > 1.645$

Test statistic, $z = \dfrac{543 - 500}{\sqrt{500}} = 1.92$

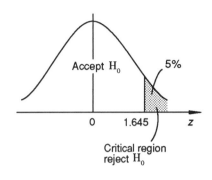

This value does lie in the critical region. Thus there is evidence, at the 5% level of significance, to suggest that the forecourt modernisation has resulted in an increase in the average number of vehicles calling for fuel.

Exercise 3D

1. In the manufacture of commercial carpet on a particular machine, small faults occur at random in the carpet at an average rate of 0.925 per 25 m². Following an overhaul of the machine, an inspection of a random sample of four 5 m × 5 m squares of carpet reveals only 2 small faults. Is there evidence, at the 5% level of significance, that, following the overhaul, the mean number of small faults has been reduced?

2. It is known that the numbers of parasites on fish in a pond follow a Poisson distribution. The total number of parasites on a random sample of 3 fish taken from the pond is 8. Test the hypothesis that the mean number of parasites per fish is 4.   (AEB)

3. The daily number of letters of complaint from customers received by a department store follows a Poisson distribution. Over a 150-day period, a total of 407 letters of complaint were received. Investigate, at the 1% level of significance, the claim that an average of fewer than 3 letters of complaint per day are received. What assumption is needed regarding the 150-day period?   (AEB)

4. It has been established over a period of time that the weekly numbers of breakages of crockery and glassware in a hotel follow a Poisson distribution with mean 27. On appointment, a new manager announces to staff that unless this mean level is reduced, bonuses will suffer as a result. Following this announcement, the weekly numbers of breakages over an eight-week period were as follows.

   23   19   17   20   25   32   22   26

   Do these data provide evidence that the manager's announcement has been heeded by the staff?

3.5   Population median

In Chapter 3 of *Statistics*, the median, m, of n items of data is defined as the $\left\{\left(\dfrac{n+1}{2}\right)\right\}$th item of data; or, in other words, the middle item.

For a random variable, X, with median η, this leads to the result

$$P(X < \eta) = P(X > \eta) = 0.5$$

or

$$P(X - \eta < 0) = P(X - \eta > 0) = 0.5$$

or

$$P(X - \eta \text{ is negative}) = P(X - \eta \text{ is positive}) = 0.5$$

These equally probable positive and negative values lead to a test for a hypothesised value of a population median based upon a binomial distribution with $p = P(+\text{sign}) = 0.5$ under H_0.

Note however that, contrary to all the other tests in this chapter, no assumption needs to be made about the distribution of X itself. As a result this sign test for a population median is an example of a **non-parametric** test.

Tests which require a knowledge of, or assumption about, the distribution of the parent population (e.g. normal, binomial, Poisson) are called **parametric** tests.

Example

The values below are the scores (maximum 20) obtained in an aptitude test by a random sample of 11 graduates. It is known that for the non-graduate population the median score is 12. Is there evidence, at the 10% significance level, that graduates achieve a higher median score than the non-graduate population?

$$14 \quad 15 \quad 9 \quad 10 \quad 10 \quad 13 \quad 14 \quad 19 \quad 12 \quad 16 \quad 13$$

Solution

$$H_0: \eta = 12$$

$$H_1: \eta > 12 \qquad \text{(one-tailed)}$$

Significance level, $\alpha = 0.10$

Signs of (score – 12) are

$$+ \quad + \quad - \quad - \quad - \quad + \quad + \quad + \quad 0 \quad + \quad +$$

Let X denote the number of + signs. Then, ignoring the one 0 in this case, under H_0,

$$X \sim B(10, 0.50) \text{ with observed value of } X = 7.$$

Now

$$P(X \geq 7) = 1 - P(X \leq 6) = 1 - 0.8281 = 0.1719 > 0.10$$

Thus there is no evidence, at the 10% level of significance, to suggest that graduates achieve a higher median score than the non-graduate population.

What additional information would be required in the above example in order to test $H_0: \mu = 12$ versus $H_1: \mu > 12$?

Activity 5 Weights and measures re-visited

Using your data collected for Activity 1, test the hypothesis that the true median value for the contents is equal to the value stated as contents.

Explain the reasons for the similarity, or difference, between your conclusions for the two activities.

Exercise 3E

1. The following values are the annual salaries, in £, of a random sample of 10 recent statistics' graduates.

    13 250   7 485   15 136   12 258   11 019
    14 268   19 536   14 326   16 326   17 984

    Investigate the claim, at the 10% significance level, that the median annual salary of all recent statistics' graduates exceeds £12 000.

2. Part of the assessment of a statistics course involves small groups of students giving a short presentation of their findings. The grades obtained by 13 such groups are as follows (highest = A, lowest = F).

    C B A B B C D C F B A B B

    Test the hypothesis that the median grade for all such group presentations is C.

3. It is claimed by a local resident that more than 50% of all the vehicles on an urban road exceed the 30 mph speed limit. The speed of each of a random sample of 24 vehicles is recorded with the following results.

    42 35 24 30 32 42 56 35
    34 30 29 41 38 38 30 29
    34 39 43 72 38 40 30 62

    Investigate the resident's claim.

4. During a working day a machine may require various adjustments. The machine's operator is asked to record the number of adjustments made to the machine each day for a period of 250 working days. She obtains the data displayed in the table below.

Number of adjustments	0	1	2	3	4	5	≥6
Number of days	61	54	65	18	12	9	31

    Test the hypothesis that the true median daily number of adjustments is 1.

    Explain why a test for the true mean daily number of adjustments would be difficult.

3.6 Miscellaneous Exercises

1. An investigation was conducted into the dust content in the flue gases of a particular type of solid-fuel boiler. Thirteen boilers were used under identical fuelling and extraction conditions. Over a similar period, the following quantities, in grams, of dust were deposited in traps inserted in each of the thirteen flues.

   73.1 56.4 82.1 67.2 78.7 75.1 48.0
   53.3 55.5 61.5 60.6 55.2 63.1

   Stating any necessary distributional assumptions, test, at the 5% level of significance, the hypothesis that

   (a) the population variance of dust deposit is 35 g²,

   (b) the population mean dust deposit is 60 g.
   (AEB)

2. As part of a research project, a random sample of 11 students sat a proposed national Physics examination and obtained the following percentage marks.

   30 44 49 50 63 38 43 36 54 40 26

   (a) Use a t-test, at the 10% significance level, to test the hypothesis that the true mean examination mark is 40%.

   (b) Use a sign test, at the 10% level, to test the hypothesis that the median mark for all candidates is 40%.

   What assumption is needed for (a) but not for (b), and do you think it is justified? (AEB)

3. Smallwoods Ltd run a weekly football pools competition. One part of this involves a fixed-odds contest where the entrant has to forecast correctly the result of each of five given matches. In the event of a fully correct forecast the entrant is paid out at odds of 100 to 1. During the last two years Miss Fortune has entered this fixed-odds contest 80 times. The table below summarises her results.

Number of matches correctly forecast per entry (x)	0	1	2	3	4	5
Number of entries with x correct forecasts (f)	4	13	27	22	13	1

   Assuming that the number of matches correctly forecast per entry follows a binomial distribution, test the hypothesis that the probability of Miss Fortune forecasting correctly the result of a single match is 0.5.

   On the evidence before you, and assuming that the point of entering is to win money, would you advise Miss Fortune to continue with this competition, and why? (AEB)

4. At a nuclear power station great care is taken to monitor employees' state of health. The table below gives the number of visits made by each of 10 employees from the reactor room to their general practitioners during one calendar year.

   3 6 5 7 4 2 3 5 1 4

   The number of such visits made by a member of the general public is known to have a Poisson distribution with mean 3. Assuming that the numbers of visits made by the nuclear power station's employees are also distributed as a Poisson random variable, test the hypothesis that the annual mean per employee is greater than 3. (AEB)

5. A random sample of 18 female computer operators each had their diastolic blood pressure measured to the nearest millimetre with the following results.

   57 64 77 82 66 94 72 83 61
   72 65 89 54 73 55 67 71 68

   (a) Stating any necessary distributional assumptions, show that there is no significant evidence to reject the hypothesis that the standard deviation of female computer operators' diastolic blood pressures is equal to that of the female population, namely 10 mm.

   (b) Making appropriate use of the statement in (a), investigate the claim that the mean diastolic blood pressure of female computer operators differs from 75 mm. (AEB)

6. The number of misprints per page in each national daily newspaper is known to follow a Poisson distribution. The mean number per page for the tabloid newspapers is 4. The Daily Planet, a quality newspaper, claims that although its pages are much bigger and contain more text than those of the tabloid papers, its mean number of misprints per page is certainly fewer.

   A random sample of 16 pages from recent editions of the Daily Planet results in the following numbers of misprints.

   0, 3, 2, 3, 1, 4, 5, 2, 3, 4, 5, 2, 4, 3, 3, 1.
   Investigate, at the 1% significance level, the Daily Planet's claim. (AEB)

7. Explain what is meant by the following terms when used in the context of an hypothesis test.

   (a) Null and alternative hypotheses.

   (b) Type 1 and Type 2 errors.

   (c) One-tailed and two-tailed tests.

   A new dietary treatment for a severe allergy is claimed to have a better cure rate than the accepted value of 60% for the well-established standard drug treatment. A random sample of 20 patients, suffering from the allergy, are given the new dietary treatment and as a result 17 are cured. Is the claim valid? (AEB)

8. A large food processing firm was considering introducing a new recipe for its ice cream. In a preliminary trial, a panel of 15 tasters were each asked to score the ice cream on a scale form 0 (awful) to 20 (excellent).Their scores were as follows.

    16 15 17 3 18 15 18 7
    12 14 6 4 19 14 17

    The mean score in a similar trial for the firm's existing ice cream was 14. Test the hypothesis that the mean score for the new ice cream was no different.

    Because of the erratic nature of the scores obtained, doubt was expressed as to the assumption that scores were normally distributed. As a result it was suggested that a sign test for a median was perhaps more appropriate. Given that the median score in the trial for their existing ice cream was 13, what can be concluded? (AEB)

9. The external diameter, in centimetres, of each of a random sample of 10 pistons manufactured on a particular machine was measured with the results below.

    9.91, 9.89, 10.06, 9.98, 10.09,
    9.81, 10.01, 9.99, 9.87, 10.09.

    Stating any necessary assumptions, test the two distinct claims that piston rings manufactured on this machine have a mean external diameter of 10 cm with a variance of 0.005 cm². (AEB)

10. A sweet shop sells chocolates which appear, at first sight, to be identical. Of a random sample of 80 chocolates, 61 had hard centres and the rest soft centres. Test the hypothesis that 70% of chocolates have hard centres.

    The chocolates are all in the shape of circular disks and the diameters, in millimetres, of the 19 soft centred chocolates were as follows.

    279 263 284 277 281 269 266
    271 262 275 266 272 281
    274 279 277 267 269 275

    Assuming that the diameters of the soft centred chocolates are normally distributed, test, at the 10% significance level, the hypothesis that their mean diameter is 275 mm.

    What changes would you make to your test if it was known that the standard deviation of the diameters of soft centred chocolates was 5 mm? (AEB)

11. It is known that repeated weighings of the same object on a particular chemical balance give readings which are normally distributed. Past evidence, using experienced operators, suggests that the mean is equal to the mass of the object and that the standard deviation is 0.25 mg.

    A trainee operator makes seven repeated weighings of the same object, which is known to have a mass of 19.5 mg, and obtains the following readings.

    19.1 19.4 19.0 18.8 19.7 19.8 19.3

    Is there any evidence that these results are more variable than those obtained by experienced operators?

    Hence investigate whether or not the trainee operator's readings are biased. (AEB)

12. As part of a statistics project, students observed five private cars passing a college and counted the number which were carrying the driver only, with no passengers. This was repeated 80 times. The results for a particular student were as follows.

Number of cars with driver only	0	1	2	3	4	5
Number of times observed	0	3	12	27	26	12

    Explain why the distribution of the number of cars with a driver only could be modelled by a binomial random variable. Assuming such a model is appropriate, state the value of the parameter n and estimate the value of the parameter p.

    Hence investigate the claim that more than 60% of cars contain the driver only. (AEB)

13. Explain **each** of the terms *significance level, critical region* and *test statistic* as used in hypothesis testing.

    The manager of a road haulage firm records the following times taken, in minutes, by a lorry to travel from the depot to a particular customer's factory.

    43 35 47 180 39 58 40 39 51

    The journey time of 3 hours was as a result of the driver being stopped by Customs & Excise Inspectors. The manager therefore removes this value before passing the data to you, as the firm's statistician, for analysis. Use the eight remaining values to test the hypothesis that the true mean journey time is 40 minutes.

    Comment on the manager's decision to remove the value of 3 hours and state what assumption may have been violated if this value had been included.

    What alternative test would you have considered if the manager had requested that all nine results should be analysed? (AEB)

14. A car insurance company found that the average amount it was paying on bodywork claims in 1992 was £435 with a standard deviation of £141. The first six bodywork payments, in £, in 1993 were

    548   209   534   198   789   633.

    Stating clearly all necessary assumptions, has there been a significant change in the average and in the variability of payments in 1993 as compared to 1992? (AEB)

15. (a) Before its annual overhaul, the mean operating time of an automatic machine was 100 seconds. After the overhaul, the following random sample of operating times, in seconds, was obtained.

    90 97 101 92 101 95 95 98 96 95

    Assuming that the time taken by the machine to perform the operation is a normally distributed random variable, test the hypothesis that the overhaul has improved the machine's operation.

    (b) The results of a survey showed that 3615 out of 10 000 families regularly purchased a specific weekly magazine. Test, at the 1% level of significance, the claim that more than 35% of families buy the magazine.

    (AEB)

16. A nurseryman decided to keep records of the first year's growth of his pine seedlings. On the first occasion he found a mean growth of 11.5 cm with a standard deviation of 2.5 cm. The following year he used an experimental soil preparation for all his seedlings and the first year's growth of a random sample of eight of the seedlings was

    7, 23, 19, 25, 11, 18, 17 and 15 cm.

    (a) Assuming these data may be regarded as a random sample from a normal distribution, test at the 5% significance level, whether there has been a change in

    (i) the standard deviation,

    (ii) the mean.

    (b) Explain to the nurseryman why the conclusions in (a) cannot necessarily be attributed to the new soil preparation. (AEB)

17. The development engineer of a company making razors records the time it takes him to shave, on seven mornings, using a standard razor made by the company. The times, in seconds, were

    217, 210, 254, 237, 232, 228, 243.

    Assuming that this may be regarded as a random sample from a normal distribution, with mean μ and variance σ^2 test, at the 5% level of significance, the hypothesis that

    (a) $\sigma = 10$ seconds,

    (b) $\mu = 240$ seconds. (AEB)

18. Packets of ground filter coffee have a nominal weight of 200 g. The distribution of weights may be assumed to be normal. A random sample of 30 packets had the following weights.

    218 207 214 189 211 206 203 217 183 186
    219 213 207 214 203 204 195 197 213 212
    188 221 217 184 186 216 198 211 216 200

    Investigate the assumption that the mean weight of all packets is 200 g.

    Test the hypothesis that 15% of packets weigh less than 190 g. (AEB)

19. (a) The number of accidents per day on a stretch of motorway is known to have a Poisson distribution. Police claim that there is an average of more than one accident per day. Over a particular 7-day period there is a total of 13 accidents. Investigate the claim of the police.

    (b) The results of a survey to establish the attitude of individuals to a particular proposal showed that three quarters of those interviewed were house owners. Of the 200 interviewed, only 12 of the 70 in favour of the proposal were not house owners. Test the hypothesis that the percentage of house holders in favour of the proposal is 40.

    (AEB)

20. The resistances (in ohms) of a sample from a batch of resistors were as follows.

    2314   2456   2389   2361   2360   2332   2402

    Stating any necessary assumptions, test the hypothesis that the true standard deviation of the resistors is 30 ohms.

    Hence test the hypothesis that the actual mean resistance of the resistors is 2400 ohms. (AEB)

21. Explain the difference between *parametric* and *non-parametric* hypothesis tests, and give an example of each type.

    A local authority offers all of its employees regular health checks. As part of the check, several physiological measurements are taken on each person.

    (a) The ordered scores for one of the measurements on nine employees were as follows.

    9 11 50 54 58 69 76 91 95

    Test the hypothesis that the median score for this measurement is 50. (AEB)

    (b) For another measurement, a random sample of 100 employees had 19 scores of exactly 50 and 30 scores above 50. Investigate the claim that the median score for this measurement is less than 50. (AEB)

22. Experimental components for use in aircraft engines were tested to destruction under extreme conditions. The survival times, X days, of ten components were as follows.

    207 381 411 673 534 294 697 344 418 554

    (a) Assuming that the survival time, under these conditions, for all the experimental components is normally distributed, assess the validity of the claim that the mean survival time exceeds 400 days.

    (b) Given that the standard deviation of survival times is known to be 150 days, what changes would you make to your test procedure in (a)? (AEB)

23. The external diameters (measured in units of 0.01 mm above nominal value) of a sample of piston rings produced on the same machine were

    11 9 32 18 29 11 21 19 6

    (a) Assuming a normal distribution, and given that the target value is 20 and a standard deviation of at most 10 is acceptable, carry out appropriate hypothesis tests so as to comment on the performance of the machine.

    (b) It was later discovered that an error had been made in zeroing the measuring device and that all the measurements in the sample should be increased by 12. How, if at all, does this affect your conclusions in (a)? (AEB)

24. Explain **each** of the terms *null hypothesis*, *critical region* and *test statistic* as used in hypothesis testing.

    Employees of a firm carrying out motorway maintenance are issued with brightly coloured waterproof jackets. These come in different sizes numbered 1 to 5. The last 40 jackets issued were of the following sizes.

2	3	3	1	3	3	2	4	3	2
5	4	1	2	3	3	2	4	5	3
2	4	4	1	5	3	3	2	3	3
1	3	4	3	3	2	5	1	4	4

    Assuming that the 40 employees may be regarded as a random sample of all employees, test the hypothesis, at the 5% significance level, that 40% of all employees require size 3.

    Test the claim that size 3 is the median size. (AEB)

4 HYPOTHESIS TESTING: TWO SAMPLE TESTS

Objectives

After studying this chapter you should

- appreciate the need for two sample tests;

- be able to carry out a test for the equality of two normal population variances;

- understand when, and be able, to carry out normal and t-tests for the equality of two normal population means using information from two independent samples;

- understand when, and be able, to carry out a t-test for the equality of two population means using information from paired samples;

- be able to carry out a sign test for a paired samples design;

- be able to analyse the results of a paired samples design using the Wilcoxon signed-ranks test.

4.0   Introduction

In the previous chapter, tests were described for a parameter of a single population. In this chapter, some of these tests will be developed, and new ones introduced, to test for the equality of a parameter in two populations.

It is a well-known and frequently stated fact that, on average, men are significantly taller than women. Less well-known is the fact that the variability in men's heights is greater than that in women's heights. However, is this latter difference significant?

In this chapter you will see how similar facts are justified, and similar questions are answered.

Activity 1   Hand span 1

Using a 30 cm ruler, measure and record the span (thumb to fourth finger) of the dominant hand of each of a random sample of between 10 and 15 males. Repeat for a random sample of females; the two sample sizes need not be equal.

(a) Calculate appropriate summary statistics for each of your two samples.

(b) Comment upon any differences or similarities between males and females as regards dominant hand span.

(c) Name a probability distribution that may be appropriate for hand span.

(d) State, in words, two possible hypotheses regarding the difference, if any, between male and female dominant hand spans.

Activity 2   Hand span 2

Using a 30 cm ruler, measure and record the span (thumb to fourth finger) of both the dominant and non-dominant hands of each of a random sample of between 10 and 15 people.

(a) For each person, calculate the difference
(dominant hand span) minus (non-dominant hand span).

(b) Calculate summary statistics for your differences.

(c) Formulate hypotheses in terms of the variable 'difference' to investigate the claim that, on average, the span of a person's dominant hand is greater than that of their non-dominant hand.

What is the key difference in experimental design between Activity 1 and Activity 2?

4.1   Two normal population variances

One possible question arising from the data collected in Activity 1 might be:

> "Is the variability in dominant hand span the same for males and females?"

This question may be formulated as the following two hypotheses.

H_0: $\sigma_1^2 = \sigma_2^2$ (1 = male, 2 = female)

H_1: $\sigma_1^2 \neq \sigma_2^2$ (where σ^2 denotes population variance)

It is important to note that, although an assumption of normal populations is required for such tests, no assumption is required as to the equality or otherwise of the population means μ_1 and μ_2.

In Section 3.2, a statistic based upon the sample variance, $\hat{\sigma}^2$ was used in testing hypotheses concerning a single normal population variance (or standard deviation). Here, when testing the equality of two normal population variances (or standard deviations), the statistic used is the ratio of the two sample variances.

In fact

$$F = \frac{\hat{\sigma}_1^2 / \sigma_1^2}{\hat{\sigma}_2^2 / \sigma_2^2}$$

has an F distribution with degrees of freedom

$$\nu_1 = n_1 - 1 \quad \text{and} \quad \nu_2 = n_2 - 1, \quad \text{written} \quad F_{(n_1-1, n_2-1)}.$$

The F distribution was developed by the American statistician, *G. W. Snedecor*, and so named in honour of *R. A. Fisher* (1890-1962) an eminent British statistician, who originally discovered the distribution in a slightly different form.

The distribution depends on the two parameters ν_1 and ν_2 for its shape and, except for large values of both, is positively skewed (like the χ^2 distribution). The distribution function for F exists for the range zero to infinity and is very complicated. The mean of $F_{(\nu_1, \nu_2)}$ exists only for $\nu_2 > 2$ and is given by $\dfrac{\nu_2}{(\nu_2 - 2)}$. The variance exists only for $\nu_2 > 4$ and is a complicated function of ν_1 and ν_2.

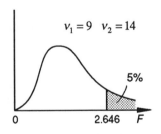

If $\quad H_0$: $\sigma_1^2 = \sigma_2^2$ is true, then $\quad F = \dfrac{\hat{\sigma}_1^2}{\hat{\sigma}_2^2} \sim F_{(n_1-1, n_2-1)}$

and, adopting the convention of always putting the larger $\hat{\sigma}^{2 \, 2}$ in the numerator, will result in H_0 being rejected when F becomes significantly large.

This significance can be assessed by making reference to tables of upper percentage points of the F distribution. For example:

the upper 5.0% point of $F_{(9,14)}$ is 2.646,

the upper 0.5% point of $F_{(4,6)}$ is 12.03.

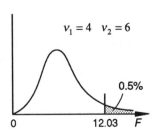

Note that, for larger values of v_1 and/or v_2, linear interpolation may be necessary to obtain accurate percentage points.

What is the upper 2.5% point for $F_{(14,9)}$?

Example

A random sample of 10 hot drinks from Dispenser A had a mean volume of 203 ml and a standard deviation of 3 ml. A random sample of 15 hot drinks from Dispenser B gave corresponding values of 206 ml and 5 ml. The amount dispensed by each machine may be assumed to be normally distributed. Test, at the 5% significance level, the hypothesis that there is no difference in the variability of the volume dispensed by the two machines.

Solution

$$H_0: \sigma_A^2 = \sigma_B^2$$

$$H_1: \sigma_A^2 \neq \sigma_B^2 \qquad \text{(two-tailed)}$$

Significance level, $\alpha = 0.05$

Since $\hat{\sigma}_A > \hat{\sigma}_B$ and the larger value is always placed in the numerator,

$$v_1 = n_B - 1 = 14 \text{ and } v_2 = n_A - 1 = 9$$

Using interpolation, the upper 2.5% point for

$$F_{(14,9)} = F_{(12,9)} - \frac{2}{3}\left(F_{(12,9)} - F_{(15,9)}\right)$$

$$= 3.868 - \frac{2}{3}(3.868 - 3.769)$$

$$= 3.802$$

Thus critical region is $F > 3.802$

Test statistic is

$$F = \frac{\hat{\sigma}_B{}^2}{\hat{\sigma}_A{}^2} = \frac{5^2}{3^2} = 2.78$$

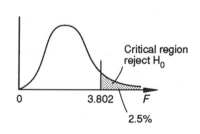

This value does not lie in the critical region. Thus there is no evidence, at the 5% level of significance, of a difference in the variability of the volume dispensed by the two machines.

Activity 3   Hand span 1 revisited

Test the hypothesis that the variability in dominant hand span for males is the same as that for females.

What assumption regarding hand span distributions did you make?

Explain why you consider the assumption to be reasonable.

Exercise 4A

1. An investigation was conducted into the dust content in the flue gases of two types of solid-fuel boilers. Thirteen boilers of type A and nine boilers of type B were used under identical fuelling and extraction conditions. Over a similar period, the following quantities, in grams, of dust were deposited in similar traps inserted in each of the twenty-two flues.

Type A	73.1	56.4	82.1	67.2
	78.7	75.1	48.0	
	53.3	55.5	61.5	
	60.6	55.2	63.1	
Type B	53.0	39.3	55.8	
	58.8	41.2	66.6	
	46.0	56.4	58.9	

Assuming that these independent samples come from normal populations, test for an equality of population variances.   (AEB)

2. Korn Krispies are a type of breakfast cereal, and they are packed in boxes with a nominal net mass of 296 grams. Owing to overwhelming demand, the manufacturers have installed a new and faster machine to fill the boxes with cereal. However, to meet government regulations, amongst other things the variability in the packed masses of these boxes should not increase over present levels. The table below gives the masses of a random sample of 10 boxes of cereal from the original packing machine, and the masses of a random sample of 12 boxes of cereal from the new machine.

Original machine		New machine	
301.0	292.4	295.3	320.4
293.6	298.7	289.4	312.2
291.1	285.1	288.5	292.9
305.1	290.0	299.8	300.2
297.0	302.2	293.6	276.3
		308.9	280.3

Assuming that these independent samples came from underlying normal populations, use a 5% level of significance to determine whether an increase in variance has occurred.   (AEB)

3. In a research study aimed at improving the design of bus cabs it was necessary to measure the functional arm reach of bus drivers. In a pilot study a research worker made this measurement on a random sample of ten bus drivers from a large depot, and next day her assistant made this measurement on a random sample of eight bus drivers from the same depot. The results, in millimetres, were as follows.

Research worker	730	698	712	686	724
	711	679	762	683	673
Assistant	701	642	651	700	672
	674	656	649		

Assuming a normal distribution for functional arm reach, test, at the 10% significance level, whether the samples could have come from populations with the same variance.   (AEB)

4. As part of a research study into pattern recognition, subjects were asked to examine a picture and see if they could distinguish a word. The picture contained the word 'technology' written backwards and camouflaged by an elaborate pattern. Of the 23 librarians who took part 11 succeeded in recognising the word whilst of 19 designers, 13 succeeded. The times, in seconds, for the successful subjects to recognise the word were as follows.

Librarians	55	18	99	54	87	11	
	62	68	27	90	57		
Designers	23	69	34	27	51	29	45
	42	48	74	31	30	31	

Stating any necessary assumptions, investigate the hypothesis that the variability of times for librarians significantly exceeds that for designers.   (AEB)

5. The light attenuation of trees may be measured by photometric methods, which are very time consuming, or by photographic techniques which are much quicker. The light attenuation of an oak tree was repeatedly measured by both methods independently. The following results, expressed as percentages, were obtained.

| Photometric | 85.6 86.1 86.5 85.1 86.8 87.3 |
| Photographic | 82.4 84.7 86.1 87.2 82.4 85.8 84.3 |

Assuming normal distributions, test at the 5% level of significance whether there is a difference in the variability of the two methods.

(AEB)

6. A firm is to buy a fleet of cars for use by its salesmen and wishes to choose between two alternative models, A and B. It places an advertisement in a local paper offering 20 litres of petrol free to anyone who has bought a new car of either model in the last year. The offer is conditional on being willing to answer a questionnaire and to note how far the car goes, under typical driving conditions, on the free petrol supplied. The following data were obtained.

	Km driven on 20 litres of petrol			
Model A	187	218	173	235
Model B	157	198	154	184
	202	174	146	173

Assuming these data to be random samples from two normal populations, test whether the population variances may be assumed equal.

List good and bad features of the experimental design ands suggest how you think it could be improved.

(AEB)

4.2 Two normal population means – case 1

Independent samples and known population variances – normal test

It is claimed that Brand A size D alkaline batteries last longer than those of Brand B.

Is this claim likely to be true for all Brand A size D alkaline batteries?

All mass-produced articles are liable to random variation which should be monitored and controlled, but cannot be eliminated entirely. Such variation is generally assumed, with good cause, to be approximately normally distributed. Thus it is quite possible that, whilst the claim may be true **on average**, it is not the case for every Brand A size D alkaline battery.

Which other population parameter may influence the validity of the claim?

Investigating claims of a population mean difference generally requires a comparison of two sample means; in the illustration above, measuring the lifetimes of all Brand A (and B) battery lifetimes would leave none for sale!

As noted earlier, the variance of a sample mean depends upon the sample size and the variance of the population from which the sample is selected. Consequently the sizes of the two samples and the variances of the two populations will influence the comparison of sample means.

From earlier work you have seen that:

(a) if $X \sim N(\mu, \sigma^2)$, then $\overline{X} \sim N\left(\mu, \dfrac{\sigma^2}{n}\right)$

(b) if $X_1 \sim N(\mu_1, \sigma_1^2)$ independent of $X_2 \sim N(\mu_2, \sigma_2^2)$,

  then $X_1 - X_2 \sim N(\mu_1 - \mu_2, \sigma_1^2 + \sigma_2^2)$

Combining these two results gives

$$\overline{X}_1 - \overline{X}_2 \sim N\left(\mu_1 - \mu_2, \frac{\sigma_1^2}{n_1} + \frac{\sigma_2^2}{n_2}\right)$$

Hence

$$z = \frac{(\overline{x}_1 - \overline{x}_2) - (\mu_1 - \mu_2)}{\sqrt{\dfrac{\sigma_1^2}{n_1} + \dfrac{\sigma_2^2}{n_2}}}$$

is a standardised normal statistic and may be used to test the equality of two normal population means, μ_1 and μ_2, based upon independent random samples.

It is perhaps worth noting here that for $n_1 > 30$ and $n_2 > 30$, the sample variances, $\hat{\sigma}_1^2$ and $\hat{\sigma}_2^2$ may be used as estimates of σ_1^2 and σ_2^2, respectively, so providing an approximate z statistic.

In this case, why can the requirement of normal populations be relaxed?

Example

The alkalinity, in milligrams per litre, of water in the upper reaches of rivers in a particular region is known to be normally distributed with a standard deviation of 10 mg/l. Alkalinity readings in the lower reaches of rivers in the same region are also known to be normally distributed, but with a standard deviation of 25 mg/l.

Ten alkalinity readings are made in the upper reaches of a river in the region and fifteen in the lower reaches of the same river with the following results.

Upper reaches	91	75	91	88	94	63	86	77	71	69
Lower reaches	86	95	135	121	68	64	113	108	79	62
	143	108	121	85	97					

Investigate, at the 1% level of significance, the claim that the true mean alkalinity of water in the lower reaches of this river is greater than that in the upper reaches.

Solution

$$H_0: \mu_1 = \mu_2 \qquad (1 = \text{ lower, } 2 = \text{ upper})$$

$$H_1: \mu_1 > \mu_2 \qquad \text{(one-tailed)}$$

Significance level, $\alpha = 0.01$

Critical region is $z > 2.326$

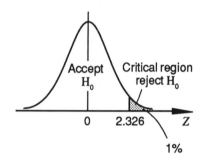

Under H_0, the test statistic is

$$z = \frac{(\bar{x}_1 - \bar{x}_2)}{\sqrt{\dfrac{\sigma_1^2}{n_1} + \dfrac{\sigma_2^2}{n_2}}}$$

Calculation gives $\bar{x}_1 = \dfrac{1485}{15} = 99.0$ and $\bar{x}_2 = \dfrac{805}{10} = 80.5$,

so

$$z = \frac{(99.0 - 80.5)}{\sqrt{\dfrac{25^2}{15} + \dfrac{10^2}{10}}} = 2.57$$

This value does lie in the critical region so H_0 is rejected. Thus there is evidence, at the 1% level of significance, to suggest that the true mean alkalinity of water in the lower reaches of the river is greater than that in the upper reaches.

Activity 4   Random numbers

Random numbers generated on calculators are claimed to be rectangularly distributed within the range 0 to 1.

(a) State the mean and variance of this distribution.

(b) Explain why the average of 10 such random numbers may be assumed to be approximately normally distributed.

Using a calculator (Model A) with a random number key, generate and calculate $n_A = 12$ such averages together with their mean $\bar{x}_A$. Repeat, using a different make of calculator (Model B), to obtain $\bar{x}_B$ from $n_B = 8$ averages of 10 random numbers each.

(c) Investigate the claim that $\mu_A = \mu_B$, assuming that

$$\sigma_A^2 = \sigma_B^2 = \frac{1}{120}.$$

(d) Explain how the assumption in (c) was obtained.

Exercise 4B

1. The mass of crisps delivered into bags by a machine is known to be normally distributed with a standard deviation of 0.5 g.

   Prior to a minor overhaul of the machine, the contents, in grams, of a random sample of six bags are as follows.

   151.7 152.6 150.8 151.9 152.3 151.5

   After the overhaul, which from past experience is known not to affect the standard deviation, the contents of a random sample of twelve bags were measured with the results below.

   151.1 150.7 149.0 150.3 151.3 151.4
   150.8 149.5 150.2 150.6 150.9 151.3

   Test, at the 5% significance level, the hypothesis that the minor overhaul has had no effect on the mean mass of crisps delivered by the machine.

2. A firm obtains its supply of steel wire of a particular gauge from each of two manufacturers A and B. The firm suspects that the mean breaking strength, in newtons(N), of wire from manufacturer A differs from that supplied by manufacturer B.

   The table below shows the breaking strengths of random samples of wire from each of the two manufacturers.

   A | 80.5 83.1 73.6 70.4 68.9 71.6 82.3 78.6 73.4

   B | 71.4 86.2 81.4 72.3 78.9 80.3 81.4 78.0

   Assuming all such breaking strengths to be normally distributed with a standard deviation of 5 N, investigate the firm's suspicion.

3. The manager of a lemonade bottling plant is interested in comparing the performance of two production lines, one of which has only recently been installed. For each line she selects 10 one-hour periods at random and records the number of crates completed in each hour. The table below gives the results.

Production line	Number of crates completed per hour
1 (new)	78 87 79 82 87 81 85 80 82 83
2 (old)	74 77 78 70 87 83 76 78 81 76

   From past experience with this kind of equipment it is known that the variance in these figures will be 10 for Line 1 and 25 for Line 2. Assuming that these samples came from normal populations with these variances, test the hypothesis that the two populations have the same mean.   (AEB)

4. Rice Pops (RP) are a type of breakfast cereal which are packed into boxes with a quoted net mass of 296 g by one of two different filling machines. The mass of RP delivered by filling machine A, an old machine, is known to be normally distributed with a standard deviation of 5 g. The mass of RP delivered by machine B, a new machine, is also known to be normally distributed but with a standard deviation of 3 g. The table below shows the net masses, in grams, of a random sample of 12 boxes filled by machine A and of a random sample of 15 boxes filled by machine B

Boxes filled by machine A

296	296	302
304	300	306
305	297	307
303	299	306

Boxes filled by machine B

296	297	299
301	297	299
298	302	304
298	299	303
297	296	299

Test the hypothesis that there is no significant difference in the mean mass of RP delivered by the two filling machines. (AEB)

5. During the first three months of 1993 a technician was timed for the repair of an electronic instrument on 12 separate occasions. In the same period a trainee technician was timed for the repair of a similar instrument on 14 occasions. These times, in minutes, are given in the table below.

Technician	344	278	267	234	212	271
	341	391	176	164	214	399

Trainee	279	351	282	280	258	267	312
	357	322	249	228	315	311	341

(a) Assuming that these observations may be regarded as independent random samples from normal populations with known standard deviations of 80 minutes (for the technician) and 40 minutes (for the trainee technician), test the hypothesis that there is no difference in the mean times.

(b) Subsequently it was learned that the times for the trainee were incorrectly recorded and that each of the values above is 30 minutes too small. What, if any, difference does this make to the result of the test you have just completed? (AEB)

6. James and his sister, Alison, each deliver 30 papers on their evening paper rounds and each are paid the same amount. One evening Alison claims this system of equal payment to be unfair as her round takes on average longer than that of her brother, James. To test her claim their father, unknown to them, records their delivery times for 12 consecutive days. One of Alison's times had to be discounted as the front tyre of her bicycle was punctured. The recorded times, in minutes, were as shown below.

	Delivery times (minutes)
James	45 30 39 32 34 43 38 35 43 39 32 34
Alison	49 42 39 45 38 49 43 36 33 41 36

(a) Assuming each child's delivery times are normally distributed with the same known standard deviation of 5 minutes, test whether Alison's claim is justified, using a 5% level of significance.

(b) If Alison had in fact claimed that the system of equal payment was unfair because the average delivery times for the two rounds were different, what changes would you make to your test procedure in (a)? (AEB)

4.3 Two normal population means – case 2

Independent samples and unknown but equal population variances – *t*-test

In Section 4.2, the test statistic z required that the two populations are normal with known variances, σ_1^2 and σ_2^2. If however both sample sizes are greater than 30, it was stated that sample variances may be used as estimates to provide an approximate z statistic.

In most practical situations, the population variances are unknown and the sample sizes are less than 30. Refer to your data collected in Activity 1.

If it may be assumed, or has been confirmed using the F-test of Section 4.1, that the population variances are equal, but unknown, then a test is available for all sample sizes providing the two populations are normal. (For small samples from normal populations with unknown and unequal variances, an involved approximate t-test is available, but it is outside the scope of this text.)

Returning to the test statistic of Section 4.1, defined by

$$z = \frac{(\bar{x}_1 - \bar{x}_2) - (\mu_1 - \mu_2)}{\sqrt{\dfrac{\sigma_1^{\,2}}{n_1} + \dfrac{\sigma_2^{\,2}}{n_2}}}$$

If $\sigma_1^2 = \sigma_2^2 = \sigma^2$, then

$$z = \frac{(\bar{x}_1 - \bar{x}_2) - (\mu_1 - \mu_2)}{\sigma \sqrt{\dfrac{1}{n_1} + \dfrac{1}{n_2}}}.$$

Now both sample variances, $\hat{\sigma}_1^{\,2}$ and $\hat{\sigma}_2^{\,2}$, are estimates of σ^2, so this information can be combined to form a pooled (weighted) estimate of variance defined by

$$\hat{\sigma}_p^{\,2} = \frac{(n_1 - 1)\hat{\sigma}_1^{\,2} + (n_2 - 1)\hat{\sigma}_2^{\,2}}{n_1 + n_2 - 2}$$

From Section 2.1 you saw that, when σ^2 is replaced by $\hat{\sigma}^2$ in a z statistic, the result is a t statistic.

Hence

$$\frac{(\bar{x}_1 - \bar{x}_2) - (\mu_1 - \mu_2)}{\hat{\sigma}_p \sqrt{\dfrac{1}{n_1} + \dfrac{1}{n_2}}}$$

is a t statistic with degrees of freedom given by $v = n_1 + n_2 - 2$.

What interpretation has the pooled estimate of variance if the two samples are of the same size?

Example

Mr Brown is the owner of a small bakery in a large town. He believes that the smell of fresh baking will encourage customers to purchase goods from his bakery. To investigate this belief, he records the daily sales for 10 days when all the bakery's windows are open, and the daily sales for another 10 days when all the windows are closed. The following sales, in £, are recorded.

Windows open	202.0 204.5 207.0 215.5 190.8
	215.6 208.8 187.8 204.1 185.7
Windows closed	193.5 192.2 199.4 177.6 205.4
	200.6 181.8 169.2 172.2 192.8

Assuming that these data may be deemed to be random samples from normal populations with the same variance, investigate the baker's belief.

Solution

H_0: $\mu_1 = \mu_2$ (1 = open, 2 = closed)

H_1: $\mu_1 > \mu_2$ (one-tailed)

Significance level, $\alpha = 0.05$ (say)

Degrees of freedom, $v = 10 + 10 - 2 = 18$

Critical region is $t > 1.734$

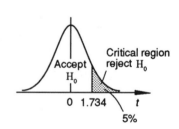

Under H_0, the test statistic is

$$t = \frac{(\bar{x}_1 - \bar{x}_2)}{\sigma_p \sqrt{\dfrac{1}{n_1} + \dfrac{1}{n_2}}}$$

Calculation gives

$$\bar{x}_1 = 202.18, \quad \hat{\sigma}_1^2 = 115.7284$$

and $\qquad \bar{x}_2 = 118.47, \quad \hat{\sigma}_2^2 = 156.6534$

Hence $\quad \hat{\sigma}_p^{\;2} = \dfrac{9 \times 115.7284 + 9 \times 156.6534}{10 + 10 - 2}$

$$\qquad\qquad = \dfrac{115.7284 + 156.6534}{2} \quad \text{(mean when } n_1 = n_2\text{)}$$

so $\qquad \hat{\sigma}_p = 11.67$

Thus $\qquad t = \dfrac{202.18 - 188.47}{11.67\sqrt{\dfrac{1}{10} + \dfrac{1}{10}}} = 2.63$

This value does lie in the critical region so H_0 is rejected. Thus there is evidence, at the 5% level of significance, to suggest that the smell of fresh baking will encourage customers to purchase goods from Mr Brown's bakery.

Example

Referring back to the Example in Section 4.1 concerning the two drink dispensers, test, at the 5% level of significance, the hypothesis that there is no difference in the mean volume dispensed by the two machines.

Solution

$H_0 \colon \mu_A = \mu_B$

$H_1 \colon \mu_A \neq \mu_B \quad$ (two-tailed)

Significance level, $\alpha = 0.05$

Degrees of freedom, $v = 10 + 15 - 2 = 23$

Critical region is $t < -1.714$ or $t > 1.714$

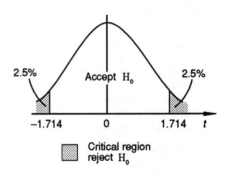

Under H_0, the test statistic is

$$t = \dfrac{\left(\bar{x}_1 - \bar{x}_2 \right)}{\hat{\sigma}_p \sqrt{\dfrac{1}{n_1} + \dfrac{1}{n_2}}}$$

$\bar{x}_A = 203$, $\hat{\sigma}_A = 3$ and $\bar{x}_B = 206$, $\hat{\sigma}_B = 5$

Hence

$$\hat{\sigma}_p^{\;2} = \dfrac{9 \times 3^2 + 14 \times 5^2}{10 + 15 - 2} = 18.7391 = 4.33^2$$

Thus $\qquad t = \dfrac{203 - 206}{4.33\sqrt{\dfrac{1}{10} + \dfrac{1}{15}}} = -1.70$

This value does not lie in the critical region so H_0 is not rejected. Thus there is no evidence, at the 5% level of significance, to suggest that there is a difference in the mean volume dispensed by the two machines.

Activity 5   Hand span 1 revisited again, perhaps!

If in Activity 3, you did NOT reject the hypothesis that the variability in dominant hand span for males is the same as that for females, now test the hypothesis that the true mean handspan for males is greater than that for females.

Activity 6   Random numbers revisited

Re-investigate the claim made in Part (c) of Activity 4, assuming only that $\sigma_A^2 = \sigma_B^2$. Compare your two conclusions.

Exercise 4C

1. A microbiologist wishes to determine whether there is any difference in the time it takes to make yoghurt from two different starters; lactobacillus acidophilus (A) and bulgarius (B). Seven batches of yoghurt were made with each of the starters. The table below shows the time taken, in hours, to make each batch.

Starter A	6.8	6.3	7.4	6.1	8.2	7.3	6.9
Starter B	6.1	6.4	5.7	5.5	6.9	6.3	6.7

   Assuming that both sets of times may be considered to be random samples from normal populations with the same variance, test the hypothesis that the mean time taken to make yoghurt is the same for both starters.

2. Referring to Question 1 of Exercise 4A, test for an equality of population means. (AEB)

3. Referring to Question 2 of Exercise 4A, test the hypothesis that the original and new machines deliver the same mean mass of Korn Krispies. (AEB)

4. Referring to Question 3 of Exercise 4A, show that, at the 1% significance level, the hypothesis that the samples are from populations with equal means is rejected. (AEB)

5. Referring to Question 5 of Exercise 4A, test, at the 5% significance level, whether there is a difference in the mean measurement by the two methods. (AEB)

6. A new chemical process is developed for the manufacture of nickel-cadmium batteries. The company believes that this new process will increase the mean lifetime of a battery by 5 hours as compared to that of batteries produced by the old process. Sixteen batteries produced by the old process were randomly selected and the mean and the standard deviation of the lifetimes of these batteries were 105.2 hours and 9.1 hours, respectively. Fifteen batteries produced by the new process were also randomly selected and calculations gave corresponding values of 112.4 and 8.3 hours.

   Assuming all battery lifetimes to be normally distributed, test at the 5% significance level whether there is

   (a) a difference in the variability of the two processes,

   (b) an increase of 5 hours in the mean lifetime of batteries produced by the new process as compared to that of batteries produced by the old process.

4.4 Two normal population means – case 3

Paired samples – *t*-test

To assess the claims of a new weight-reducing diet programme, a researcher weighs each of a random sample of 10 people about to enrol on the programme. The researcher then calculates correctly their mean and standard deviation to be 72.1 kg and 6.8 kg, respectively. Later, the researcher weighs each of a random sample of 12 people who have adhered strictly to the programme for three months. Correct calculations give their mean weight as 80.4 kg with a standard deviation of 5.1 kg. The researcher therefore concludes that, rather than reduce people's weights, the diet programme actually appears to cause people to gain weight!

Why would the researcher's data and conclusion be challenged, even ridiculed, by the diet programme's sponsors?

In some investigations, the inherent variation of the subjects or items used in the study can negate, mask or enhance the actual differences of interest. However in many of these cases, with sensible planning of the investigation, the differences of interest can be assessed separately from the inherent variation.

Thus in the previous illustration regarding a diet programme, the researcher should have weighed the same 10 people after three months as were weighed before enrolment. The measure of weight loss for each person would then be 'weight before minus weight after 3 months'. The mean and standard deviation of the 10 differences so calculated could then be validly used to assess the programme's claim. Note that variations in weight between the 10 people are no longer confused with weight loss. On the other hand, the two samples are no longer independent since the same 10 people form each sample, with the results thereby occurring in pairs; hence the name, paired samples.

Assuming that the two populations from which the paired samples of size n are selected are distributed with means μ_1 and μ_2, respectively, then from earlier work the differences between pairs will also be normally distributed with means $\mu_1 - \mu_2 = \mu_d$ and variance σ_d^2, say. Thus a test of H_0: $\mu_1 = \mu_2$ is equivalent to a test of H_0: $\mu_d = 0$.

Although the two populations may well be normally distributed, the key distributional assumption for the test is that the difference between pairs of values are approximately normally distributed.

Let $\bar{d}$ and $\hat{\sigma}_d^2$ denote the variance of the sample of n differences.

Then $\qquad \bar{d} \sim N\left(\mu_d, \dfrac{\sigma_d^2}{\sqrt{n}}\right)$

or $\qquad \dfrac{\bar{d} - \mu_d}{\dfrac{\sigma_d}{\sqrt{n}}} \sim N(0, 1)$

Thus, from Section 4.1,

$$\boxed{\dfrac{\bar{d} - \mu_d}{\dfrac{\hat{\sigma}_d}{\sqrt{n}}}}$$

is a t statistic with degrees of freedom, $v = n - 1$.

Example

A school mathematics teacher decides to test the effect of using an educational computer package, consisting of geometric designs and illustrations, to teach geometry. Since the package is expensive, the teacher wishes to determine whether using the package will result in an improvement in the pupils' understanding of the topic. The teacher randomly assigns pupils to two groups; a control group receiving standard lessons and an experimental group using the new package. The pupils are selected in pairs of equal mathematical ability, with one from each pair assigned at random to the control group and the other to the experimental group. On completion of the topic the pupils are given a test to measure their understanding. The results, percentage marks, are shown in the table.

Pair	1	2	3	4	5	6	7	8	9	10
Control	72	82	93	65	76	89	81	58	95	91
Experimental	75	79	84	71	82	91	85	68	90	92

Assuming percentage marks to be normally distributed, investigate the claim that the educational computer package produces an improvement in pupils' understanding of geometry.

Solution

$H_0: \mu_d = 0$ Difference $=$ Experimental $-$ Control

$H_1: \mu_d > 0$ (one-tailed)

Significance level, $\alpha = 0.05$ (say)

Degrees of freedom, $v = 10 - 1 = 9$

Critical region is $t > 1.833$

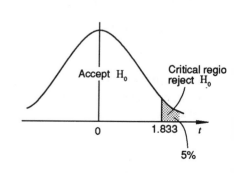

Under H_0, the test statistic is

$$t = \frac{\bar{d}}{\frac{\hat{\sigma}_d}{\sqrt{n}}}$$

The 10 differences (Experimental - Control) are

$$d: \quad 3 \quad -3 \quad -9 \quad 6 \quad 6 \quad 2 \quad 4 \quad 10 \quad -5 \quad 1$$

Hence $\qquad \sum d = 15$ and $\sum d^2 = 317$

so $\qquad \bar{d} = 1.5$ and $\hat{\sigma}_d = 5.72$

Thus $\qquad t = \dfrac{1.5}{\frac{5.72}{\sqrt{10}}} = 0.83$

This value does not lie in the critical region so H_0 is not rejected. Thus there is no evidence, at the 5% level of significance, to suggest that the educational computer package produces an improvement in pupils' understanding of geometry.

Activity 7   Hand span 2 revisited

Assuming the difference between dominant and non-dominant hand spans to be normally distributed, investigate the claim made in Part (c) of Activity 2.

Exercise 4D

1. A random sample of eleven students sat a Chemistry examination consisting of one theory paper and one practical paper. Their marks out of 100 are given in the table below.

Student	A	B	C	D	E	F	G	H	I	J	K
Theory mark	30	42	49	50	63	38	43	36	54	42	26
Practical mark	52	58	42	67	94	68	22	34	55	48	17

Assuming differences in pairs to be normally distributed, test, at the 5% level of significance, the hypothesis of no difference in mean mark on the two papers.   (AEB)

2. A convenience food, known as 'Quicknosh', was introduced into the British market in January 1992. After a poor year for sales the manufacturers initiated an intensive advertising campaign during January 1993. The table in the column opposite records the sales, in thousands of pounds, for a one-month period before and a one-month period after the advertising campaign, for each of eleven regions.

Region	A	B	C	D	E	F	G	H	I	J	K
Sales before campaign	2.4	2.6	3.9	2.0	3.2	2.2	3.3	2.1	3.1	2.2	2.8
Sales after campaign	3.0	2.5	4.0	4.1	4.8	2.0	3.4	4.0	3.3	4.2	3.9

Determine, at the 5% significance level, whether an increase in mean sales has occurred by using the *t*-test for paired values.   (AEB)

3. In an investigation to compare the accuracy of Crackshot and Fastfire 12-bore shotguns in clay pigeon shooting, ten competitors each fired 100 shots with each make of gun. Their scores are shown in the table below.

Competitor	A	B	C	D	E	F	G	H	I	J
Crackshot	93	99	90	86	85	94	87	91	96	79
Fastfire	87	91	86	87	78	95	89	84	88	74

It may be assumed that the differences between pairs of scores are approximately normally distributed. Examine the claim that the Crackshot shotgun is the more accurate for clay pigeon shooting. (AEB)

4. The following data are the third and fourth round scores of a random sample of five competitors in an open golf tournament.

Competitor	A	B	C	D	E
3rd round	76	75	72	75	79
4th round	70	73	71	68	76

Use a paired t-test and a 5% significance level to test whether there is a difference in the mean score of all competitors in the two rounds. (AEB)

5. In a study of memory recall, 12 students were given ten minutes to try to memorise a list of 20 nonsense words. Each student was then asked to list as many of the words as he or she could remember both one hour and twenty-four hours later. The numbers of words recalled correctly for each student are shown below.

Student	A	B	C	D	E	F	G	H	I	J	K	L
1 hr later	14	9	18	12	13	17	16	16	19	8	15	7
24 hrs later	10	6	14	6	8	10	12	10	14	5	10	5

Stating any necessary assumptions, used a paired t-test to determine whether there is evidence, at the 5% level of significance, that for all such students, the mean number of words recalled after one hour exceeds that recalled after twenty-four hours by 5 words. (AEB)

6. The temperature of the earth may be measured either by thermometers on the ground (x), which is an accurate but tedious method, or by sensors mounted in space satellites (y), which is a less accurate method and may be biased. The following table gives readings (°C) taken by both methods at eleven sites.

Site	Ground therm, x	Satellite sensors, y
1	4.6	4.7
2	17.3	19.5
3	12.2	12.5
4	3.6	4.2
5	6.2	6.0
6	14.8	15.4
7	11.4	14.9
8	14.9	17.8
9	9.3	9.7
10	10.4	10.5
11	7.2	7.4

Given that all readings are normally distributed, investigate the hypothesis that satellite sensors give, on average, significantly higher readings than the ground thermometers. (AEB)

4.5 Two population medians – case 1

Paired samples – sign test

The table below shows the grades obtained by each of a random sample of ten students in two pieces of Statistics coursework.

Student	1	2	3	4	5	6	7	8	9	10
Coursework 1 grade	A	B	B	C	D	C	C	A	B	C
Coursework 2 grade	B	C	B	D	C	D	C	B	C	D

What distinguishes these data from those considered so far in this Chapter?

The above grades are the results of a paired samples study since the same ten students constituted both samples. However the paired *t*-test of the previous Section requires the differences in pairs to be normally distributed. This is certainly not the case here so a non-parametric test is required. In fact since the grades are letters, rather than numbers, differences can reasonably be listed only as:

$$+ \quad + \quad 0 \quad + \quad - \quad + \quad 0 \quad + \quad + \quad +$$

where

     +   denotes (coursework 1 grade > coursework 2 grade)

     0   denotes (coursework 1 grade = coursework 2 grade)

     −   denotes (coursework 1 grade < coursework 2 grade)

Now if the distribution of grades in the two courseworks is the same, then the two population median grades, η_1 and η_2, will be the same.

Hence, under the null hypothesis of no difference between the grades in the two courseworks,

$$P(\text{difference is positive } ve) = P(\text{difference is negative } ve)$$

$$= 0.5.$$

This hypothesis can therefore be tested by reference to a binomial distribution with n = number of non-zero differences and $p = 0.5$.

What probability is required in the above illustration?

In the above illustration, the number of non-zero differences is $10 - 2 = 8$, so X = number of $+ve$ signs $\sim B(8, 0.5)$ under H_0, with the observed value of X being 7.

Since for $X \sim B(8, 0.5)$

$$P(X \geq 7) = 1 - P(X \leq 6)$$

$$= 1 - 0.9648$$

$$= 0.0352 < 0.025 \quad (5\% \text{ two-tailed})$$

there is no significant evidence to suggest that there is a difference between the grades achieved in the two statistics courseworks.

What probability would have been evaluated if the observed value of X had been 1?

Example

On a particular day the incoming mail in each of twelve selected towns was randomly divided into two similar batches prior to sorting. In each town one batch was then sorted by the traditional hand sorting method, the other by a new Electronic Post Code Sensor Device (EPCSD). The times taken, in hours, to complete the sorting of the batches are recorded below.

Town	A	B	C	D	E	F	G	H	I	J	K	L
Hand sort time	4.3	4.1	5.6	4.0	5.9	4.9	4.3	5.4	5.6	5.2	6.1	4.7
EPCSD sort time	3.7	5.3	4.5	3.1	4.8	4.9	3.5	4.9	4.6	4.1	5.7	4.7

Use the sign test and a 1% level of significance to investigate the claim that the EPCSD method is quicker.

Solution

Let   difference = (Hand sort time) − (EPCSD sort time)

H_0: No difference in the times $(\eta_1 = \eta_2)$

H_1: EPCSD method is quicker $(\eta_1 > \eta_2;$ one-tailed$)$

Significance level, $\alpha = 0.01$

Signs of differences are

$$+ \; - \; + \; + \; + \; 0 \; + \; + \; + \; + \; 0$$

Let X denote the number of + signs.

Then, ignoring the two 0's in this case, under H_0,

$X \sim B(10, 0.50)$ with observed value of $X = 9$

From tables, $P(X \geq 9) = 1 - P(X \leq 8)$

$$= 1 - 0.9893$$

$$= 0.0107 < 0.01 \quad \text{(one-tailed)}$$

Thus there is no evidence, at the 1% level of significance, that the EPSCD method is quicker than the traditional hand sorting method.

Activity 8   Brand preference

Obtain from your local supermarket two large bottles of cola (or orange or lemonade); one bottle having a well-known brand label, the other having the supermarket's own brand label.

(You may alternatively, or additionally, investigate crisps, biscuits, chocolate, baked beans, etc, providing that they are comparable in taste and cannot be identified readily by observation.)

Arrange for between 10 and 20 tasters to sample a small amount of each drink in (plastic) beakers labelled simply I or II with only you knowing which beaker contains the well-known brand and which contains the supermarket's own brand.

Ask the tasters independently to grade the quality of each of their samples as either

A: excellent, B: good, C: acceptable or D: unacceptable.

Using the sign test, investigate the claim that people cannot taste the difference between a well-known brand of soft drink and a supermarket's own brand.

Exercise 4E

1. Fifteen girls were each given an oral examination and a written examination in French. Their grades (highest = A, lowest = F) in the two examinations were as follows.

Girl	1	2	3	4	5	6	7	8
Oral exam	A	B	C	D	E	C	B	E
Written exam	B	D	D	C	E	D	C	D

Girl	9	10	11	12	13	14	15
Oral exam	E	C	D	C	E	C	B
Written exam	C	C	E	E	F	D	C

Using the sign test, investigate the hypothesis that one examination produces significantly different grades from the other. (AEB)

2. Apply the sign test to the data in Question 1 of Exercise 4D. Compare your conclusion with that obtained previously. (AEB)

3. Apply the sign test to the data in Question 2 of Exercise 4D. What assumption, made when using the paired *t*-test, is not needed for the sign test? (AEB)

4. Apply the sign test to the data in Question 3 of Exercise 4D. Comment on your conclusions to the two analyses. (AEB)

5. To measure the effectiveness of a drug for asthmatic relief, twelve subjects, all susceptible to asthma, were each randomly administered either the drug or a placebo during two separate asthma attacks. After one hour an asthmatic index was obtained on each subject with the following results.

Subject	1	2	3	4	5	6	7	8	9	10	11	12
Drug	28	31	17	18	31	12	33	24	18	25	19	17
Placebo	32	33	23	26	34	17	30	24	19	23	21	24

Making no distributional assumptions, investigate the claim that the drug significantly reduces the asthmatic index. (AEB)

6. Two methods for measuring the level of vitamin B12 in red blood cells were compared. Blood samples were taken from ten healthy adults, and, for each blood sample, the B12 level was determined using both methods. The resultant data are given below.

Adult	1	2	3	4	5	6	7	8	9	10
Method 1	204	238	209	277	197	226	203	131	282	76
Method 2	199	230	198	253	180	209	213	137	250	82

Use the signs of the differences to test the hypothesis that there is no difference between the two methods as regards the measurement of the B12 level in red blood cells. (AEB)

4.6 Two population medians – case 2

Paired samples – Wilcoxon signed-rank test

As stated earlier, the paired t-test of Section 4.4 requires the differences in pairs to be normally distributed. In addition, the relative magnitudes of the differences are taken into account by the calculations of $\bar{d}$ and $\hat{\sigma}_d^2$.

The sign test of the previous section requires no such assumption of normality but, on the other hand, it makes no account for the relative magnitudes of the differences.

The alternative test for paired samples now to be considered, called the Wilcoxon (signed-rank) test, may be considered to be a compromise between the two previous methods in that it

  (i)   does not require any distributional assumptions of normality, so is non-parametric;

  (ii) does take into account for the relative magnitudes of the differences.

It is therefore to be preferred to the sign test when the sizes of the differences can be determined readily.

What do you understand by the term 'rank'?

The Wilcoxon test procedure is best developed using a specific example.

In a comparison of two computerised methods, A and B, for measuring physical fitness, a random sample of eight people were assessed by both methods. Their scores (maximum 20) were recorded as follows.

Subject	1	2	3	4	5	6	7	8
Method A	11.2	8.6	6.5	17.3	14.3	10.7	9.8	13.3
Method B	10.4	12.1	9.1	15.6	16.7	10.7	12.8	15.5
Difference (A - B)	+0.8	−3.5	−2.6	+1.7	−2.4	0.0	−3.0	−2.2

Since previous investigations of each method have concluded that scores are not normally distributed, a paired t-test is not appropriate.

A sign test could be used, but this would only use the signs of the differences (2 positive, 5 negative, with 1 zero).

A closer examination of these differences reveals that the 2 positive ones are the smallest in absolute value. This suggests that they are less important than the five negative values, which are all greater in absolute value. This idea is the basis of the **Wilcoxon test**.

Having determined the differences, they are ranked ignoring their signs, or, in other words, the absolute differences are ranked. Next the signs of the differences are attached to the ranks, hence the term 'signed-rank'.

The test statistic, T, is the determined as

$$T = \text{maximum of } T_+ \text{ and } T_-,$$

where $T_+ = $ sum of ranks with positive sign

and $T_- = $ sum of ranks with negative sign.

What will be sum of T_+ and T_- for n ranked differences?

Thus for the current example,

Difference $(A-B)$	+0.8	−3.5	−2.6	+1.7	−2.4	0.0	−3.0	−2.2
Absolute difference $\mid A-B \mid$	0.8	3.5	2.6	1.7	2.4	0.0	3.0	2.2
Rank of $\mid A-B \mid$	1	7	5	2	4		6	3
Signed -rank of difference	+1	−7	−5	≠2	−4		−6	−3

and hence,

$$T_+ = 1+2 = 3 \quad T_- = 3+4+5+6+7 = 25$$

giving $\quad T = 25$

Note that here, $n = 8 - 1$ (zero difference) $= 7$,

$$(T_+ + T_-) = 28 = (7 \times 8) \div 2,$$

and in general, $(T_+ + T_-) = n(n+1) \div 2.$

Under the null hypothesis of no real difference (i.e. $\eta_A = \eta_B$), each rank is equally likely to be associated with a positive or negative sign. Thus in this example, the list of signed ranks consists of all the possible combinations of

$$\pm 1 \quad \pm 2 \quad \pm 3 \quad \pm 4 \quad \pm 5 \quad \pm 6 \quad \pm 7$$

There are $2^7 = 128$ possible combinations, all equally likely under H_0, and this enables probabilities for each tail to be calculated as follows.

Value of T	Possible arrangements (ranks of same sign)	Probability	Cumulative probability
28	all	$\left(\frac{1}{2}\right)^7$	0.0078125
27	rank 1	$\left(\frac{1}{2}\right)^7$	0.0156250
26	rank 2	$\left(\frac{1}{2}\right)^7$	0.0234375
25	rank 3 or ranks 1 & 2	$2\times\left(\frac{1}{2}\right)^7$	0.0390625
24	rank 4 or ranks 1 & 3	$2\times\left(\frac{1}{2}\right)^7$	0.0546875

Thus under the null hypothesis, H_0, $P(T \geq 25) = 0.0391$

For a two-tailed 5% test, this probability is greater than 0.025, so the null hypothesis of no difference between the two methods A and B would not be rejected.

What is the smallest value of T for which H_0 would have been rejected?

When two or more differences have the same absolute value they are termed ties. In such cases the general rule is to replace the ties by the average rank of all the observations involved in the tie.

e.g. The ranks for   2.5 2.7 2.8 2.8 2.8 3.1 3.2 3.2

would be   1   2   4   4   4   6   7.5 7.5

Probability calculations as above for values of T are not in general necessary since tables of (approximate) critical values are available.

Example

An athletics coach wishes to test the value to his athletes of an intensive period of weight training and so he selects twelve 400-metre runners from his region and records their times, in seconds, to complete this distance. They then undergo his programme of weight training and have their times, in seconds, for 400 metres measured again. The table below summarises the results.

Athlete	A	B	C	D	E	F	G	H	I	J	K	L
Before	51.0	49.8	49.5	50.1	51.6	48.9	52.4	50.6	53.1	48.6	52.9	53.4
After	50.6	50.4	48.9	49.1	51.6	47.6	53.5	49.9	51.0	48.5	50.6	51.7

Use the Wilcoxon signed-rank test to investigate the hypothesis that the training programme will significantly improve athletes' times for the 400 metres.

Solution

Let   difference = (Time before)– (Time after)

H_0: Training programme has no effect $\left(\eta_B = \eta_A\right)$

H_1: Training programme improves time $\left(\eta_B > \eta_A\right)$

(one-tailed)

Significance level, $\alpha = 0.05$, say

$n = 12 - 1 = 11$ (1 zero difference)

From tables, critical region is $T > 52$

d	+0.4	−0.6	+0.6	+1.0	0.0	+1.3	−1.1	+0.7	+2.1	+0.1	+2.3	+1.7
$\lvert d\rvert$	0.4	0.6	0.6	1.0	0.0	1.3	1.1	0.7	2.1	0.1	2.3	1.7
rank	2	3.5	3.5	6		8	7	5	10	1	11	9
s-rank	+2	−3.5	+3.5	+6		+8	−7	+5	+10	+1	+11	+9

Hence $T_+ = 55.5$ and $T_- = 10.5$

(Check: $T_+ + T_- = 66 = (11 \times 12) \div 2$)

Thus $T = 55.5$

This value does lie in the critical region so H_0 is rejected. There is evidence, at the 5% level of significance, that the weight training programme does improve athletes' times for the 400 metres.

What alternative tests are available to you for these data, and what, if any, assumptions are necessary?

Activity 9   Faster with practice

Construct a simple random shape such as that printed here. Arrange for it to be printed at least 5 times on a plain sheet of A4 white paper.

Ask between 10 and 20 subjects to draw round each shape using their non-dominant hand. Time each subjects first and last tracings.

Investigate the hypothesis that tracing times improve with practice.

Chapter 4 Hypothesis Testing: Two Sample Tests

Exercise 4F

1. Apply the Wilcoxon signed-rank test to the data in Question 2 of Exercise 4D. Compare your conclusion with those obtained previously.
(AEB)

2. Apply the Wilcoxon test to the data in Question 3 of Exercise 4D. List and discuss your three conclusions to this set of data.   (AEB)

3. Apply the Wilcoxon test to the data in Question 5 of Exercise 4E. Compare your conclusion with that from the sign test.   (AEB)

4. As part of her research into the behaviour of the human memory, a psychologist asked 15 schoolgirls to talk for five minutes on 'my day at school'. Each girl was then asked to record how many times she thought that she had used the word nice during this period. The table below gives their replies together with the true values.

Girl	A	B	C	D	E	F	G	H
True value	12	20	1	8	0	12	12	17
Recorded value	9	19	3	14	4	12	16	14

Girl	I	J	K	L	M	N	O
True value	6	5	24	23	10	18	16
Recorded value	5	9	20	16	11	17	19

Use Wilcoxon's test to investigate whether schoolgirls can remember accurately the frequency with which they use a particular word in a verbal description.   (AEB)

5. Re-analyse the data in Question 6 of Exercise 4E using Wilcoxon's signed-rank test. Compare your conclusion with that obtained from the sign test. What other test could be applied to the data, and what assumption would be necessary?
(AEB)

6. The Ministry of Defence is considering which of two shoe leathers it should adopt for its new Army boot. They are particularly interested in how boots made from these leathers wear and so 15 soldiers are selected at random and each man wears one boot of each type. After six months the wear, in millimetres, for each boot is recorded as follows.

Soldier	1	2	3	4	5	6	7	8
Leather A	5.4	2.6	4.3	1.1	3.3	6.6	4.4	3.5
Leather B	4.7	3.2	3.8	2.3	3.6	7.2	4.4	3.9

Soldier	9	10	11	12	13	14	15
Leather A	1.2	1.3	4.8	1.2	2.8	2.0	6.1
Leather B	1.9	1.2	5.8	2.0	3.7	1.8	6.1

Use the Wilcoxon signed-rank test to investigate the hypothesis that the wear in the two leathers is the same. Why may this test be considered a better approach to this problem than the sign test?   (AEB)

4.7   Miscellaneous Exercises

1. The vitamin content of the flesh of each of a random sample of eight oranges and of a random sample of five lemons was measured. The results are given in milligrams per 10 grams.

   Oranges   1.14 1.59 1.57 1.33 1.08 1.27 1.43 1.36
   Lemons   1.04 0.95 0.63 1.62 1.11

   Assuming vitamin content to be normally distributed, test the hypothesis that both samples come from populations with the same variance.
(AEB)

2. Over a certain period of time, a random sample of 15 private subscribers connected to telephone exchange X used a total of 7980 units. Over the same period of time, a random sample of 20 subscribers connected to exchange Y used a total of 10 220. It is known that, for both exchanges, the numbers of units used by private subscribers during the period are normally distributed with standard deviation 100.

   Test the hypothesis that there is no difference between the mean number of units used by private subscribers at exchanges X and Y.

3. An economist believes that a typical basket of weekly provisions, purchased by a family of four, costs more in Southville than it does in Nortown. Six stores were randomly selected in each of these two cities and the following costs, for identical baskets of provisions, were observed.

   Southville   12.32 13.10 12.11 12.84 12.52 12.71
   Nortown   11.95 11.84 12.22 12.67 11.53 12.03

   (a) Explain why a paired test would not be appropriate here.

   (b) Assuming costs in both towns to be normally distributed with the same variance, test the economist's belief.   (AEB)

4. A high nitrate intake in food consumption is suspected of retarding the growth of some animals. The following data are the results of an experiment to measure the percentage gain in mass of young laboratory mice given either a standard diet (A) or an extra 200 parts per million of nitrate in their diet (B).

A	18.2	25.8	16.8	14.9	19.6	26.5	17.5
B	13.4	18.8	20.5	6.5	22.2	15.0	12.2
	14.3	18.0	15.1				

Assuming that both percentages are normally distributed with a standard deviation of 4.5, test, at the 1% level of significance, the hypothesis that a high nitrate intake retards the mean percentage gain in mass of mice.

After the experiment was performed it was discovered that the laboratory mice used were not a homogeneous population. In fact, most of the mice in the control group were appreciably heavier than those in the experimental group. Discuss briefly the possible effect of this information on the validity of your analysis.

(AEB)

5. As part of an investigation into the effects of alcohol on the human body at high altitude, ten male subjects were taken to a simulated altitude of 8000 m and given several tasks to perform. Each subject was carefully observed for deterioration in performance due to lack of oxygen, and the time, in seconds, at which useful consciousness ended was recorded. Three days later, the experiment was repeated one hour after the same ten subjects had unknowingly consumed 1 ml of 100%-proof alcohol per 5 kilograms of body mass. The time, in seconds, of useful consciousness was again recorded. The resulting data are given below.

Subject	1	2	3	4	5
No alcohol	260	565	900	630	280
Alcohol	185	375	310	240	215

Subject	6	7	8	9	10
No alcohol	365	400	735	430	900
Alcohol	420	405	205	255	900

Using an appropriate parametric test, determine whether or not these data support the hypothesis that the consumption of the stated amount of alcohol reduces the mean time of useful consciousness at high altitudes.

Name an alternative non-parametric test, and indicate the assumption that is then no longer required.

(AEB)

6. An on-line catalogue of books is being introduced into a college library. Formerly the catalogue was held on microfiche. To test the new system, students were selected at random and asked to obtain some specified information from the microfiche catalogue and a further sample of students was asked to obtain the same information from the on-line catalogue. The times, in seconds, were as follows.

Microfiche	68	91	71	96	97	75		
On-line	85	69	93	79	117	79	78	102

(a) Assuming a normal distribution, test, at the 5% significance level, whether there is a difference in

(i) the standard deviations of times for the two methods,

(ii) the means of the times for the two methods.

(b) One student had taken 297 seconds to obtain the information using the on-line catalogue due to an initial misunderstanding of how to use the equipment. It had been decided to exclude this result from the data above. Comment on this decision and on the effect the inclusion of this result would have had on the assumptions you made in carrying out the test in (a)(ii).

(AEB)

7. Two analysers are used in a hospital laboratory to measure blood creatinine levels. These are used as a measure of kidney function.

(a) To compare the performance of the two machines a technician took eight specimens of blood and measured the creatinine level (in micromoles per litre) of each specimen using each machine. The results were as follows.

Specimen	1	2	3	4	5	6	7	8
Analyser A	119	173	100	99	77	121	84	73
Analyser B	106	153	83	95	69	123	84	67

The technician carried out a paired t-test and reported that there was a difference between analysers at the 5% significance level. Verify that this is in fact the case, assuming a normal distribution.

(b) A statistician requested that each analyser should be used repeatedly to measure a standard solution which should give a creatinine level of 90.

(i) Analyser A was used 7 times and gave a mean result of 93.5 and a standard deviation of 4.7. Test at the 5% significance level whether these results could have come from a population with mean 90, assuming a normal distribution.

(ii) Results were also obtained for Analyser B. Explain why the results requested by the statistician are more useful in comparing the performance of the two analysers than the results in (a). What further analysis would you carry out if all the results were available to you? Justify your answer. (AEB)

8. It is claimed that Examiner V is more severe than Examiner W. This claim is based upon an analysis of the marks awarded by each examiner to independent random samples of scripts from a particular examination which had been marked by the two examiners. Some details of the marks awarded are as follows.

	Sample size	Sum of marks
Examiner V	25	1060
Examiner W	15	819

Investigate the claim that Examiner W awards, on average, more marks than Examiner V, assuming all marks are normally distributed with a standard deviation of 15.

Give **two** reasons why the outcome of the test may not necessarily imply that Examiner V is really more severe than Examiner W.

Suggest a more effectively designed study to investigate the claim.

9. Students on a statistics course are assessed on coursework and by a written examination. The marks obtained by a sample of 14 students were as follows (3 of the students failed to hand in any coursework).

Student	A	B	C	D	E	F	G
Coursework (%)	68	66	0	65	0	66	69
Examination (%)	53	45	67	52	43	71	37

Student	H	I	J	K	L	M	N
Coursework (%)	68	70	67	0	67	69	68
Examination (%)	43	68	27	34	79	57	54

(a) Use the sign test on all these results to examine whether coursework marks are higher than examination marks.

(b) Use the Wilcoxon signed-rank test, ignoring the 3 students who failed to hand in any coursework, to examine whether coursework marks are higher than examination marks.

(c) Compare your conclusions to (a) and (b) and indicate with reasons which analysis you consider to be the more appropriate. (AEB)

10. A large consignment of similarly graded apples arrived at a company's warehouse for distribution to retail outlets. Two varieties were chosen and a random sample of each had their masses, in grams, measured. The results are tabulated below.

Variety I	110.5	89.6	89.1	85.6	115.0	98.2
	113.1	92.0	104.3	100.7	97.5	106.1
Variety II	125.6	118.3	118.0	110.8	116.5	108.7
	108.2	104.4	114.4	98.4	111.2	

Assuming that these independent samples came from underlying normal populations, use a 5% significance level to test the hypothesis that the population variances are the same.

Further, use a 5% level of significance to test the hypothesis that the population means are the same.

Later it transpired that the measuring device used to determine the above masses was inaccurate. The true masses of the 23 apples considered were all 10 grams more than the results given above. What effect do you think this information will have on the above test results and why? (Further tests are not required.) (AEB)

11. A large food processing firm is considering introducing a new recipe for its ice cream. In a preliminary trial, a panel of 11 tasters were asked to score ice cream made from both the existing and the new recipe for sweetness. The results, on a scale from 0 to 100 with the sweeter ice cream being given the higher score, were as follows.

Taster	A	B	C	D	E	F
Existing recipe	88	35	67	17	24	32
New recipe	94	49	66	82	25	96

Taster	G	H	I	J	K
Existing recipe	8	44	73	47	25
New recipe	14	56	27	44	79

Use the sign test, at the 5% significance level, to test whether the new recipe is sweeter than the existing one.

Because of the erratic nature of the scores obtained, it was decided to repeat the trial with a new panel of 10 tasters, this time giving some guidance as to the scores to allocate. Two other ice creams were tasted first. One was very sweet and the tasters were told that it had a score of 90. The other was not sweet and had a score of 10. The new trial gave the following results.

Taster	L	M	N	O	P	Q	R	S	T	U
Existing recipe	52	44	57	49	61	55	49	69	64	46
New recipe	74	65	66	47	71	55	62	66	73	59

Use a paired t-test, stating any necessary assumptions, to test the hypothesis that there is no difference in sweetness between the two recipes at the 1% significance level.

Discuss briefly the suitability of the choice of the sign test for the first set of data and the paired t-test for the second. (AEB)

12. Industrial waste dumped in rivers reduces the amount of dissolved oxygen in the water. A factory was suspected of illegally dumping waste in the river. Samples of water were taken from the river, six above the factory and eight below the factory and the dissolved oxygen content in parts per million (ppm) were as follows.

   Above factory   4.9 5.1 4.7 5.0 5.3 4.6
   Below factory   3.8 4.9 4.0 3.6 5.0 3.4 3.5 3.9

   Making any necessary assumptions, test, at the 5% significance level, whether

   (a) the variability of the dissolved oxygen content is the same above and below the factory,

   (b) the mean of the dissolved oxygen content is less below than above the factory.   (AEB)

13. Two trainee estate agents, A and B, each valued independently a random sample of eight small properties. Their valuations, in £000s, are shown below.

Property	A	B	C	D
Trainee A	83.7	58.8	77.7	85.1
Trainee B	79.6	59.2	75.8	84.3

Property	E	F	G	H
Trainee A	91.9	66.4	69.8	48.5
Trainee B	90.1	65.2	66.9	53.8

   (a) Stating any assumptions necessary, use a paired t-test to investigate whether there is evidence that the two trainees differ in their valuations.

   (b) Repeat the test in (a) using an appropriate non-parametric test.

14. The manager of a road haulage firm records the time, in minutes, taken on six occasions for a lorry to travel from the depot to a particular customer's factory. Roadworks are due to start on the usual route so the manager decides to try an alternative route and records the times, in minutes, of eight journeys on this new route.

Old route	34 45 36 48 49 38
Alternative route	43 35 47 39 58 40 39 51

   Test, at the 5% significance level, whether there is a difference in

   (a) the variances of the times taken on the two routes,

   (b) the means of the times taken on the two routes.

   One driver had taken 99 minutes on the alternative route. Investigation showed that this was due to losing his way and it was decided to exclude this result from the above tests. Comment on this decision and state what assumptions may have been violated if the result had been included in the analysis.   (AEB)

15. Celebrity endorsement of a product is a common advertising technique.
   In one study, a randomly selected group of 125 people was shown a TV commercial involving a celebrity endorsement. A second randomly selected group of 75 people was shown the same TV commercial, but involving an unknown actress rather than the celebrity. Each of the 200 people was asked to rate on a scale from 0 (not persuaded) to 20 (totally persuaded) the effect on them of the commercial. An summary of the scores is shown below.

	With celebrity	Without celebrity
Sum of scores	1275	705
Sum of squares of scores	16485	9705

   Explain why the sample variances may be used as accurate estimates of the corresponding population variances.

   Hence investigate the claim that the celebrity endorsement of this particular TV commercial increases its mean persuasiveness score.

   Why were no distributional assumptions necessary in carrying out your test?

16. A biologist weighs each individual mouse in a random sample consisting of ten mice and records each weight to the nearest gram. The mice are then fed on a special diet and after 15 days each mouse is weighed again and the weight to the nearest gram is recorded. The results are as follows.

Initial weight (x)	50 49 48 52 40 43 51 46 41 42
Weight after 15 days (y)	52 50 50 55 42 45 52 48 42 44

   (You may assume that $\sum x^2 = 21520$ and $\sum y^2 = 23226$.)

   (a) Assuming that the results are given in random order on both occasions,

   (i) test the hypothesis that $\sigma_x^2 = \sigma_y^2$, where σ_x^2 and σ_y^2 are the variances of the populations from which these data are taken,

   (ii) examine the possibility that there has been a significant increase in mean weight over the 15 days.

   (b) If the results are given in the same order on both occasions, explain (without calculation) how this fact would alter your analysis of these data.   (AEB)

17. Trace metals in drinking water affect the flavour of the water and high concentrations can pose a health hazard. The following table shows the zinc concentrations, in milligrams per 1000 litres, of water on the surface and on the river bed at each of twelve locations on a river.

Location	1	2	3	4	5	6
Surface	387	515	721	341	689	599
Bed	435	532	817	366	827	735

Location	7	8	9	10	11	12
Surface	734	541	717	523	524	445
Bed	812	669	808	622	476	387

(a) Using a Wilcoxon signed-rank test, examine the claim that zinc concentration of water in this river is higher on the river bed than on the surface. Explain why this test is preferred here to the sign test.

(b) If differences in zinc concentrations of water in this river may be assumed to be normally distributed, re-examine the claim in (a) using an appropriate alternative test.

18. Samples are taken from two batches of paint and the viscosity, x poise, measured. The information is summarised below.

Paint	Mean	Standard deviation	Size
A	114.44	0.62	4
B	114.93	0.94	6

Assuming named distributions, test, at the 5% significance level, whether

(a) the mean viscosity of Paint A is more than 114,

(b) the standard deviations of the viscosities of the two paints are equal,

(c) the mean viscosities of the two paints are equal. (AEB)

19. Five joints of meat were each cut in half. One half was frozen and wrapped using a standard process and the other half using a new process. The ten halves were placed in a freezer and the number of days to spoilage (which can be detected by the colour of the package) was noted for each pack.

Joint number	1	2	3	4	5
Standard process	96	194	149	185	212
New process	117	190	186	776	263

A statistician queried the observation on the new process for joint 4. The experimenter agreed that an error must have been made but said that he was certain that, for this joint, the half frozen by the new process had lasted longer than the other half.

He had used the sign test on the five joints and had accepted, at the 5% significance level, that there was no difference in the number of days to spoilage.

(a) Confirm, by making any necessary calculations, that the sign test applied to these data does lead to the experimenter's conclusion.

(b) Use a paired *t*-test on joints 1, 2, 3 and 5 to test whether there is a difference, at the 5% significance level, in the mean number of days to spoilage.

Comment on the validity and advisability of using each of these tests on these data. A larger trial is to be carried out and, before the data are collected, you are asked to advise on which test should be used. List the advantages of each. (AEB)

20. The development engineer of a company making razors records the time it takes him to shave on seven mornings using a standard razor made by the company. The times, in seconds, were

$$217, \quad 210, \quad 254, \quad 237, \quad 232, \quad 228, \quad 243.$$

He wishes to compare the time taken by different designs of razor. He decides that rather than test all the design himself it would be quicker to find other employees who would be willing to test one design each. As a preliminary step his assistant agrees to test the standard razor and produces the following times.

$$186, \quad 219, \quad 168, \quad 202, \quad 191, \quad 184.$$

Regarding the samples as coming from normal distributions,

(a) show that there is no significant evidence of a difference between variances,

(b) test whether the mean shaving times of the engineer and his assistant are the same.

Advise the engineer how to proceed with his investigation. (AEB)

5 GOODNESS OF FIT TESTS

Objectives

After studying this chapter you should

• be able to calculate expected frequencies for a variety of probability models;

• be able to use the χ^2 distribution to test if a set of observations fits an appropriate probability model.

5.0   Introduction

The chi-squared test is a particular useful technique for testing whether observed data are representative of a particular distribution. It is widely used in biology, geography and psychology.

Activity 1   How random are your numbers?

Can you make up your own table of random numbers? Write down 100 numbers 'at random' (taking values from 0 to 9). Do this without the use of a calculator, computer or printed random number tables. Draw up a frequency table to see how many times you wrote down each number. (These will be called your **observed** frequencies.)

If your random numbers really are random, roughly how many of each do you think there ought to be? (These are referred to as **expected** frequencies.)

What model are you using for this distribution of expected frequencies?

What assumptions must you make in order to use this model?

Do you think you were able to fulfil those assumptions when you wrote them down?

Can you think of a way to test whether your numbers have a similar frequency distribution to what we would expect for true random numbers?

For analysing data of the sort used in Activity 1 where you are comparing observed with expected values, a chart as shown opposite is a useful way of writing down the data.

Number	Frequency Observed, O_i	Frequency Expected, E_i
1		
2		
3		
4		
.		
.		
.		

5.1 The chi-squared table

For your data in Activity 1, try looking at the differences $O_i - E_i$.

What happens if you total these?

Unfortunately the positive differences and negative differences always cancel each other out and you always have a zero total.

To overcome this problem the differences $O_i - E_i$ can be squared.

So $\sum (O_i - E_i)^2$ could form the basis of your 'difference measure'. In this particular example, however, each figure has an equal expected frequency, but this will not always be so (when you come to test other models in other situations). The importance assigned to a difference must be related to the size of the expected frequency. A difference of 10 must be more important if the expected frequency is 20 than if it is 100.

One way of allowing for this is to divide each squared difference by the expected frequency for that category.

Here is an example worked out for you:

Number	Observed frequency O_i	Expected frequency E_i	$O_i - E_i$	$(O_i - E_i)^2$	$\dfrac{(O_i - E_i)^2}{E_i}$
0	11	10	1	1	0.1
1	12	10	2	4	0.4
2	8	10	−2	4	0.4
3	14	10	4	16	1.6
4	7	10	−3	9	0.9
5	9	10	−1	1	0.1
6	9	10	−1	1	0.1
7	8	10	−2	4	0.4
8	14	10	4	16	1.6
9	8	10	−2	4	0.4
					6.0

For this set of 100 numbers $\displaystyle\sum \frac{\left(O_i - E_i\right)^2}{E_i} = 6$

But what does this measure tell you?

How can you decide whether the observed frequencies are close to the expected frequencies or really quite different from them?

Firstly, consider what might happen if you tried to test some true random numbers from a random number table.

Would you actually get 10 for each number?

The example worked out here did in fact use 100 random numbers from a table and not a fictitious set made up by someone taking part in the experiment.

Each time you take a sample of random numbers you will get a slightly different distribution and it would certainly be surprising to find one with all the observed frequencies equal to 10. So, in fact, each different sample of 100 true random numbers will give a different value for

$$\sum \frac{\left(O_i - E_i\right)^2}{E_i}$$

The distribution of

$$\sum \frac{\left(O_i - E_i\right)^2}{E_i}$$

is approximately χ_v^2 where the parameter v is termed the **degrees of freedom**.

For any χ^2 **goodness of fit test**, the number of degrees of freedom shows the number of independent free choices which can be made in allocating values to the expected frequencies. In these examples, there are ten expected frequencies (one for each of the numbers 0 to 9). However, as the total frequency must equal 100, only nine of the expected frequencies can vary independently and the tenth one must take whatever value is required to fulfil the 'constraint'. To calculate the number of degrees of freedom

$$v = \text{number of classes or groups } - \text{ number of constraints.}$$

Here there are ten classes and one constraint, so

$$v = 10 - 1$$

$$= 9$$

Significance testing

A high value of χ^2 implies a poor fit between the observed and expected frequencies, so the upper tail of the distribution is used for most hypothesis testing in goodness of fit tests.

From χ^2 tables, only 5% of all samples of true random numbers will give a value of χ_9^2 greater than 16.919. Thus if the value of

$$\chi^2 = \sum \frac{\left(O_i - E_i\right)^2}{E_i} < 16.919$$

it would support the view that the numbers are random. If not, there is evidence, at the 5% significance level, to suggest that the numbers are not truly random.

What do you conclude from the worked example above, where $\chi^2 = 6$?

The above procedure may be summarised usefully as a hypothesis test as follows:

H_0: numbers are random

H_1: numbers are not random

Significance level, $\alpha = 0.05$

Degrees of freedom, $v = 10 - 1 = 9$

Critical region is $\quad \chi^2 > 16.919$

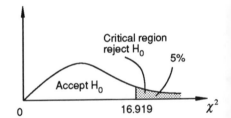

Test statistic is $\quad \chi^2 = \sum \frac{\left(O_i - E_i\right)^2}{E_i} = 6$

This value does not lie in the critical region. There is no evidence, at the 5% significance level, to suggest that the numbers are not random.

Activity 2

What happens when you test your made up 'random' numbers? Is their distribution close to what you would expect for true random numbers?

Example

Nadir is testing an octahedral die to see if it is biased. The results are given in the table below.

Score	1	2	3	4	5	6	7	8
Frequency	7	10	11	9	12	10	14	7

Test the hypothesis that the die is fair.

Solution

H_0: die is fair

H_1: die is not fair

Significance level, $\alpha = 0.05$

Degrees of freedom, $v = 8 - 1 = 7$

Critical region is $\chi^2 > 14.067$

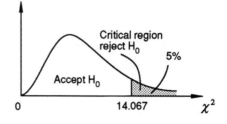

As before, the expected frequencies are based on a uniform distribution which gives each E_i as

$$\frac{1}{8}(7 + 10 + 11 + 9 + 12 + 10 + 14 + 7) = 10$$

Hence

Score	O_i	E_i	$O_i - E_i$	$\left(O_i - E_i\right)^2$	$\dfrac{\left(O_i - E_i\right)^2}{E_i}$
1	7	10	−3	9	0.9
2	10	10	0	0	0
3	11	10	1	1	0.1
4	9	10	−1	1	0.1
5	12	10	2	4	0.4
6	10	10	0	0	0
7	14	10	4	16	1.6
8	7	10	−3	9	0.9
					4.0

Thus the test statistic is $\qquad \chi^2 = \sum \dfrac{\left(O_i - E_i\right)^2}{E_i} = 4.0$

This value does not lie in the critical region. There is no evidence, at the 5% significance level, to suggest that the die is not fair.

Exercise 5A

1. Nicki made a tetrahedral die using card and then tested it to see whether it was fair. She got the following scores:

Score	1	2	3	4
Frequency	12	15	19	22

   Does this seem fair?

2. Joe has a die which has faces numbered from 1 to 6. He got the following scores:

Score	1	2	3	4	5	6
Frequency	17	20	29	20	18	16

   He thinks that the die may be biased. What do you think?

3. The table below shows the number of pupils absent on particular days in the week.

Day	M	Tu	W	Th	F
Number	125	88	85	94	108

   Find the expected frequencies if it is assumed that the number of absentees is independent of the day of the week.

   Test, at 5% level, whether the differences in observed and expected frequencies are significant.

4. Over a long period of time, a research team monitored the number of car accidents which occurred in a particular county. The following table summarises the data relating to the day of the week on which the accident occurred.

Day	M	Tu	W	Th	F	S	Su
Number of accidents	60	54	48	53	53	75	77

   Investigate the hypothesis that these data are a random sample from a uniform distribution.
   (AEB)

5. Entrance to, and exit from, a large departmental store is via one of four sets of doors. The number of customers entering or leaving the store is counted at each set of doors for a period of time with the following results.

Set of doors	North	South	East	West
Number of customers	327	402	351	380

   It is claimed that the numbers of customers using each of the four sets of doors is the same. Investigate this claim.

6. The proportions of blood types O, A, B and AB in the general population of a particular country are known to be in the ratio 49:38:9:4, respectively. A research team, investigating a small isolated community in the country, obtained the following frequencies of blood type.

Blood type	O	A	B	AB
Frequency	87	59	20	4

   Test the hypothesis that the proportions in this community do not differ significantly from those in the general population.

5.2   Discrete probability models

Four identical six-sided dice, each with faces marked 1 to 6, are rolled 200 times. At each rolling, a record is made of the number of dice whose score on the uppermost face is even. The results are as follows.

Number of even scores (x_i)	0	1	2	3	4
Frequency (f_i)	10	41	70	57	22

Why might a binomial model describe the distribution of X?

What values would you suggest for the two binomial parameters n and p?

Based upon your suggested values, how would you then obtain the expected frequencies for comparative purposes?

The number of computer malfunctions per day is recorded for 260 days with the following results.

Number of malfunctions (x_i)	0	1	2	3	4	5
Number of days (f_i)	77	90	55	30	5	3

Which probability model might be suitable for describing the number of malfunctions per day?

How would you estimate the value for the parameter of your model?

How might the suitability of your model be tested?

In each of the above examples, a comparison is required of observed frequencies $(O_i = f_i)$ and expected frequencies (E_i) calculated from an assumed or hypothesised probability model.

This comparison is tested for significance again using

$$\chi^2 = \sum \frac{\left(O_i - E_i\right)^2}{E_i}$$

However, some complications are encountered when values for the parameters of the assumed distribution are unknown and/or when some expected frequencies are small. To demonstrate how these complications arise and show how they are overcome is best illustrated by considering each of the above two examples in turn.

Example (binomial)

Four identical six-sided dice, each with faces marked 1 to 6, are rolled 200 times. At each rolling, a record is made of the number of dice whose score on the uppermost face is even. The results are as follows.

Number of even scores (x_i)	0	1	2	3	4
Frequency (f_i)	10	41	70	57	22

Explain why a binomial model might describe the distribution of X, and test its goodness of fit.

Solution

A binomial distribution might be appropriate on the basis of:

(a) a fixed number (4) of repeated, independent (dice identical and scores independent) trials,

(b) each trial can result in success (even) or failure (odd),

(c) constant probability (dice identical) of success at each trial.

Assuming the dice are unbiased, then

$$P(\text{even score on a die}) = \frac{3}{6} = 0.5$$

Hence $\qquad X \sim B(4, 0.5)$

Using the p.d.f. of the binomial distribution, or from the table in the Appendix, with $n = 4$ and $p = 0.50$, gives the following probability and hence expected frequency ($200 \times$ probability) for each value of X.

x_i	$O_i = f_i$	$P(X = x_i)$	E_i	$(O_i - E_i)$	$(O_i - E_i)^2$	$\dfrac{(O_i - E_i)^2}{E_i}$
0	10	0.0625	12.5	-2.5	6.25	0.500
1	41	0.2500	50.0	-9.0	81.00	1.620
2	70	0.3750	75.0	-5.0	25.00	0.333
3	57	0.2500	50.0	7.0	49.00	0.980
4	22	0.0625	12.5	9.5	90.25	7.220
		1.0000				10.653

H_0: number of even scores is $\sim B(4, 0.5)$

H_1: number of even scores is not $\sim B(4, 0.5)$

Significance level, $\alpha = 0.05$

Degrees of freedom, $v = 5 - 1 = 4$

(5 classes: 0, 1, 2, 3, 4; 1 constraint: $\Sigma E_i = \Sigma O_i$)

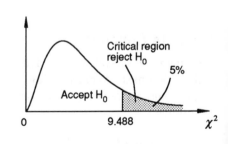

Critical region is $\quad \chi^2 > 9.488$

Test statistic is $\quad \chi^2 = \sum \dfrac{(O_i - E_i)^2}{E_i} = 10.653$

This value does lie in the critical region. There is evidence, at the 5% significance level, to suggest that the number of even scores is not distributed as $B(4, 0.5)$.

Suppose that it is now revealed that the dice are equally biased in some unknown way.

Can you now think of a way of estimating the probability of an even score on one of the dice?

The mean number of even scores per single rolling of the four dice is given by

$$\bar{x} = \frac{\sum f_i x_i}{\sum f_i}$$

$$= \frac{(10 \times 0 + 41 \times 1 + 70 \times 2 + 57 \times 3 + 22 \times 4)}{200}$$

$$= \frac{440}{200} = 2.2$$

Thus

$$P(\text{even score on a single die}) = \hat{p} = \frac{2.2}{4} = 0.55$$

Again using the p.d.f. of the binomial distribution, or from the table in the Appendix, with $n = 4$ and $p = 0.55$ ($1 - \hat{p} = 0.45$ for use in tables), gives the following probability and hence the expected frequency ($200 \times$ probability) for each value of X.

x_i	$O_i = f_i$	$P(X = x_i)$	E_i	$(O_i - E_i)$	$(O_i - E_i)^2$	$\dfrac{(O_i - E_i)^2}{E_i}$
0	10	0.0410	8.2	1.8	3.24	0.395
1	41	0.2005	40.1	0.9	0.81	0.020
2	70	0.3675	73.5	−3.5	12.25	0.167
3	57	0.2995	59.9	−2.9	8.41	0.140
4	22	0.0915	18.3	3.7	13.69	0.748
		1.0000				1.470

What is the value of $\sum E_i x_i$?

H_0: number of even scores is $\sim B(4, p)$

H_1: number of even scores is not $\sim B(4, p)$

Significance level, $\alpha = 0.05$

Degrees of freedom, $v = 5 - 2 = 3$

(5 classes: 0, 1, 2, 3, 4; 2 constraints: $\sum E_i = \sum O_i$ and
$\sum E_i x_i = \sum O_i x_i$ from estimation of p)

Critical region is $\chi^2 > 7.815$

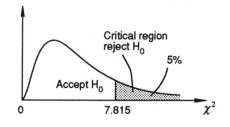

Test statistic is $\chi^2 = \sum \dfrac{\left(O_i - E_i\right)^2}{E_i} = 1.470$

This value does not lie in the critical region. There is no evidence, at the 5% significance level, to suggest that the number of even scores cannot be modelled by a binomial distribution with $n = 4$ and $p = 0.55$.

Example (Poisson)

The number of computer malfunctions per day is recorded for 260 days with the following results.

Number of malfunctions (x_i)	0	1	2	3	4	5
Number of days (f_i)	77	90	55	30	5	3

Test the goodness of fit of an appropriate probability model.

Solution

An appropriate probability model here could be a Poisson distribution on the basis of the following assumptions.

(a) Malfunctions occur independently.

(b) Simultaneous malfunctions are impossible.

(c) Malfunctions occur randomly in time.

(d) Malfunctions occur uniformly (mean number per time period proportional to the period length).

Can you devise an approximate, but quick, method for checking whether a Poisson distribution might be a suitable model?

A Poisson distribution has one parameter, λ, which is the mean (and also the variance). Thus the sample mean may be used to estimate λ.

Mean $\qquad \bar{x} = \dfrac{\sum f_i x_i}{\sum f_i} = \dfrac{325}{260} = 1.25$

[Note that $\sum f_i x_i^2 = 735$, so variance, $s^2 = \dfrac{735}{260} - 1.25^2 = 1.26$]

Hence with $\quad \lambda = 1.25$,

$$P(X = x) = \frac{e^{-1.25} 1.25^x}{x!}, \quad x = 0, 1, 2, 3, \ldots\ldots$$

which gives the following probabilities and expected frequencies $(260 \times \text{probability})$ for each value of X.

x_i	$P(X = x_i)$	E_i
0	0.2865	74.5
1	0.3581	93.1
2	0.2238	58.2
3	0.0933	24.2
4	0.0291	7.6
5	0.0073	1.9
$\geq 6^*$	0.0019	0.5
	1.0000	260.0

*Since a Poisson distribution is valid for all positive values of X, this additional class is necessary, and $P(X \geq 6) = 1 - P(X \leq 5)$.

What is the value of $\sum E_i x_i$ if ≥ 6 is read as 6?

The test statistic

$$\sum \frac{\left(O_i - E_i\right)^2}{E_i}$$

is approximated by χ^2 providing none of the expected frequencies are less than 5. When expected frequencies fall below 5, then groups or classes must be combined.

In the current example, this rule necessitates combining 4, 5 and ≥ 6 malfunctions into ≥ 4 malfunctions, so giving the following table.

O_i	$O_i = f_i$	$P(X = x_i)$	E_i	$(O_i - E_i)$	$(O_i - E_i)^2$	$\dfrac{(O_i - E_i)^2}{E_i}$
0	77	0.2865	74.5	2.5	6.25	0.084
1	90	0.3581	93.1	−3.1	9.61	0.103
2	55	0.2238	58.2	−3.2	10.24	0.176
3	30	0.0933	24.2	5.8	33.64	1.390
≥ 4	8	0.0383	10.0	−2.0	4.00	0.400
		1.0000				2.153

H_0 : number of daily malfunctions is ~ Poisson

H_1 : number of daily malfunctions is not ~ Poisson

Significance level, $\alpha = 0.05$

Degrees of freedom, $v = 5 - 2 = 3$

(5 classes: 0, 1, 2, 3, ≥ 4; 2 constraints: $\sum E_i = \sum O_i$ and $\sum E_i x_i = \sum O_i x_i$ from estimation of λ)

Critical region is $\chi^2 > 7.815$

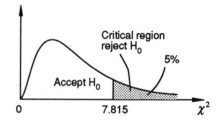

Critical region
reject H_0

5%

Accept H_0

0

7.815

χ^2

Test statistic is $\chi^2 = \sum \dfrac{(O_i - E_i)^2}{E_i} = 2.153$

This value does not lie in the critical region. There is no evidence, at the 5% significance level, to suggest that the number of computer malfunctions per day does not have a Poisson distribution.

Activity 3 Shuffled cards

Obtain the use of a standard pack of 52 playing cards.

Shuffle the cards thoroughly, deal the top two cards, and record how many (0, 1 or 2) are diamonds.

Repeat this process at least 80 times.

Test the hypothesis that the number of diamonds per deal can be modelled by a distribution which is $B(2, 0.25)$.

Activity 4   Binomial quiz

[You may already have some data for this activity from Activity 5 in Chapter 5 of *Statistics*.]

Ask your fellow students, and anyone else who will participate, whether the following statements are 'true' or 'false'.

1.   The *Portrait of a Lady* was written by Henry James.
2.   *Psalms* is the 20th book of the *Old Testament*.
3.   The equatorial diameter of Mercury is about 3032 miles.
4.   Mankoya is a place in Zambia.
5.   'The Potato Eaters' is a painting by Cezanne.
6.   The Battle of Sowton was fought in 1461.

Make a frequency table to show the number of correct answers out of six for those asked. You will need to ask about 200 people.

Calculate expected frequencies on the assumption that people are simply guessing the answers. Compare observed and expected frequencies using a χ^2 goodness of fit test.

Estimate the probability, $\hat{p}$, of a correct answer. Hence test the appropriateness of the distribution $B(6, \hat{p})$.

Activity 5   Simulated spelling errors

The random variable X denotes the number of spelling errors made by a typist per 1000 words typed.

Use a three-digit random number, y, to generate an 'observed' value, x, of X using the following rules.

$$000 \leq y \leq 135 \Rightarrow x = 0$$
$$136 \leq y \leq 406 \Rightarrow x = 1$$
$$407 \leq y \leq 677 \Rightarrow x = 2$$
$$678 \leq y \leq 857 \Rightarrow x = 3$$
$$858 \leq y \leq 947 \Rightarrow x = 4$$
$$948 \leq y \leq 999 \Rightarrow x \geq 5$$

Using the above rules, obtain at least 100 'observed' values of X.

Test the hypothesis that $X \sim Po(2)$ using the χ^2 goodness of fit test.

Activity 6 Customer arrivals

[You may already have some data for this activity from Activity 3 in Chapter 6 of *Statistics*.]

Record the number of arrivals of customers at a post office, bank or supermarket in 2-minute intervals until you have at least 120 results. The 2-minute interval may well be shortened in the case of a large and busy site.

At the same time ask a friend to record the times, in seconds, between successive arrivals of customers. (This information is required for Activity 8.) Alternatively, record, to the nearest second, the actual arrival time of each customer. Numbers of arrivals per interval and inter-arrival times can then be listed later.

Construct a frequency distribution of the numbers of arrivals per interval.

Use a χ^2 goodness of fit test to investigate whether a Poisson distribution provides a suitable model.

Exercise 5B

1. A farmer kept a record of the number of heifer calves born to each of his cows during the first five years of breeding of each cow. The results are summarised below.

Number of heifers	0	1	2	3	4	5
Number of cows	4	19	41	52	26	8

Test, at the 5% level of significance, whether or not the binomial distribution with parameters $n = 5$ and $p = 0.5$ is an adequate model for these data.

Explain briefly (without doing any further calculations) what changes you would make in your analysis if you were testing whether or not the binomial distribution with $n = 5$ and unspecified p fitted the data. (AEB)

2. The number of misprints on 200 randomly selected pages from the 1981 editions of the *Daily Planet*, a quality newspaper, were recorded. The table below summarises these results.

Number of misprints per page (x)	0	1	2	3	4	5	6	7	8	>8
Frequency (f)	5	12	31	40	38	29	22	14	5	4

Use a χ^2 distribution to test the claim that a suitable model for these data is Poisson with a mean of 4. (AEB)

3. Smallwoods Ltd run a weekly football competition. One part of this involves a fixed-odds contest where the entrant has to forecast correctly the result of each of five given matches. In the event of a fully correct forecast the entrant is paid out at odds of 100 to 1. During the last two years Miss Fortune has entered this fixed-odds contest 80 times. The table below summarises her results.

Number of matches correctly forecast per entry (x)	0	1	2	3	4	5
Number of entries with x correct forecasts (f)	8	19	25	22	5	1

(a) Find the frequencies of the number of matches correctly forecast per entry given by a binomial distribution having the same mean and total as the observed distribution.

(b) Use the χ^2 distribution and a 10% level of significance to test the adequacy of the binomial distribution as a model for these data.

(c) On the evidence before you, and assuming that the point of entering is to win money, would you advise Miss Fortune to continue with this competition and why? (AEB)

4. The table below gives the distribution of the number of hits by flying bombs in 450 equally sized areas in South London during World War II.

Number of hits (x)	0	1	2	3	4	5
Frequency (f)	180	173	69	20	6	2

(a) Find the expected frequencies of hits given by a Poisson distribution having the same mean and total as the observed distribution.

(b) Use the χ^2 distribution and a 10% level of significance to test the adequacy of the Poisson distribution as a model for these data.   (AEB)

5.3 Continuous probability models

For a continuous random variable, probabilities for precise values do not exist so a comparison of observed and expected frequencies of individual values is not possible.

However, it is possible to calculate, by integration or using tables, the probability that the value of a continuous random variable falls within some specified interval.

Hence for continuous probability models, χ^2 goodness of fit tests are based upon a comparison of observed and expected frequencies in non-overlapping intervals which together constitute the complete range for the random variable.

Example

The following table summarises the waiting times, in minutes, of a random sample of 200 people at a taxi rank.

Waiting time (x)	0 –	0.5 –	1.0 –	1.5 – 2.5
Number of people (f)	77	60	35	28

Test the claim that the waiting time, X, can be modelled by the probability density function

$$f(x) = \begin{cases} 0.8 - 0.32x & 0 \le x < 2.5 \\ 0 & \text{otherwise} \end{cases}$$

Solution

$$P(X < x) = \int_0^a (0.8 - 0.32x)\,dx = 0.16a(5 - a),$$

so that

$$P(X < 2.5) = 1.00 \qquad P(0.0 \le X < 0.5) = 0.36$$

$$P(X < 1.5) = 0.84 \qquad P(0.5 \le X < 1.0) = 0.28$$

$$P(X < 1.0) = 0.64 \qquad P(1.0 \le X < 1.5) = 0.20$$

$$P(X < 0.5) = 0.36 \qquad P(1.5 \le X < 2.5) = 0.16$$

Using $E_i = (200 \times \text{probability})$ gives the following table of calculations.

x	$O_i = f_i$	E_i	$(O_i - E_i)$	$(O_i - E_i)^2$	$\dfrac{(O_i - E_i)^2}{E_i}$
0.0 –	77	72	5	25	0.347
0.5 –	60	56	4	16	0.286
1.0 –	35	40	–5	25	0.625
1.5 – 2.5	28	32	–4	16	0.500
					1.758

H_0: suggested model is appropriate

H_1: suggested model is not appropriate

Significance level, $\alpha = 0.10$ (say)

Degrees of freedom, $v = 4 - 1 = 3$

(4 classes; 1 constraint: $\Sigma E_i = \Sigma O_i$)

Critical region is $\quad \chi^2 > 6.251$

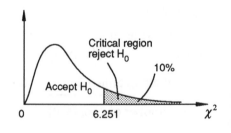

Test statistic is $\quad \chi^2 = \sum \dfrac{(O_i - E_i)^2}{E_i} = 1.758$

This value does not lie in the critical region. There is no evidence, at the 10% significance level, to suggest that waiting times cannot be modelled by the suggested probability density function.

Activity 7   Response times

Using a stopwatch or a watch with a stopwatch facility in hundredths of a second, set the watch going and try to stop at exactly 5 seconds. Record the exact time on the stopwatch. At this stage it is easier to work in pairs. Repeat this at least 100 times and then construct a grouped frequency distribution using the following classes:

$$4.5 -, 4.7 -, 4.8 -, 4.9 -, 5.0 -, 5.1 -, 5.2 -, 5.3 - 5.5.$$

{Discard the few, if any, times outside the range 4.5 to 5.5.}

Hence test the goodness of fit of your data to the distribution defined by

$$f(x) = \begin{cases} 4(x - 4.5) & 4.5 < x \le 5.0 \\ 4(5.5 - x) & 5.0 < x \le 5.5 \\ 0 & \text{otherwise} \end{cases}$$

Draw a relative frequency histogram of your grouped frequency distribution and superimpose the graph of the above distribution.

Comment on the similarities and/or differences.

Example (exponential)

The table below shows the time intervals, in seconds, between successive white cars in free flowing traffic on an open road. Can these times be modelled by an exponential distribution?

Time	0 –	20 –	40 –	60 –	90 –	120 –180
Frequency	41	19	16	13	9	2

Solution

The p.d.f. of an exponential distribution is given by

$$f(x) = \begin{cases} \lambda e^{-\lambda x} & x > 0 \\ 0 & \text{otherwise} \end{cases}$$

where λ^{-1} is the mean.

Hence the sample mean can be used as an estimate of λ^{-1}.

Using class mid-points (x) of 10, 30, 50, 75, 105 and 150 gives

$$\bar{x} = \hat{\lambda}^{-1} = \frac{\Sigma fx}{\Sigma f} = \frac{4000}{100} = 40$$

Hence $$P(X < a) = \int_0^a \frac{e^{-\frac{x}{40}}}{40}\, dx = 1 - e^{-\frac{a}{40}}$$

The following probabilities and expected frequencies can now be calculated.

			Class probability		E_i
$P(X < \infty)$	$= 1.000$	$P(0 \le X < 20)$	$= 0.393$		39.3
$P(X < 180)$	$= 0.989$	$P(20 \le X < 40)$	$= 0.239$		23.9
$P(X < 120)$	$= 0.950$	$P(40 \le X < 60)$	$= 0.145$		14.5
$P(X < 90)$	$= 0.895$	$P(60 \le X < 90)$	$= 0.118$		11.8
$P(X < 60)$	$= 0.777$	$P(90 \le X < 120)$	$= 0.055$		5.5
$P(X < 40)$	$= 0.632$	$P(120 \le X < 180)$	$= 0.039$		3.9*
$P(X < 20)$	$= 0.393$	$P(180 \le X < \infty)$	$= 0.011$		1.1*
				1.000	100.0

* Combine classes so that all $E_i \ge 5$

What will be the value now for the degrees of freedom?

The calculation of the value of χ^2 is completed as follows.

x	O_i	E_i	$(O_i - E_i)$	$(O_i - E_i)^2$	$\dfrac{(O_i - E_i)^2}{E_i}$
0 –	41	39.3	1.7	2.89	0.074
20 –	19	23.9	−4.9	24.01	1.005
40 –	16	14.5	1.5	2.25	0.155
60 –	13	11.8	1.2	1.44	0.122
90 –	9	5.5	3.5	12.25	2.227
120 –	2	5.0	−3.0	9.00	1.800
					5.383

H_0: exponential distribution is appropriate

H_1: exponential distribution is not appropriate

Significance level, $\alpha = 0.05$

Degrees of freedom, $v = 6 - 2 = 4$

(6 classes; 2 constraints: $\sum E_i = \sum O_i$ and $\sum E_i x_i = \sum O_i x_i$ from estimation of λ)

Critical region is $\quad \chi^2 > 9.488$

Test statistic is $\quad \chi^2 = \sum \dfrac{\left(O_i - E_i\right)^2}{E_i} = 5.383$

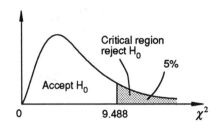

This value does not lie in the critical region. There is no evidence, at the 5% significance level, to suggest that an exponential distribution is not appropriate.

What changes would need to be made to this solution if the question had suggested an exponential distribution with $\lambda = 0.025$?

Example (normal)

An analysis of the fat content, $X\%$, of a random sample of 175 hamburgers of a particular grade resulted in the following summarised information.

Fat content	Number of hamburgers (f)
$26 \leq x < 28$	7
$28 \leq x < 30$	22
$30 \leq x < 32$	36
$32 \leq x < 34$	45
$34 \leq x < 36$	33
$36 \leq x < 38$	28
$38 \leq x < 40$	4

Can it be assumed that the fat content of this grade of hamburger is normally distributed?

Solution

What parameters will need to be estimated?

Here it is necessary to estimate the parameters μ and σ^2 of the normal distribution by $\bar{x}$ and $\hat{\sigma}^2$ respectively.

What will now be the number of constraints?

Using class mid-points of 27, 29, ..., 39 results in

$$\sum fx = 5775 \quad \text{and} \quad \sum fx^2 = 192047$$

so that $\qquad \bar{x} = \dfrac{5775}{175} = 33$

and $\qquad \hat{\sigma} = \sqrt{\dfrac{1}{174}\left[192047 - \dfrac{5775^2}{175}\right]} = 2.91$

Using the standardisation $\quad z = \dfrac{x-\mu}{\sigma} = \dfrac{x-33}{2.91} \quad$ gives the following probabilities and hence expected frequencies.

			Class probability	E_i
$P(X < \infty)$	$= P(Z < \infty)$	$= 1.000$	$P(-\infty < X < 26) = 0.008$	1.4*
$P(X < 40)$	$= P(Z < 2.405)$	$= 0.992$	$P(26 \le X < 28) = 0.035$	6.1*
$P(X < 38)$	$= P(Z < 1.718)$	$= 0.957$	$P(28 \le X < 30) = 0.108$	18.9
$P(X < 36)$	$= P(Z < 1.031)$	$= 0.849$	$P(30 \le X < 32) = 0.214$	37.5
$P(X < 34)$	$= P(Z < 0.344)$	$= 0.635$	$P(32 \le X < 34) = 0.270$	47.2
$P(X < 32)$	$= P(Z < -0.344)$	$= 0.365$	$P(34 \le X < 36) = 0.214$	37.5
$P(X < 30)$	$= P(Z < -1.031)$	$= 0.151$	$P(36 \le X < 38) = 0.108$	18.9
$P(X < 28)$	$= P(Z < -1.718)$	$= 0.043$	$P(38 \le X < 40) = 0.035$	6.1*
$P(X < 26)$	$= P(Z < -2.405)$	$= 0.008$	$P(40 \le X < \infty) = 0.008$	1.4*
			1.000	175.0

* Combine classes so that all $E_i \ge 5$

The calculation of the value of χ^2 is now completed as follows.

Class	O_i	E_i	$\left(O_i - E_i\right)$	$\left(O_i - E_i\right)^2$	$\dfrac{\left(O_i - E_i\right)^2}{E_i}$
$-\infty < x < 28$	7	7.5	−0.5	0.25	0.033
$28 \le x < 30$	22	18.9	3.1	9.61	0.508
$30 \le x < 32$	36	37.5	−1.5	2.25	0.060
$32 \le x < 34$	45	47.2	−2.2	4.84	0.103
$34 \le x < 36$	33	37.5	−4.5	20.25	0.540
$36 \le x < 38$	28	18.9	9.1	82.81	4.381
$38 \le x < \infty$	4	7.5	−3.5	12.25	1.633
					7.258

H_0: normal distribution is appropriate

H_1: normal distribution is not appropriate

Significance level, $\alpha = 0.10$

Degrees of freedom, $v = 7 - 3 = 4$

(7 classes; 3 constraints:

$$\sum E_i = \sum O_i \,,$$
$$\sum E_i x_i = \sum O_i x_i \text{ from estimation of } \mu \,,$$

and $\quad \sum E_i x_i^2 = \sum O_i x_i^2$ from estimation of σ^2)

Critical region is $\quad \chi^2 > 7.779$

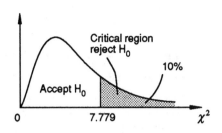

Test statistic is $\quad \chi^2 = \sum \dfrac{\left(O_i - E_i\right)^2}{E_i} = 7.258$

This value does not lie in the critical region. There is no evidence, at the 10% significance level, to suggest that a normal distribution is not appropriate.

What changes would need to be made to this solution if the question had suggested a normal distribution with

(a) $\mu = 33$ **(b)** $\sigma = 3$ **(c)** $\mu = 33$ and $\sigma = 3$?

Activity 8   Customer arrivals revisited

Construct a grouped frequency distribution of the inter-arrival times recorded in Activity 6.

Draw a histogram of your results and observe its shape.

Examine whether or not inter-arrival times may be modelled by an exponential distribution.

Activity 9   Textbook weights

Using a suitable random selection procedure, obtain and weigh, in grams, a sample of at least 100 textbooks from your school or college library. A set of electronic kitchen scales should give sufficient accuracy.

Construct a grouped frequency distribution of your results and draw the corresponding histogram.

Investigate the claim that textbook weights are normally distributed.

Exercise 5C

1. A sample of 300 electronic circuit components is selected at random from a production process. The lifetime, in hours, of each component is measured by testing it to destruction with the following summarised results.

Lifetime	0-	50-	100-	150-	200-	300-	400-	500
Frequency	63	47	55	34	29	27	24	21

Use a goodness of fit test to test the hypothesis that the lifetimes of components from this production process follow an exponential distribution with mean 200 hours.

2. The duration, in hours, of the effect of the standard dose of a certain drug on a healthy adult female is thought to be exponentially distributed. The table below shows the results for a random sample of 200 healthy females all given the standard dose.

Duration	0	3-	6-	9-	12-	18-	24-36
Females	40	31	31	22	23	22	31

Test the hypothesis that the duration of the effect is exponentially distributed.

3. The table below summarises the times taken, in seconds, by 250 nine-year-old children to tie their shoe laces.

Time	<10	10-	20-	30-	40-	50-	60-
Frequency	9	16	51	72	79	11	12

Apply a χ^2 goodness of fit test to investigate whether or not the times taken by nine-year-old children to tie their shoe laces are normally distributed with a mean of 35 seconds and a standard deviation of 10 seconds.

4. The shape of the human head was the subject of an international project financed by the World Council for Health and Welfare. Observations were taken in many countries and the nose lengths, to the nearest millimetre, of 150 Italians are summarised below.

Nose lengths (mm) x	Frequency f
$-\infty < x \le 44$	4
$45 \le x \le 47$	12
$48 \le x \le 50$	63
$51 \le x \le 53$	59
$54 \le x \le 56$	10
$57 \le x < \infty$	2

Estimate the mean and the standard deviation of the population from which these observations were taken. (For these calculations you should assume that the lower and upper classes have the same width as the other classes.)

Use the χ^2 distribution and a 1% level of significance to test the adequacy of the normal distribution as a model for these data.

(AEB)

5.4   Miscellaneous Exercises

1. At a vinegar bottling plant, samples of five bottles are taken at regular intervals and their contents measured. During a particular week 170 samples were taken and the number of bottles in each sample containing less than 1160 ml recorded. The results are given in the following table.

Number of bottles containing less than 1160 ml	0	1	2	3	4	5
Number of samples	41	62	49	12	5	1

Estimate p, the proportion of bottles produced containing less than 1160 ml.

Find the expected frequencies of a binomial distribution with the same sample size, value of p and total frequency as the observed data.

Applying a goodness of fit test, investigate whether the data support the view that the numbers of bottles in samples of size 5, containing less than 1160 ml, have a binomial distribution.

(AEB)

2. A factory operates four production lines. Maintenance records show that the daily number of stoppages due to mechanical failure were as follows (it is possible for a production line to break down more than once on the same day).

Number of stoppages (x)	Number of days (f)
0	728
1	447
2	138
3	48
4	26
5	13
6 or more	0

You may assume that $\sum f = 1400$ $\sum fx = 1036$

(a) Use a χ^2 distribution and a 1% significance level to determine whether the Poisson distribution is an adequate model for the data.

(b) The maintenance engineer claims that breakdowns occur at random and that the mean rate has remained constant throughout the period. State, giving a reason, whether your answer to (a) is consistent with this claim.

(c) Of the 1036 breakdowns which occurred, 230 were on production line A, 303 on B, 270 on C and 233 on D. Test at the 5% significance level whether these data are consistent with breakdowns occurring at an equal rate on each production line. (AEB)

3. In a European country, registration for military service is compulsory for all eighteen-year-old males. All males must report to a barracks where, after an inspection, some, including all those less than 1.6 m tall, are excused service. The heights of a sample of 125 eighteen-year-olds measured at the barracks were as follows.

Height	1.2–	1.4–	1.6–	1.8–	2.0–2.2
Frequency	6	34	31	42	12

(a) Use a χ^2 test and a 5% significance level to confirm that the normal distribution is not an adequate model for these data.

(b) Show that, if the second and third classes (1.4– and 1.6–) are combined, the normal distribution does appear to fit the data. Comment on this apparent contradiction in the light of the information at the beginning of the question. (AEB)

4. (a) The number of books borrowed from a library during a certain week were 518 on Monday, 431 on Tuesday, 485 on Wednesday, 443 on Thursday and 523 on Friday.

Is there any evidence that the number of books borrowed varies between the five days of the week? Use a 1% level of significance.

Interpret fully your conclusions.

(b) The following 50 observations were believed to be a random sample from the discrete probability distribution defined by

$$P(X = r) = (r-1)p^2(1-p)^{r-2} \quad r = 2, 3, \ldots$$

r	2	3	4	5	≥6
Frequency	18	17	12	3	0

An appropriate estimate of p is $\dfrac{2}{\bar{x}}$, where $\bar{x}$ is the sample mean. Use a χ^2 test, at the 5% significance level, to investigate whether these data are consistent with the postulated distribution. (AEB)

5. (a) The table below summarises the values of 600 pseudo random numbers as generated by a particular model of calculator.

Value	0.0–	0.2–	0.4–	0.6–	0.8–1.0
Frequency	10	14	112	107	135

Can it be assumed that pseudo random numbers, as generated by this model of calculator, are distributed uniformly over the interval zero to unity?

(b) The table below shows the results of the measurement of the lifetime, in thousands of hours, of each of a random sample of 200 Type A transistors.

Lifetime	0–	5–	10–	15–	20–	30–	50–
Frequency	47	34	28	25	22	33	11

Perform a χ^2 goodness of fit test of the hypothesis that the lifetimes of Type A transistors follow an exponential distribution with mean 20000 hours.

Outline, without calculation, the modifications necessary to your analysis, if the hypothesis did not specify the mean value.

6. A mill weaves cloth in standard lengths. When a length of cloth contains a serious blemish, the damaged section is cut out and the two remaining parts stitched together. This is known as a string. An analysis of the number of strings in 220 lengths of a particular type revealed the following data.

Number of strings	0	1	2	3	4	5	6	7
Frequency	14	29	57	48	31	41	0	0

(a) Test whether a Poisson distribution is an adequate model for these data, using a 5% significance level.

(b) On seeing the analysis, the manager pointed out that lengths of cloth containing more than 5 strings were unsaleable. If necessary, larger sections of cloth would be removed so that no length contained more than 5 strings. Without this restriction, she estimated that there would be an average of 3 strings per length.

If a Poisson distribution with mean 3 is fitted to the data the expected numbers are as follows.

Number of strings	0	1	2	3	4	≥5
Expected number	10.96	32.85	49.29	49.29	36.98	40.63

Test whether a Poisson distribution with mean 3 is an adequate model for the data provided all observations of 5 or more are classified together (as is the case in this part). Use a 5% significance level.

(c) In the light of your calculations in (a) and (b), discuss whether it is likely that serious blemishes occur at random at a constant average rate through the cloth.   (AEB)

7. A company sells clothes by mail order catalogue. The size of clothes is defined by the hip size; thus the height of customers of a particular size may vary considerably.

Data sent in by female customers of size 18 showed the following distribution of heights, in centimetres.

Class	Class mid-mark (x)	Frequency (f)
130–	135	8
140–	145	129
150–	155	61
160–	165	34
170–	175	22
180–	185	11

(a) Given that

$$\Sigma f = 265 \quad \Sigma fx = 40735 \quad \Sigma fx^2 = 6299425$$

estimate the mean and standard deviation of heights.

(b) Test, at the 1% significance level, whether the normal distribution provides an adequate model for the heights.

(c) The company decides, for economic reasons, that it is not possible to produce a range of garments of a particular size suitable for customers of different heights. A single height must be chosen and it is proposed that this should be the mean height. Comment on this suggestion as it applies to customers of size 18 and make an alternative proposal.
        (AEB)

8. A biased coin is tossed 5 times and the number of heads obtained is recorded. This is repeated 200 times. The table below summarises the results.

Number of heads (x)	0	1	2	3	4	5
Frequency (f)	5	39	70	52	25	9

Find the frequencies of the number of heads given by a binomial distribution having the same mean and total as the observed distribution.

Instead of calculating the usual goodness of fit statistic $\chi^2 = \sum \dfrac{(O-E)^2}{E}$, calculate the values of the following:

(a) $\chi_1^2 = \sum \dfrac{(O-E)}{E}$

(b) $\chi_2^2 = \sum \dfrac{|O-E|}{E}$

How useful do you think these new statistics may be in measuring the goodness of fit in the above situation?   (AEB)

9. The owner of a small country inn observes that during the holiday season the demand for rooms is as follows.

Rooms required	0	1	2	3	4	5	6	7	8
Number of nights	2	9	16	26	33	25	20	11	5

Calculate the mean demand for rooms per night.

Use a χ^2 test with a 5% significance level to determine whether the Poisson distribution is an adequate model for the data.

The inn has only four rooms available to let. Assuming demand follows a Poisson distribution with mean 4.17, calculate the mean and variance of the number of rooms occupied per night.
        (AEB)

.0. (a) As part of a statistics project, students observed five private cars passing a college and counted the number which were carrying the driver only, with no passengers. This was repeated 80 times.

The results of a particular student were as follows.

Number of cars with driver only	0	1	2	3	4	5
Number of times observed	0	3	12	27	26	12

Use the χ^2 distribution and a 5% significance level to test whether the binomial distribution provides an adequate model for the data.

(b) In a further part of the project the students counted the number of cars passing the college in 130 intervals each of length 5 seconds. The following table shows the results obtained by the same student together with the expected numbers if a Poisson distribution, with the same mean as the observed data, is fitted.

Number of cars passing a point in a 5 second interval	Number of intervals	
	Observed	Expected
0	28	25.85
1	40	41.75
2	32	33.72
3	19	18.16
4	7	7.33
5	3	2.37
6	1	0.64
7 or more	0	0.18

Use as χ^2 distribution and a 5% significance level to test whether the Poisson distribution provides an adequate model for the data.

(c) The teacher suspected that this student had not observed the data but invented them. Explain why the teacher was suspicious and comment on the strength of the evidence supporting her suspicions.   (AEB)

6 EXPERIMENTAL DESIGN

Objectives

After studying this chapter you should

*   understand what is meant by experimental error, bias , replication and blocking;
*   appreciate why experimental and control groups are used;
*   understand what is meant by blind and double blind trials.

6.0 Introduction

A greengrocer normally obtained her fruit and vegetables from a market in Manchester. She wished to find out whether obtaining her supplies from a different market in Preston would increase her takings. As an experiment she used the Preston market on eight days and recorded her daily takings. The results together with her takings on ten days when she used the Manchester market are shown below.

	Takings, £
Preston market	323 274 269 552 435 391 208 529
Manchester market	286 517 492 264 367 399 198 581 362 303

The first point to note is that the takings for both markets vary. If every time she bought from Preston her takings were £323 and every time she bought from Manchester her takings were £286 it would be obvious that buying from Preston increased her takings and there would be no need for any statistical analysis.

However the takings do vary and this is said to be caused by **experimental error**. This does not mean that a mistake has been made. It simply means that factors other than the market she is buying from will affect the takings. In this case, it is probable that the weather, the traffic conditions in the area and the types of fruit and vegetables available will affect the takings. Almost certainly the shop will be busier at the weekend than in the middle of the week and this will have a substantial effect on the takings.

What other factors might affect the takings?

The problem with experimental error is that if there is a difference in the average takings from the two markets, it may be difficult or impossible to tell whether this is due to the effect of the factor(s) being investigated - in this case the market - or due to experimental error.

Experimental error should be minimised by keeping factors which are not being investigated as constant as possible and by experimental design. In this case it may be impossible to standardise the weather or the traffic conditions but the opening hours of the shop and the number of assistants working there should be kept constant. In a laboratory experiment temperature, humidity and various other factors could be held constant.

What factors could be kept constant in an experiment to compare the petrol consumption of two different makes of car?

If repeated observations under apparently identical conditions are made then the magnitude of the experimental error may be estimated. The repeated observations are known as **replicates** and the magnitude of the experimental error is usually estimated by calculating the standard deviation of the replicates. In the experiment above there were 8 replicates of the takings from Preston and 10 replicates of the takings from Manchester. As far as the factor under investigation was concerned (i.e. the market), the conditions were identical. The data could be analysed using an unpaired t-test (see Section 4.3) to compare the means. This involves making a pooled estimate of the standard deviation, i.e. estimating the size of the experimental error.

6.1   Experimental design

Rather than carrying out the analysis on the data above, it would first be better to use **experimental design** to try to reduce the size of the experimental error. The simplest experimental design is the use of **paired comparisons**. Here two treatments being compared are each applied to similar raw material. For example, if yield of two types of wheat were to be compared, a field might be split into small plots and the two types of wheat planted in adjacent plots. This is to minimise differences in the conditions in which the wheat grows and reduce experimental error due to the two types of wheat growing under different conditions.

Similarly, to compare the weight loss due to two different slimming diets, an ideal design would be to secure the cooperation of several pairs of identical twins. One twin of each pair would follow one diet and the other twin the other diet. Thus experimental error due to physiological differences in the people undertaking the diets would be minimised.

To return to the greengrocer, an obvious source of experimental error is the day of the week. Takings are likely to be much higher at weekends. Therefore if we examine the differences between the takings from each market on the same day of the week, one major source of experimental error will have been eliminated.

The experiment might be carried out as follows

Week 1	Manchester market					
	Mon	Tue	Wed	Thur	Fri	Sat
Takings	272	295	318	307	532	599

Week 2	Preston market					
	Mon	Tue	Wed	Thur	Fri	Sat
Takings	268	272	324	352	511	604

The data can now be analysed using a paired *t*-test (see Section 4.4). This would be perfectly satisfactory for analysing data of weight loss by identical twins who had followed different diets. However in this case, the design can be improved further. Suppose that Week 1 was fine and dry but Week 2 was wet and windy. Alternatively, suppose new potatoes were available from the market in Week 2 but not in Week 1. If a difference was found between the takings in the two weeks we would not know whether this was due to a difference between the markets or whether it was due to the different weather conditions (or the availability of new potatoes). The two effects are said to be confounded.

A better arrangement would be as follows

Week 1	Mon	Tue	Wed	Thur	Fri	Sat
Market	A	B	A	B	A	B
Takings £	284	296	333	376	494	517

Week 2	Mon	Tue	Wed	Thur	Fri	Sat
Market	B	A	B	A	B	A
Takings £	276	308	307	400	482	512

Why is this a better arrangement?

A and B represent the two markets. The final decision to be taken is whether A represents Manchester and B represents Preston or the other way round. Where there is no obvious reason for choosing one way in preference to the other the choice should be made by a random process such as tossing a coin. This is known as **randomisation** and is to prevent unconscious or unsuspected **bias** from affecting the result. There are no obvious further improvements which can be made to this design. Suppose A was chosen to be Manchester, the analysis would be as follows:

	Mon	Tue	Wed	Thur	Fri	Sat
Manchester	284	308	333	400	494	512
Preston	276	296	307	376	482	517
Difference	12	12	26	24	12	–5

H_0 : mean difference $= 0$ H_1 : mean difference $\neq 0$

This can be tested using the paired t-test. This assumes that the differences are normally distributed. The sample mean will be approximately normally distributed even if the individual differences do not exactly follow a normal distribution. It is therefore safe to apply this test unless it is quite clear that the distribution is extremely skew.

The mean difference $\bar{d} = 13.5$ and the standard deviation of the differences $\hat{\sigma} = 11.095$. So

$$ t = \frac{13.5}{\left(\dfrac{11.095}{\sqrt{6}} \right)} = 2.98 $$

Critical values of t_5 for a 5% 2-sided risk of **Type 1 error** are ± 2.571.

H_0 is rejected and, since the mean difference for Manchester - Preston is positive, we conclude that the takings are higher when the Manchester market is used.

It is impossible to rule out completely the possibility that the difference is due to some factor other than the markets. Chance is always a possibility. However, a well-designed experiment eliminates all likely alternative explanations.

Activity 1

A road haulage firm moves lorryloads of slate from a quarry to a depot 70 miles away. You are asked to advise the firm how to investigate which of two alternative routes is quicker.
Design an experiment to compare the routes efficiently. Explain the role of replication and randomisation in your design.

Activity 2

You are asked to compare the effect of two different fertiliser treatments on the yield of a particular variety of carrots. Describe how you might design this experiment and the precautions you might take to ensure any conclusions you came to were valid. Explain the role of replication and randomisation in your design.

Blocking

If the greengrocer wished to compare the effect on takings of several possible markets she could visit each market on randomly chosen days and record her takings.

	Takings £					
Kirkham	344	479	503	290	207	
Manchester	459	234	602	222	598	479
Oldham	322	600	308	344	506	
Preston	292	588	347	399	544	406

This is known as a **completely randomised design** and would be analysed using **one factor analysis of variance** (see Section 7.3).

However, the ideas of the paired comparison can be extended to this case. The experiment could be carried out as follows.

	Takings £					
	Mon	Tue	Wed	Thur	Fri	Sat
Kirkham	294	306	343	386	494	527
Manchester	277	318	399	360	524	566
Oldham	299	265	302	410	488	530
Preston	260	289	299	391	460	488

This is known as a **randomised block design**. The markets are blocked by days of the week. This design is analysed using **two factor analysis of variance** (see Section 7.4). One of the factors - in this case the markets - is the object of the investigation. The other factor - in this case the day of the week - is introduced because it is thought that it might have a substantial effect on the results. As with the paired comparison, the introduction of the days of the week as a factor will, if the design is successful, reduce the experimental error. It will therefore make it easier to detect a difference between markets, if such a difference exists.

Control groups

In the examples above two or more different markets were compared. Sometimes there are not two or more treatments, but only one. For example, we may wish to observe the effect of a particular medical treatment on arthritis or the effect of a coaching course on a student's tennis playing skills. The effect of these treatments cannot be judged in isolation. An arthritis sufferer may improve (or deteriorate) with no treatment. Similarly, a tennis player may improve without attending a coaching course.

It is necessary to have a **control group** and an **experimental group**. These two groups should be matched as closely as possible. That is, the people in one group should be as similar as possible to the people in the other group as far as characteristics relevant to the investigation are concerned. This does not mean that all the people in a particular group must be similar to each other, but that the group as a whole must be similar to the other group.

For example, in the case of the arthritis sufferers the two groups should contain people of similar age, sex, general health and severity of arthritis. In the case of the tennis players, the groups should contain students of similar age, sex, fitness and tennis playing ability.

The groups should be selected and then one group should be chosen at random to receive the experimental treatment (or tennis coaching) and the other group will be the control group. The control group will receive no treatment (or coaching) or will continue with the standard treatment. The effect on the two groups can then be compared.

Blind and double blind trials

In the case of medical treatment, it is sometimes thought that patients will improve or recover without treatment and that in some cases this improvement will be greater or quicker if they are told they are having treatment, even if they are not. Thus it is standard practise in drugs tests to give the control group a **placebo**. This is a harmless substance which looks like the real medication but, in fact, does not contain any drug. Many patients will improve after taking placebos. To show a drug to be effective, significantly more patients who took the drug must show improvement than those who took the placebo. (There are, of course, other issues such as possible side effects to consider as well).

If the patients who took the placebos knew that they were taking placebos the effect would of course be lost. It is essential that the patients should not know whether or not they are taking placebos and this is known as a **blind trial**.

Even more subtle effects can be at work. It has been found that, even if the patients do not know whether or not they are taking placebos, the doctor may expect those patients taking the drug to fare better than those taking placebos. This expectation may somehow transmit itself to the patient whose condition may improve as a result. It is therefore, necessary that the doctor does not know which patients are receiving placebos and which are receiving the drugs. Of course, someone must know who is receiving the drugs otherwise it would be impossible to analyse the results. However, it should be someone who has no direct contact with the patient. Trials where neither the patient nor the doctor know who is receiving the drugs are known as **double blind trials**.

It has been suggested that the person carrying out the statistical analysis should also not know which patients took the drug to prevent this influencing the analysis. This would be described as a triple blind trial.

Drug trials are greatly affected by the ethical problems involved. Firstly, it is of course essential that patients taking part should be fully informed of the nature and possible risks of the experiment. Secondly, once a treatment has been established as beneficial, it would be wrong not to let all the patients taking part in the trial benefit from it even if this interferes with strictly statistical considerations. Thirdly, it is clearly wrong to carry out an experiment, with all the inconvenience it may cause and false hopes it may raise, if it has not been well designed. Trials have been carried out which have been too small to establish the effectiveness of a treatment, whatever the results obtained. In other cases, lack of effective design has made the experimental error much larger than it need be thus making a real effect impossible to detect. The statistician has an important role to play in this fascinating area.

7 ANALYSIS OF VARIANCE (ANOVA)

Objectives

After studying this chapter you should

- appreciate the need for analysing data from more than two samples;

- understand the underlying models to analysis of variance;

- understand when, and be able, to carry out a one way analysis of variance;

- understand when, and be able, to carry out a two way analysis of variance.

7.0 Introduction

What is the common characteristic of all tests described in Chapter 5?

Consider the following two investigations.

(a) A car magazine wishes to compare the average petrol consumption of THREE similar models of car and has available six vehicles of each model.

(b) A teacher is interested in a comparison of the average percentage marks attained in the examinations of FIVE different subjects and has available the marks of eight students who all completed each examination.

In both these investigations, interest is centred on a comparison of **more than two populations**; THREE models of car, FIVE examinations.

In (a), six vehicles of each of the three models are available so there are three **independent samples**, each of size six. This example requires an extension of the test considered in Section 4.3, which was for two normal population means using independent samples and a pooled estimate of variance.

In (b) however, there is the additional feature that the same eight students each completed the five examinations, so there are five **dependent samples** each of size eight. This example requires an extension of the test considered in Section 4.4, which was for two normal population means using dependent (paired) samples.

This chapter will show that an appropriate method for investigation (a) is a **one way** anova to test for differences between the three models of car. For (b), an appropriate method is a two way anova to test for differences between the five subjects and, if required, for differences between the eight students.

7.1   Ideas for data collection

Undertake at least one of Activities 1 and 2 AND at least one of Activities 3 and 4. You will require your data for subsequent analysis later in this chapter.

Activity 1   Estimating length

Draw a straight line of between 20 cm and 25 cm on a sheet of plain white card. (Only you should know its exact length.)

Collect 6 to 10 volunteers from each of school years 7, 10 and 13. Ask each volunteer to estimate independently the length of the line.

Do differences in year means appear to outweigh differences within years?

Activity 2   Apples

Obtain random samples of each of at least three varieties of apple. The samples should be of at least 5 apples but need not be of the same size.

Weigh, as accurately as you are able, each apple.

Compare variation within varieties with variability between varieties.

Activity 3   Shop prices

Make a list of 10 food/household items purchased regularly by your family.

Obtain the current prices of the items in three different shops; preferably a small 'corner' shop, a small supermarket and a large supermarket or hyper market.

Compare total shop prices.

Activity 4   Weighing scales

Obtain the use of at least three different models of bathroom scales, preferably one of which is electronic. Collect about 10 volunteers and record their weights on each scale. If possible, also have each volunteer weighed on more accurate scales such as those found in health centres or large pharmacies.

You will need to ensure that your volunteers are each wearing, as far as is possible, the same apparel at every weighing.

Assess the differences in total weights between the weighing devices used.

Which model of bathroom scales appears the most accurate?

7.2   Factors and factor levels

Two new terms for analysis of variance need to be introduced at this stage.

> **Factor** – a characteristic under consideration, thought to influence the measured observations.
>
> **Level** – a value of the factor.

In Activity 1, there is one factor (school year) at three levels (7, 10 and 13).

In Activity 3, there are two factors (item and shop) at 10 and 3 levels, respectively.

What are the factors and levels in Activities 2 and 4?

7.3 One way (factor) anova

In general, one way anova techniques can be used to study the effect of $k(> 2)$ levels of a single factor.

To determine if different levels of the factor affect measured observations differently, the following hypotheses are tested.

$$H_0: \mu_i = \mu \quad \text{all} \ \ i = 1, 2, ..., k$$

$$H_1: \mu_i \neq \mu \quad \text{some} \ i = 1, 2, ..., k$$

where μ_i is the population mean for level i.

Assumptions

When applying one way analysis of variance there are three key assumptions that should be satisfied. They are essentially the same as those assumed in Section 5.3 for $k = 2$ levels, and are as follows.

1. The observations are obtained independently and randomly from the populations defined by the factor levels.

2. The population at each factor level is (approximately) normally distributed.

3. These normal populations have a common variance, σ^2.

Thus for factor level i, the population is assumed to have a distribution which is $N\left(\mu_i, \sigma^2\right)$.

Example

The table below shows the lifetimes under controlled conditions, in hours in excess of 1000 hours, of samples of 60W electric light bulbs of three different brands.

Brand		
1	**2**	**3**
16	18	26
15	22	31
13	20	24
21	16	30
15	24	24

Assuming all lifetimes to be normally distributed with common variance, test, at the 1% significance level, the hypothesis that there is no difference between the three brands with respect to mean lifetime.

Solution

Here there is one factor (brand) at three levels (1, 2 and 3). Also the sample sizes are all equal (to 5), though as you will see later this is not necessary.

$$H_0: \mu_i = \mu \quad \text{all} \quad i = 1, 2, 3$$

$$H_1: \mu_i \neq \mu \quad \text{some} \quad i = 1, 2, 3$$

The sample mean and variance (divisor $(n-1)$) for each level are as follows.

	Brand		
	1	**2**	**3**
Sample size	5	5	5
Sum	80	100	135
Sum of squares	1316	2040	3689
Mean	16	20	27
Variance	9	10	11

Since each of these three sample variances is an estimate of the common population variance, σ^2, a pooled estimate may be calculated in the usual way as follows.

$$\hat{\sigma}_W^2 = \frac{(5-1) \times 9 + (5-1) \times 10 + (5-1) \times 11}{5+5+5-3} = 10$$

This quantity is called the **variance within samples**. It is an estimate of σ^2 based on $v = 5 + 5 + 5 - 3 = 12$ degrees of freedom. This is irrespective of whether or not the null hypothesis is true, since differences between levels (brands) will have no effect on the within sample variances.

The variability between samples may be estimated from the three sample means as follows.

	Brand		
	1	**2**	**3**
Sample mean	16	20	27
Sum		63	
Sum of squares		1385	
Mean		21	
Variance		21	

This variance (divisor $(n-1)$), denoted by $\hat{\sigma}_B^2$ is called the **variance between sample means**. Since it calculated using sample means, it is an estimate of

$$\frac{\sigma^2}{5} \text{ (that is } \frac{\sigma^2}{n} \text{ in general)}$$

based upon $(3-1)=2$ degrees of freedom, but only if the null hypothesis is true. If H_0 is false, then the subsequent 'large' differences between the sample means will result in $5\hat{\sigma}_B^2$ being an inflated estimate of σ^2.

The two estimates of σ^2, $\hat{\sigma}_W^2$ and $5\hat{\sigma}_B^2$, may be tested for equality using the F-test of Section 4.1 with

$$F = \frac{5\hat{\sigma}_B^2}{\hat{\sigma}_W^2}$$

as lifetimes may be assumed to be normally distributed.

Recall that the F-test requires the two variances to be independently distributed (from independent samples). Although this is by no means obvious here (both were calculated from the same data), $\hat{\sigma}_W^2$ and $\hat{\sigma}_B^2$ are in fact independently distributed.

The test is always one-sided, upper-tail, since if H_0 is false, $5\hat{\sigma}_B^2$ is inflated whereas $\hat{\sigma}_W^2$ is unaffected.

Thus in analysis of variance, the convention of placing the larger sample variance in the numerator of the F statistic is NOT applied.

The solution is thus summarised and completed as follows.

$H_0: \mu_i = \mu$ all $i = 1, 2, 3$

$H_1: \mu_i \neq \mu$ some $i = 1, 2, 3$

Significance level, $\alpha = 0.01$

Degrees of freedom , $v_1 = 2$, $v_2 = 12$

Critical region is $F > 6.927$

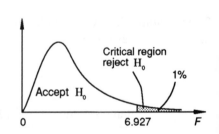

Test statistic is $F = \dfrac{5\hat{\sigma}_B^2}{\hat{\sigma}_W^2} = \dfrac{155}{10} = 15.5$

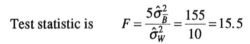

This value does lie in the critical region. There is evidence, at the 1% significance level, that the true mean lifetimes of the three brands of bulb do differ.

What is the value of the variance (divisor $(n-1)$), $\hat{\sigma}_T^2$, of the lifetimes, if these are considered simply as one sample of size 15?

What is the value of $14\hat{\sigma}_T^2$?

What is the value of $12\hat{\sigma}_W^2 + 10\hat{\sigma}_B^2$?

At this point it is useful to note that, although the above calculations were based on (actual lifetimes - 1000), the same value would have been obtained for the test statistic (F) using actual lifetimes. This is because F is the ratio of two variances, both of which are unaffected by subtracting a working mean from all the data values. Additionally, in analysis of variance, data values may also be scaled by multiplying or dividing by a constant without affecting the value of the F ratio. This is because each variance involves the square of the constant which then cancels in the ratio. Scaling of data values can make the subsequent analysis of variance less cumbersome and, sometimes, even more accurate

Notation and computational formulae

The calculations undertaken in the previous example are somewhat cumbersome, and are prone to inaccuracy with non-integer sample means. They also require considerable changes when the sample sizes are unequal. Equivalent computational formulae are available which cater for both equal and unequal sample sizes.

First, some notation.

Number of samples (or levels)	$= k$
Number of observations in ith sample	$= n_i, \quad i = 1, 2, \ldots, k$
Total number of observations	$= n = \sum_i n_i$
Observation j in ith sample	$= x_{ij}, \quad j = 1, 2, \ldots, n_i$
Sum of n_i observations in ith sample	$= T_i = \sum_j x_{ij}$
Sum of all n observations	$= T = \sum_i T_i = \sum_i \sum_j x_{ij}$

The computational formulae now follow.

Total sum of squares,	$SS_T = \sum_i \sum_j x_{ij}^2 - \dfrac{T^2}{n}$
Between samples sum of squares,	$SS_B = \sum_i \dfrac{T_i^2}{n_i} - \dfrac{T^2}{n}$
Within samples sum of squares,	$SS_W = SS_T - SS_B$

A mean square (or unbiased variance estimate) is given by

$$(\text{sum of squares}) \div (\text{degrees of freedom})$$

e.g.

$$\hat{\sigma}^2 = \frac{\Sigma(x - \bar{x})^2}{n - 1}$$

Hence

Total mean square ,	$MS_T = \dfrac{SS_T}{n - 1}$
Between samples mean square,	$MS_B = \dfrac{SS_B}{k - 1}$
Within samples mean square,	$MS_W = \dfrac{SS_W}{n - k}$

Note that for the degrees of freedom: $(k - 1) + (n - k) = (n - 1)$

Activity 5

For the previous example on 60W electric light bulbs, use these computational formulae to show the following.

(a) $SS_T = 430$ (b) $SS_B = 310$

(c) $MS_B = 155 \ \left(5\hat{\sigma}_B^2\right)$ (d) $MS_W = 10 \ \left(\hat{\sigma}_W^2\right)$

Note that $F = \dfrac{MS_B}{MS_W} = \dfrac{155}{10} = 15.5$ as previously.

Anova table

It is convenient to summarise the results of an analysis of variance in a table. For a one factor analysis this takes the following form.

Source of variation	Sum of squares	Degrees of freedom	Mean square	F ratio
Between samples	SS_B	$k - 1$	MS_B	$\dfrac{MS_B}{MS_W}$
Within samples	SS_W	$n - k$	MS_W	
Total	SS_T	$n - 1$		

Example

In a comparison of the cleaning action of four detergents, 20 pieces of white cloth were first soiled with India ink. The cloths were then washed under controlled conditions with 5 pieces washed by each of the detergents. Unfortunately three pieces of cloth were 'lost' in the course of the experiment. Whiteness readings, made on the 17 remaining pieces of cloth, are shown below.

Detergent

A	B	C	D
77	74	73	76
81	66	78	85
61	58	57	77
76		69	64
69		63	

Assuming all whiteness readings to be normally distributed with common variance, test the hypothesis of no difference between the four brands as regards mean whiteness readings after washing.

Solution

H_0: no difference in mean readings $\qquad \mu_i = \mu$ all i

H_1: a difference in mean readings $\qquad \mu_i \neq \mu$ some i

Significance level, $\alpha = 0.05$

Degrees of freedom, $v_1 = k - 1 = 3$

$\qquad$ and $\quad v_2 = n - k = 17 - 4 = 13$

Critical region is $\quad F > 3.411$

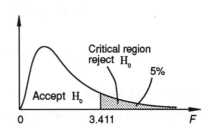

	A	B	C	D	Total
n_i	5	3	5	4	$17 = n$
T_i	364	198	340	302	$1204 = T$

$$\sum\sum x_{ij}^2 = 86362$$

$$SS_T = 86362 - \frac{1204^2}{17} = 1090.47$$

$$SS_B = \left(\frac{364^2}{5} + \frac{198^2}{3} + \frac{340^2}{5} + \frac{302^2}{4} \right) - \frac{1204^2}{17} = 216.67$$

$$SS_W = 1090.47 - 216.67 = 873.80$$

The anova table is now as follows.

Source of variation	Sum of squares	Degrees of freedom	Mean square	F ratio
Between detergents	216.67	3	72.22	1.07
Within detergents	873.80	13	67.22	
Total	1090.47	16		

The F ratio of 1.07 does not lie in the critical region.

Thus there is no evidence, at the 5% significance level, to suggest a difference between the four brands as regards mean whiteness after washing.

Activity 6

Carry out a one factor analysis of variance for the data you collected in either or both of Activities 1 and 2.

Model

From the three assumptions for one factor anova, listed previously,

$$x_{ij} \sim N\left(\mu_i, \sigma^2\right) \quad \text{for } j = 1, 2, \ldots, n_i \text{ and } i = 1, 2, \ldots, k$$

Hence $\quad x_{ij} - \mu_i = \varepsilon_{ij} \sim N\left(0, \sigma^2\right)$

where ε_{ij} denotes the variation of x_{ij} about its mean μ_i and so represents the inherent random variation in the observations.

If $\mu = \dfrac{1}{k}\sum_{i=1}^{k}\mu_i$, then $\sum_i(\mu_i - \mu) = 0$.

Writing $\mu_i - \mu = L_i$ results in $\mu_i = \mu + L_i$ where $\sum_i L_i = 0$.

Hence L_i can be interpreted as the mean effect of factor level i relative to the overall mean μ.

Combining $x_{ij} - \mu_i = \varepsilon_{ij}$ with $\mu_i - \mu = L_i$ results in

$$x_{ij} = \mu + L_i + \varepsilon_{ij} \quad \text{for } j = 1, 2, \ldots, n_i \text{ and } i = 1, 2, \ldots, k$$

This formally defines a model for one way (factor) analysis of variance, where

x_{ij} = jth observation at ith level (in ith sample),

μ = overall factor mean,

L_i = mean effect of ith level of factor relative to μ, where $\sum\limits_{i} L_i = 0$,

ε_{ij} = inherent random variation $\sim N\left(0, \sigma^2\right)$.

Note that as a result,

$$H_0: \mu_i = \mu \ (\text{all } i) \implies H_0: L_i = 0 \ (\text{all } i)$$

Estimates of μ, L_i and ε_{ij} can be calculated from observed measurements by

$$\frac{T}{n}, \ \left(\frac{T_i}{n_i} - \frac{T}{n}\right) \ \text{and} \ \left(x_{ij} - \frac{T_i}{n_i}\right), \ \text{respectively.}$$

Thus for the example on 60W electric light bulbs for which the observed measurements (x_{ij}) were

Brand

1	2	3
16	18	26
15	22	31
13	20	24
21	16	30
15	24	24

with $n = 15$, $n_1 = n_2 = n_3 = 5$, $T = 315$, $T_1 = 80$, $T_2 = 100$ and $T_3 = 135$.

Hence, estimates of μ, L_1, L_2 and L_3 are 21, –5, –1 and +6, respectively.

Estimates of the ε_{ij} are best tabulated as shown.

Brand (estimates of ε_{ij})

1	2	3
0	–2	–1
–1	2	4
–3	0	–3
5	–4	3
–1	4	–3

Notice that, relative to the original measurements, these values representing inherent random variation are quite small.

What is the sum of these values?

What is sum of squares of these values and how was it found earlier?

Activity 7

Calculate estimates of μ, L_i and ε_{ij} for the data you collected in either of Activities 1 and 2.

Exercise 7A

1. Four treatments for fever blisters, including a placebo (A), were randomly assigned to 20 patients. The data below show, for each treatment, the numbers of days from initial appearance of the blisters until healing is complete.

Treatment	Number of days
A	5 8 7 7 8
B	4 6 6 3 5
C	6 4 4 5 4
D	7 4 6 6 5

Test the hypothesis, at the 5% significance level, that there is no difference between the four treatments with respect to mean time of healing.

2. The following data give the lifetimes, in hours, of three types of battery.

	I	50.1	49.9	49.8	49.7	50.0
Type	II	51.0	50.8	50.9	50.9	50.6
	III	49.5	50.1	50.2	49.8	49.3

Analyse these data for a difference between mean lifetimes. (Use a 5% significance level.)

3. Three different brands of magnetron tubes (the key component in microwave ovens) were subjected to stress testing. The number of hours each operated before needing repair was recorded.

	A	36	48	5	67	53
Brand	B	49	33	60	2	55
	C	71	31	140	59	424

Although these times may not represent lifetimes, they do indicate how well the tubes can withstand stress.

Use a one way analysis of variance procedure to test the hypothesis that the mean lifetime under stress is the same for the three brands.

What assumptions are necessary for the validity of this test? Is there reason to doubt these assumptions for the given data?

4. Three special ovens in a metal working shop are used to heat metal specimens. All the ovens are supposed to operate at the same temperature. It is known that the temperature of an oven varies, and it is suspected that there are significant mean temperature differences between ovens. The table below shows the temperatures, in degrees centigrade, of each of the three ovens on a random sample of heatings.

Oven	Temperature (°C)
1	494 497 481 496 487
2	489 494 479 478
3	489 483 487 472 472 477

Stating any necessary assumptions, test for a difference between mean oven temperatures.

Estimate the values of μ (1 value), L_i (3 values) and ε_{ij} (15 values) for the model (temperature) $_{ij} = x_{ij} = \mu + L_i + \varepsilon_{ij}$. Comment on what they reveal.

5. Eastside Health Authority has a policy whereby any patient admitted to a hospital with a suspected coronary heart attack is automatically placed in the intensive care unit. The table below gives the number of hours spent in intensive care by such patients at five hospitals in the area.

		Hospital		
A	**B**	**C**	**D**	**E**
30	42	65	67	70
25	57	46	58	63
12	47	55	81	80
23	30	27		
16				

Use a one factor analysis of variance to test, at the 1% level of significance, for differences between hospitals. (AEB)

6. An experiment was conducted to study the effects of various diets on pigs. A total of 24 similar pigs were selected and randomly allocated to one of the five groups such that the control group, which was fed a normal diet, had 8 pigs and each of the other groups, to which the new diets were given, had 4 pigs each. After a fixed time the gains in mass, in kilograms, of the pigs were measured. Unfortunately by this time two pigs had died, one which was on diet A and one which was on diet C. The gains in mass of the remaining pigs are recorded below.

Diets	Gain in mass (kg)			
Normal	23.1	9.8	15.5	22.6
	14.6	11.2	15.7	10.5
A	21.9	13.2	19.7	
B	16.5	22.8	18.3	31.0
C	30.9	21.9	29.8	
D	21.0	25.4	21.5	21.2

Use a one factor analysis of variance to test, at the 5% significance level, for a difference between diets.

What further information would you require about the dead pigs and how might this affect the conclusions of your analysis? (AEB)

7.4 Two way (factor) anova

This is an extension of the one factor situation to take account of a second factor. The levels of this second factor are often determined by groupings of subjects or units used in the investigation. As such it is often called a **blocking factor** because it places subjects or units into homogeneous groups called **blocks**. The design itself is then called a **randomised block design**.

Example

A computer manufacturer wishes to compare the speed of four of the firm's compilers. The manufacturer can use one of two experimental designs.

(a) Use 20 similar programs, randomly allocating 5 programs to each compiler.

(b) Use 4 copies of any 5 programs, allocating 1 copy of each program to each compiler.

Which of (a) and (b) would you recommend, and why?

Solution

In (a), although the 20 programs are similar, any differences between them may affect the compilation times and hence perhaps any conclusions. Thus in the 'worst scenario', the 5 programs allocated to what is really the fastest compiler could be the 5 requiring the longest compilation times, resulting in the compiler appearing to be the slowest! If used, the results would require a one factor analysis of variance; the factor being compiler at 4 levels.

In (b), since all 5 programs are run on each compiler, differences between programs should not affect the results. Indeed it may be advantageous to use 5 programs that differ markedly so that comparisons of compilation times are more general. For this design, there are two factors; compiler (4 levels) and program (5 levels). The factor of principal interest is compiler whereas the other factor, program, may be considered as a blocking factor as it creates 5 blocks each containing 4 copies of the same program.

Thus (b) is the better designed investigation.

The actual compilation times, in milliseconds, for this two factor (randomised block) design are shown in the following table.

	Compiler			
	1	2	3	4
Program A	29.21	28.25	28.20	28.62
Program B	26.18	26.02	26.22	25.56
Program C	30.91	30.18	30.52	30.09
Program D	25.14	25.26	25.20	25.02
Program E	26.16	25.14	25.26	25.46

Assumptions and interaction

The three assumptions for a two factor analysis of variance when there is only one observed measurement at each combination of levels of the two factors are as follows.

1. The population at each factor level combination is (approximately) normally distributed.

2. These normal populations have a common variance, σ^2.

3. The effect of one factor is the same at all levels of the other factor.

Hence from assumptions 1 and 2, when one factor is at level i and the other at level j, the population has a distribution which is

$$N\left(\mu_{ij}, \sigma^2\right).$$

Assumption 3 is equivalent to stating that there is no interaction between the two factors.

Now interaction exists when the effect of one factor depends upon the level of the other factor. For example consider the effects of the two factors:

> sugar (levels none and 2 teaspoons),

and > stirring (levels none and 1 minute),

on the sweetness of a cup of tea.

Stirring has no effect on sweetness if sugar is not added but certainly does have an effect if sugar is added. Similarly, adding sugar has little effect on sweetness unless the tea is stirred.

Hence factors sugar and stirring are said to interact.

Interaction can only be assessed if more than one measurement is taken at each combination of the factor levels. Since such situations are beyond the scope of this text, it will always be assumed that interaction between the two factors does not exist.

Thus, for example, since it would be most unusual to find one compiler particularly suited to one program, the assumption of no interaction between compilers and programs appears reasonable.

Is it likely that the assumption of no interaction is valid for the data you collected in each of Activities 3 and 4?

Notation and computational formulae

As illustrated earlier, the data for a two factor anova can be displayed in a two-way table. It is thus convenient, in general, to label the factors as

> a **row factor** and a **column factor**.

Notation, similar to that for the one factor case, is then as follows.

Number of levels of row factor	$= r$
Number of levels of column factor	$= c$
Total number of observations	$= rc$
Observation in (ij) th cell of table	$= x_{ij}$
(ith level of row factor and	$i = 1, 2, ..., r$
jth level of column factor)	$j = 1, 2, ..., c$

Sum of c observations in ith row $= T_{Ri} = \sum_j x_{ij}$

Sum of r observations in jth column $= T_{Cj} = \sum_i x_{ij}$

Sum of all rc observations $= T = \sum_i \sum_j x_{ij} = \sum_i T_{Ri} = \sum_j T_{Cj}$

These lead to the following computational formulae which again are similar to those for one factor anova except that there is an additional sum of squares, etc for the second factor.

Total sum of squares, $SS_T = \sum_i \sum_j x_{ij}^2 - \dfrac{T^2}{rc}$

Between rows sum of squares, $SS_R = \sum_i \dfrac{T_{Ri}^2}{c} - \dfrac{T^2}{rc}$

Between columns sum of squares, $SS_C = \sum_j \dfrac{T_{Cj}^2}{r} - \dfrac{T^2}{rc}$

Error (residual) sum of squares, $SS_E = SS_T - SS_R - SS_C$

What are the degrees of freedom for SS_T, SS_R and SS_C when there are 20 observations in a table of 5 rows and 4 columns?

What is then the degrees of freedom of SS_E?

Anova table and hypothesis tests

For a two factor analysis of variance this takes the following form.

Source of variation	Sum of squares	Degrees of freedom	Mean square	F ratio
Between rows	SS_R	$r-1$	MS_R	$\dfrac{MS_R}{MS_E}$
Between columns	SS_C	$c-1$	MS_C	$\dfrac{MS_C}{MS_E}$
Error (residual)	SS_E	$(r-1)(c-1)$	MS_E	
Total	SS_T	$rc-1$		

Notes:

1. The three sums of squares, SS_T, SS_R and SS_C are independently distributed.

2. For the degrees of freedom:

$$(r-1)+(c-1)+(r-1)(c-1)=(rc-1).$$

Using the F ratios, tests for significant row effects and for significant column effects can be undertaken.

H_0: no effect due to row factor	H_0: no effect due to column factor
H_1: an effect due to row factor	H_1: an effect due to column factor
Critical region,	Critical region,
$F > F^{(\alpha)}_{[(r-1),\,(r-1)(c-1)]}$	$F > F^{(\alpha)}_{[(c-1),\,(r-1)(c-1)]}$
Test statistic,	Test statistic,
$F_R = \dfrac{MS_R}{MS_E}$	$F_C = \dfrac{MS_C}{MS_E}$

Example

Returning to the compilation times, in milliseconds, for each of five programs, run on four compilers.

Test, at the 1% significance level, the hypothesis that there is no difference between the performance of the four compilers.

Has the use of programs as a blocking factor proved worthwhile? Explain.

The data, given earlier, are reproduced below.

	Compiler			
	1	**2**	**3**	**4**
Program A	29.21	28.25	28.20	28.62
Program B	26.18	26.02	26.22	25.56
Program C	30.91	30.18	30.52	30.09
Program D	25.14	25.26	25.20	25.02
Program E	26.16	25.14	25.26	25.46

Solution

To ease computations, these data have been transformed (coded) by

$$x = 100 \times (\text{time} - 25)$$

to give the following table of values and totals.

	Compiler 1	2	3	4	Row totals (T_{Ri})
Program A	421	325	320	362	1428
Program B	118	102	122	56	398
Program C	591	518	552	509	2170
Program D	14	26	20	2	62
Program E	116	14	26	46	202
Column totals (T_{Cj})	1260	985	1040	975	4260 $= T$

$$\sum\sum x_{ij}^2 = 1757768$$

The sums of squares are now calculated as follows.

(Rows = Programs, Columns = Compilers)

$$SS_T = 1757768 - \frac{4260^2}{20} = 850388$$

$$SS_R = \frac{1}{4}\left(1428^2 + 398^2 + 2170^2 + 62^2 + 202^2\right) - \frac{4260^2}{20} = 830404$$

$$SS_C = \frac{1}{5}\left(1260^2 + 985^2 + 1040^2 + 975^2\right) - \frac{4260^2}{20} = 10630$$

$$SS_E = 850388 - 830404 - 10630 = 9354$$

Anova table

Source of variation	Sum of squares	Degrees of freedom	Mean square	F ratio
Between programs	830404	4	207601.0	266.33
Between compilers	10630	3	3543.3	4.55
Error (residual)	9354	12	779.5	
Total	850388	19		

H_0: no effect on compilation times due to compilers

H_1: an effect on compilation times due to compilers

Significance level, $\alpha = 0.01$

Degrees of freedom, $v_1 = c - 1 = 3$

$$\text{and} \quad v_2 = (r-1)(c-1) = 4 \times 3 = 12$$

Critical region is $F > 5.953$

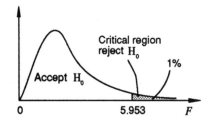

Test statistic $F_C = 4.55$

This value does not lie in the critical region. Thus there is no evidence, at the 1% significance level, to suggest a difference in compilation times between the four compilers.

The use of programs as a blocking factor has been very worthwhile. From the anova table

(a) SS_R accounts for $\dfrac{830404}{850388} \times 100 = 97.65\%$ of the total

variation in the observations, much of which would have been included in SS_E had not programs been used as a blocking variable,

(b) $F_R = 266.33$ which indicates significance at any level!

Activity 8

Carry out a two factor analysis of variance for the data you collected in either or both of Activities 3 and 4.

In each case identify the blocking factor, and explain whether or not it has made a significant contribution to the analysis.

Model

With x_{ij} denoting the one observation in the ith row and jth column, (ij)th cell, of the table, then

$$x_{ij} \sim N\left(\mu_{ij}, \sigma^2\right) \quad \text{for } i = 1, 2, \dots, r \text{ and } j = 1, 2, \dots, c$$

or $x_{ij} - \mu_{ij} = \varepsilon_{ij} \sim N\left(0, \sigma^2\right)$

However, it is assumed that the two factors do not interact but simply have an additive effect, so that

$\mu_{ij} = \mu + R_i + C_j$ with $\sum_i R_i = \sum_j C_j = 0$, where

μ = overall mean

R_i = mean effect of ith level of row factor relative to μ

C_j = mean effect of jth level of column factor relative to μ

ε_{ij} = inherent random variation.

As a result, when testing for an effect due to rows, the hypotheses may be written as

$H_0: R_i = 0$ (all i)

$H_1: R_i \neq 0$ (some i)

What are the corresponding hypotheses when testing for an effect due to columns?

If required, estimates of μ, R_i, C_j and ε_{ij} can be calculated from observed measurements by

$$\frac{T}{rc}, \quad \left(\frac{T_{Ri}}{c} - \frac{T}{rc}\right), \quad \left(\frac{T_{Cj}}{r} - \frac{T}{rc}\right), \quad \left(x_{ij} - \frac{T_{Ri}}{c} - \frac{T_{Cj}}{r} + \frac{T}{rc}\right),$$

respectively.

What are the estimates of μ, R_1, C_2 and ε_{12} in the previous example, based upon the transformed data?

Activity 9

Calculate estimates of some of μ, R_i, C_j and ε_{ij} for the data you collected in either of Activities 3 and 4.

Exercise 7B

1. Prior to submitting a quotation for a construction project, companies prepare a detailed analysis of the estimated labour and materials costs required to complete the project. A company which employs three project cost assessors, wished to compare the mean values of these assessors' cost estimates. This was done by requiring each assessor to estimate independently the costs of the same four construction projects. These costs, in £0000s, are shown in the next column.

	Assessor		
	A	B	C
Project 1	46	49	44
Project 2	62	63	59
Project 3	50	54	54
Project 4	66	68	63

Perform a two factor analysis of variance on these data to test, at the 5% significance level, that there is no difference between the assessors' mean cost estimates.

2. In an experiment to investigate the warping of copper plates, the two factors studied were the temperature and the copper content of the plates. The response variable was a measure of the amount of warping. The resultant data are as follows.

Temp (°C)	Copper content (%)			
	40	60	80	100
50	17	19	23	29
75	12	15	18	27
100	14	19	22	30
125	17	20	22	30

Stating all necessary assumptions, analyse for significant effects.

3. In a study to compare the body sizes of silkworms, three genotypes were of interest: heterozygous (HET), homozygous (HOM) and wild (WLD). The length, in millimetres, of a separately reared cocoon of each genotype was measured at each of five randomly chosen sites with the following results.

Silkworm	Site				
	1	2	3	4	5
HOM	29.87	28.24	32.27	31.21	29.85
HET	32.51	30.82	34.46	34.01	32.99
WLD	35.76	34.14	36.54	34.95	36.11

Identify the blocking factor. Has it proved useful? Explain.

Test, at the 1% significance level, for a difference in mean lengths between genotypes.

4. Four different washing solutions were being compared to study their effectiveness in retarding bacteria growth in milk containers. The study was undertaken in a laboratory, and only four trials could be run on any one day. As days could represent a potential source of variability, the experimenter decided to use days as a blocking variable. Observations were made for five days with the following (coded) results.

Solution	Day				
	1	2	3	4	5
A	12	21	17	38	29
B	15	23	16	43	35
C	6	11	7	32	28
D	18	27	23	43	35

Stating any necessary assumptions, analyse for significant differences between solutions.

Was the experimenter wise to use days as a blocking factor? Justify your answer.

5. The Marathon of the South West took place in Bristol in April 1982. The table below gives the times taken, in hours, by twelve competitors to complete the course, together with their type of occupation and training method used.

Training methods	Types of occupation		
	Office worker	Manual worker	Professional sportsperson
A	5.7	2.9	3.6
B	4.5	4.8	2.4
C	3.9	3.3	2.6
D	6.1	5.1	2.7

Carry out an analysis of variance and test, at the 5% level of significance, for differences between types of occupation and between training methods.

The age and sex of each of the above competitors are subsequently made available to you. Is this information likely to affect your conclusions and why? (AEB)

6. Information about the current state of a complex industrial process is displayed on a control panel which is monitored by a technician. In order to find the best display for the instruments on the control panel, three different arrangements were tested by simulating an emergency and observing the reaction times of five different technicians. The results, in seconds, are given below.

Arrangement	Technician				
	P	Q	R	S	T
A	2.4	3.3	1.9	3.6	2.7
B	3.7	3.2	2.7	3.9	4.4
C	4.2	4.6	3.9	3.8	4.5

Carry out an analysis of variance and test for differences between technicians and between arrangements at the 5% significance level.

Currently arrangement C is used and it is suggested that this be replaced by arrangement A. Comment, briefly, on this suggestion and on what further information you would find useful before coming to a definite decision. (AEB)

7.5 Miscellaneous Exercises

1. After completing a six month typing course with the Speedyfingers Institute, four people, A, B, C and D, had their typing speed measured, in words per minute, on each of five kinds of work. The results are given in the table below.

	Legal	Business	Numeric	Prose I	Prose II
A	40	47	42	45	53
B	34	32	14	36	44
C	33	40	31	48	44
D	24	26	25	27	45

Carry out an analysis of variance and test, at the 5% level of significance, for differences between the people and between kinds of work.

Subsequently it transpired that A and C used electric typewriters, whilst B and D used manual typewriters. Does this information affect your conclusions and why? (AEB)

2. A batch of bricks was randomly divided into three parts and each part was stored by a different method. After one week the percentage water content of a number of bricks stored by each method was measured.

Method of storage	% water content
1	7.4　8.5　7.1　6.2　7.8
2	5.5　7.1　5.6
3	4.8　5.1　6.2　4.9　6.1　7.1

Making any necessary assumptions, use a one factor analysis of variance to test, at the 5% significance level, for differences between methods of storage.

If low water content is desirable, state which method of storage you would recommend, and calculate a 95% confidence interval for its mean percentage water content after one week. [You may assume that the estimated variance of a sample mean is given by (Within samples mean square) ÷ (sample size).] (AEB)

3. A textile factory produces a silicone proofed nylon cloth for making into rainwear. The chief chemist thought that a silicone solution of about 12% strength would yield a cloth with a maximum waterproofing index. It was also suspected that there might be some batch to batch variation because of slight differences in the cloth.

To test this, five different strengths of solution were tested on each of three different batches of cloth. The following values of the waterproofing index were obtained.

Cloth	Strength of silicone solution (%)				
	6	9	12	15	18
A	20.8	20.6	22.0	22.6	20.9
B	19.4	21.2	21.8	23.9	22.4
C	19.9	21.1	22.7	22.7	22.1

[You may assume that the total sum of squares of the observations $\left(\sum x^2\right) = 7022.79$.]

Carry out an analysis of variance to test, at the 5% significance level, for differences between strengths of silicone solution and between cloths.

Comment on the chief chemist's original beliefs in the light of these results and suggest what actions the chief chemist might take. (AEB)

4. (a) A catering firm wishes to buy a meat tenderiser, but was concerned with the effect on the weight loss of meat during cooking. The following results were obtained for the weight loss of steaks of the same pre-cooked weight when three different tenderisers were used.

		Weight loss in grams				
	A	36	28	42	58	
Tenderiser	B	17	59	33		
	C	36	74	29	55	48

Carry out a one factor analysis of variance and test at the 5% significance level whether there is a difference in weight loss between tenderisers.

(b) Time and temperature are important factors in the weight loss during cooking. As these had not been taken account of during the first trial, a further set of results was obtained where all the steaks were cooked at the same temperature and cooking times of 20, 25 and 30 minutes were used. An analysis of these data led to the following table.

Source of variation	Sum of squares	Degrees of freedom
Between tenderisers	321	2
Between times	697	2
Error	85	4
Total	1103	8

Test at the 5% significance level for differences between tenderisers and between times.

(c) Contrast the results obtained in (a) and (b) and comment on why the two sets of data can lead to different conclusions. (AEB)

5. A commuter in a large city can travel to work by car, bicycle or bus. She times four journeys by each method with the following results, in minutes.

Car	Bicycle	Bus
27	34	26
45	38	41
33	43	35
31	42	46

(a) Carry out an analysis of variance and test at the 5% significance level whether there are differences in the mean journey times for the three methods of transport.

(b) The time of day at which she travels to work varies. Bearing in mind that this is likely to affect the time taken for the journey, suggest a better design for her experiment and explain briefly why you believe it to be better.

(c) Suggest a factor other than leaving time which is likely to affect the journey time and two factors other than journey time which might be considered when choosing a method of transport. (AEB)

6. (a) As part of a project to improve the steerability of trucks, a manufacturer took three trucks of the same model and fitted them with soft, standard and hard front springs, respectively. The turning radius (the radius of the circle in which the truck could turn full circle) was measured for each truck using a variety of drivers, speeds and surface conditions. Use the following information to test for a difference between springs at the 5% significance level.

Source	Sum of squares	Degrees of freedom
Between springs	37.9	2
Within springs	75.6	18
Total	113.5	20

(b) A statistician suggested that the experiment would be improved if the same truck was used all the time with the front springs changed as necessary and if the speed of the truck was controlled.

The following results for turning circle, in metres, were obtained.

Speed	Springs Soft	Standard	Hard
15 km/h	42	43	39
25 km/h	48	50	48

Carry out a two factor analysis of variance and test at the 5% significance level for differences between springs and between speeds. [You may assume that the total sum of squares about the mean (SS_T) is 92.]

(c) Compare the two experiments and suggest a further improvement to the design. (AEB)

7. A drug is produced by a fermentation process. An experiment was run to compare three similar chemical salts, X, Y and Z, in the production of the drug. Since there were only three of each of four types of fermenter A, B, C and D available for use in the production, three fermentations were started in each type of fermenter, one containing salt X, another salt Y and the third salt Z. After several days, samples were taken from each fermenter and analysed. The results, in coded form, were as follows.

	Fermenter type		
A	**B**	**C**	**D**
X 67	Y 73	X 72	Z 70
Z 68	Z 65	Y 80	X 68
Y 78	X 69	Z 73	Y 69

State the type of experimental design used.

Test, at the 5% level of significance, the hypothesis that the type of salt does not affect the fermentation.

Comment on what assumption you have made about the interaction between type of fermenter and type of salt. (AEB)

8. A factory is to introduce a new product which will be assembled from a number of components. Three different designs are considered and four employees are asked to compare their speed of assembly. The trial is carried out one morning and each of the four employees assembled design A from 8.30 am to 9.30 am, design B from 10.00 am to 11.00 am and design C from 11.30 am to 12.30 pm. The number of products completed by each of the employees is shown in the following table.

Design	Employee 1	2	3	4
A	17	4	38	8
B	21	6	52	20
C	28	9	64	22

(a) Carry out a two factor analysis of variance and test at the 5% significance level for differences between designs and between employees. [You may assume that the total sum of squares about the mean (SS_T) is 3878.9.]

(b) Comment on the fact that all employees assembled the designs in the same order. Suggest a better way of carrying out the experiment.

(c) The two factor analysis assumes that the effects of design and employee may be added. Comment on the suitability of this model for these data and suggest a possible improvement.   (AEB)

9. In a hot, third world country, milk is brought to the capital city from surrounding farms in churns carried on open lorries. The keeping quality of the milk is causing concern. The lorries could be covered to provide shade for the churns relatively cheaply or refrigerated lorries could be used but these are very expensive. The different methods were tried and the keeping quality measured. (The keeping quality is measured by testing the pH at frequent intervals and recording the time taken for the pH to fall by 0.5. A high value of this time is desirable.)

Transport method	Keeping quality (hours)
Open	16.5 20.0 14.5 13.0
Covered	23.5 25.0 30.0 33.5 26.0
Refrigerated	29.0 34.0 26.0 22.5 29.5 30.5

(a) Carry out a one factor analysis of variance and test, at the 5% level, for differences between methods of transport.

(b) Examine the method means and comment on their implications.

(c) Different farms have different breeds of cattle and different journey times to the capital, both of which could have affected the results. How could the data have been collected and analysed to allow for these differences?   (AEB)

8 STATISTICAL PROCESS CONTROL

Objectives

After studying this chapter you should

- understand the purpose of statistical process control;

- be able to set up and use charts for means, ranges, standard deviations and proportion non-conforming;

- be able to use an appropriate method to estimate short-term standard deviation;

- be able to interpret the variability of a process in relation to the required tolerances.

8.0   Introduction

Statistical process control may be used when a large number of similar items - such as Mars bars, jars of jam or car doors are being produced. Every process is subject to variability. It is not possible to put exactly the same amount of jam in each jar or to make every car door of exactly the same width. The variability present when a process is running well is called the **short term** or **inherent variability**. It is usually measured by the standard deviation.

Most processes will have a **target value**. Too much jam in a jar will be uneconomic to the manufacturer but too little will lead to customer complaints. A car door which is too wide or too narrow will not close smoothly.

The purpose of statistical process control is to give a signal when the process mean has moved away from the target. A second purpose is to give a signal when item to item variability has increased. In either case appropriate action must then be taken by a machine operator or an engineer. Statistics can only give the signal, the action relies on other skills.

8.1   Control charts

The most common method of statistical process control is to take samples at regular intervals and to plot the sample mean on a control chart.

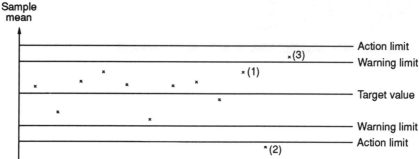

If the sample mean lies within the **warning limits** (as point (1)) the process is assumed to be on target. If it lies outside the **action limits** (as point (2) the process is off target and the machine must be reset or other action taken. If the mean is between the **warning and action limits** (as point (3)) this is a signal that the process may be off target. In this case another sample is taken immediately. If the mean is still outside the warning limits action is taken. If however the second sample mean is within the warning limits production is assumed to be on target.

Setting the limits

If the limits are too far from the target value small deviations from the target may go undetected but if the limits are too close to the target value there will be a large number of false alarms (that is there will be a signal for action when the process mean is on target and no action is necessary). To decide where to set the limits a measure of short term variability is needed.

Activity 1

Here are the weights, in grams, of 100 Mars Bars (unwrapped)

```
59.55  62.33  63.68  67.10  56.85  57.84  64.40  60.26  62.05  64.29
64.57  60.14  62.51  62.02  60.16  61.45  58.42  58.19  65.65  65.90
63.34  60.01  59.11  62.57  58.48  60.25  61.42  63.25  63.46  63.33
58.55  65.36  63.03  61.71  62.26  62.05  60.42  58.77  62.69  66.20
59.80  61.45  60.78  61.89  63.91  58.53  59.29  62.24  61.12  60.60
61.82  58.98  62.63  59.68  62.79  63.90  62.64  61.96  64.14  60.70
59.90  57.73  67.08  63.25  64.20  61.16  61.03  65.79  62.43  62.75
62.17  61.29  69.01  63.31  62.92  64.13  62.46  60.61  61.58  60.71
68.11  65.46  57.81  64.73  63.27  64.63  59.70  54.59  61.83  59.21
60.46  59.05  61.06  55.08  61.60  63.85  64.42  62.91  63.54  60.69
```

Check that the standard deviation is 2.60 g.

If the target weight for Mars bars is 61.5g and production is to be controlled by weighing samples of size 5 at regular intervals then the sample means will have a standard deviation of

$$\frac{2.60}{\sqrt{5}} = 1.16 \text{ g.}$$

It has been found convenient in practice to set the **warning limits** so that, if the mean is on target, 95% of sample means will lie within them. The **action limits** are set so that 99.8% of sample means lie within them when the mean is on target. Since we are dealing with sample means it is reasonable to assume they are normally distributed. Hence in this case the warning limits will be set at

$$61.5 \pm 1.96 \times \frac{2.6}{\sqrt{5}}$$

$\Rightarrow$ 61.5 ± 2.28

$\Rightarrow$ 59.22 and 63.78

the action limits will be set at

$$61.5 \pm 3.09 \times \frac{2.6}{\sqrt{5}}$$

$\Rightarrow$ 61.5 ± 3.59

$\Rightarrow$ 57.91 and 65.09

In general the warning limits will be set

$$\boxed{\mu \pm 1.96 \frac{\sigma}{\sqrt{n}}}$$

and the action limits at

$$\boxed{\mu \pm 3.09 \frac{\sigma}{\sqrt{n}}}$$

where μ is the target value and σ is the short term standard deviation (that is the standard deviation over a short period of time when the mean is constant and only short term variability is present).

The standard deviation will in practice only be an estimate of the true value and 95% and 99.8% are somewhat arbitrary figures. For these reasons and for simplicity the limits are often set at

$$\boxed{\mu \pm \frac{2\sigma}{\sqrt{n}} \text{ and } \mu \pm \frac{3\sigma}{\sqrt{n}}}$$

Activity 2

(a) Draw a control chart for means for the Mars bars.

(b) Calculate the sample mean for each of the following ten samples. Plot the means on the chart.

Sample

1	2	3	4	5	6	7	8	9	10
59.55	64.57	63.34	58.55	59.80	61.82	59.90	62.17	68.11	60.46
62.33	60.14	60.01	65.36	61.45	58.98	57.73	61.29	65.46	59.05
63.68	62.51	59.11	63.03	60.78	62.63	66.03	69.01	57.81	65.06
67.10	62.02	62.57	60.72	61.89	59.68	64.25	63.31	64.73	55.08
56.85	60.16	58.48	62.26	63.91	62.70	65.20	62.92	63.27	61.60

(c) Have any signals to stop production been given.

Activity 3

A machine filling packets of breakfast cereal is known to operate with a standard deviation of 3 g. The target is to put 500 g of cereal in each packet. Production is to be controlled by taking 4 packets at regular intervals and weighing their contents.

(a) Set up a control chart for means.

(b) What action, if any, would you recommend if the next sample weighed

   (i)   503,497,499,496

   (ii) 501,491,492,492

   (iii) 502,500,507,505

   (iv) 500,501,501,501?

In what way are statistical processes controled by hypothesis testing ralated?

Target values

In some cases the target value is not known or not attainable. For example the target for strength of malleable iron castings is 'as large as possible'. The target value for percentage impurity is probably zero but it will be recognised that this is unattainable (and even if it was attainable it would be nonsense to set up charts with lower limits set at negative values of impurity). In these cases a large sample should be taken when the process is believed to be running satisfactorily and the sample mean used as a **target value**.

For example, tests on the tensile strength of malleable iron castings at a foundry at a time when production was thought to be satisfactory gave a mean of 148 and a standard deviation of 2.5 (the units are Newtons $m^{-2} \times 10^9$).

The process is to be controlled by testing the strength of samples of size 3 at regular intervals.

Warning limits are

$$148 \pm 1.96 \times \frac{2.5}{\sqrt{3}}$$

$\Rightarrow \quad 145.2 - 150.8$

Action limits are

$$148 \pm 3.09 \times \frac{2.5}{\sqrt{3}}$$

$\Rightarrow \quad 143.5 - 152.5$

A sample mean less than 143.5 would lead to action being taken in the usual way. A sample mean greater than 152.5 would indicate that the average strength had increased. This would not of course lead to action to reduce the mean but might lead to an investigation to see how the improvement may be maintained.

Control of variability

Referring back to the Mars bar example, the next sample weighed

59.35 62.46 48.67 68.79 71.23.

The sample mean is 62.1 which is comfortably within the warning limits and no action is signalled. However closer examination of this sample shows that something has gone drastically wrong with production. Although the mean is acceptable the variability within the sample has increased alarmingly. The means chart is not reliable for detecting a change in variability. We need an additional chart for this purpose.

The best measure of **variability** is the standard deviation. However, since the sample range is simpler both to understand and calculate, traditionally it has been used as a measure of variability in statistical process control. With the ready availability of calculators there is now little reason for not using the standard deviation as a measure of variability. Whichever measure is chosen the charts are constructed in the same way. They depend on an estimate of standard deviation being available. They also assume that the data are normally distributed. It is no longer enough only to assume that the sample means are normally distributed. No target value is shown on the charts. The target for variability is zero but this is an unrealistic value to use on the charts.

8.2   Chart for ranges

The limits for the range are found by multiplying the short term standard deviation by the appropriate value of D found from tables.

In the case of the Mars bars with samples of size 5 and a short term standard deviation of 2.6

the upper action limit is	$5.484 \times 2.6 = 14.26$
the upper warning limit is	$4.197 \times 2.6 = 10.9$
the lower warning limit is	$0.850 \times 2.6 = 2.21$
the lower action limit is	$0.367 \times 2.6 = 0.95$

Activity 4

Draw a control chart for sample ranges for the Mars bars. Plot the ranges of the ten samples given in activity 2. Are there any signals to stop production?

8.3   Charts for sample standard deviations

These are calculated and operated in exactly the same way as the charts for ranges. The only difference being that the appropriate factor is selected from a different table. The standard deviation chart gives a slightly better chance of detecting an increase in the variability when one exists. The risk of a false alarm is the same for both charts.

For the Mars bar example

the upper action limit is	$2.15 \times 2.6 = 5.59$
the upper warning limit is	$1.67 \times 2.6 = 4.34$
the lower warning limit is	$0.35 \times 2.6 = 0.91$
the lower action limit is	$0.15 \times 2.6 = 0.39$

As with the range charts the lower limits often are not used.

Note the sample standard deviations should be calculated using the

formula $\hat{\sigma} = \sqrt{\sum \frac{(x-\bar{x})^2}{n-1}}$.

Activity 5

Draw a control chart for sample standard deviations for the Mars bars. Plot the sample standard deviations for the ten samples given in activity 2. Are there any signals to stop production?

Activity 6

Set up a chart for sample standard deviations for the packets of breakfast cereal in activity 3.

What action, if any, would you recommend if the next sample weighed

    (i)   502,496,499,496,

    (ii) 505,495,496,496,

    (iii) 499,490,505,505,

    (iv) 506,510,508,508,

    (v) 497,498,498,497?

Note that a sample must lie within the warning limits on both the mean and the standard deviation (or range) chart for production to be considered satisfactory without further checking.

8.4 Estimating the short term standard deviation

The best way of estimating the short term standard deviation is to take a large sample when the process is running well and calculate the standard deviation using the formula

$$\hat{\sigma} = \sqrt{\sum \frac{(x-\bar{x})^2}{n-1}}$$

This is how the standard deviation was estimated for the Mars bars. The same sample may also be used for estimating a suitable target value when one is required. This procedure is called a **process capability study**.

Because data is often collected in small samples for statistical process control purposes the short term standard deviation is often calculated from a number of small samples. If the process is running well at the time the standard deviation should be constant but it may be that there have been some small changes in the mean. If this is the case pooling the small samples and regarding them as one large sample will tend to over estimate the short term standard deviation. It is better to make an estimate of variability from each sample individually and then take the average. This estimate may be the sample range or the sample standard deviation.

For example, a company manufactures a drug with a nominal potency of 5.0 mg cm^{-3}. For prescribing purposes it is important that the mean potency of tablets should be accurate and the variability low. Ten samples each of four tablets were taken at regular intervals during a particular day when production was thought to be satisfactory. The potency of the tablets was measured.

Sample	1	2	3	4	5	6	7	8	9	10
	4.97	4.98	5.13	5.03	5.19	5.13	5.16	5.11	5.07	5.11
	5.09	5.15	5.05	5.18	5.12	4.96	5.15	5.07	5.11	5.19
	5.08	5.08	5.12	5.06	5.10	5.02	4.97	5.09	5.01	5.13
	5.06	4.99	5.11	5.05	5.04	5.09	5.09	5.08	4.96	5.17

The ranges of the ten samples are

0.12   0.17   0.08   0.15   0.15   0.17   0.19   0.04   0.15   0.08

giving a mean sample range of 0.13. This mean range can be converted to a standard deviation by multiplying by an appropriate factor from the table in the Appendix. For samples of size 4 the estimated standard deviation would be

$$0.4857 \times 0.13 = 0.063$$

The factors in the table assume that the data is normally distributed.

Alternatively the sample standard deviations for the ten samples are

0.0548   0.0804   0.0359   0.0678   0.0618

0.0753   0.0873   0.0171   0.0660   0.0365

For mathematical reasons, the best way of estimating the standard deviation is to find the mean of the 10 variances and take the square root, i.e.

$$\sqrt{\frac{0.0548^2 + 0.0804^2 + 0.0359^2 + 0.0678^2 + 0.0618^2 + 0.0753^2 + 0.0873^2 + 0.0171^2 + 0.0660^2 + 0.0365^2}{10}}$$

$$= 0.062.$$

As can be seen, there is little difference in the two estimates. Although the second method is mathematically preferable the first method is perfectly adequate for most purposes.

Example 1

In the production of bank notes samples are taken at regular intervals and a number of measurements made on each note. The following table shows the width, mm, of the top margin in eight samples each of size 4. The target value is 9 mm.

Sample 1	2	3	4	5	6	7	8
9.0	10.4	8.2	7.9	8.2	8.4	7.4	7.6
8.1	9.0	9.2	7.7	9.0	8.1	8.0	8.5
8.7	7.9	7.9	7.7	7.4	8.4	8.9	8.1
7.5	7.2	7.7	9.3	8.6	8.7	9.8	8.8

(a) Calculate the mean sample range and, assuming a normal distribution, use it to estimate the standard deviation of the process.

(b) Use the estimate made in (a) to draw a control chart for means showing 95% warning limits and 99.8% action limits. Plot the eight means.

(c) Draw a control chart for ranges showing the upper and lower action and warning limits. Plot the eight ranges.

(d) Comment on the current state of the process.

(e) What action, if any, would you recommend in each of the following cases.

The next sample is

(i)   9.1, 10.2, 8.9, 9.7

(ii) 7.3, 6.9, 8.8, 7.1

(iii) 10.4, 10.1, 9.2, 6.8

(iv) 10.9, 9.8, 8.8, 11.1

(v)   9.3, 9.2, 9.3, 9.3

(f) Suggest two methods, other than the one used in (a), to estimate the short term standard deviation of the process. Compare the relative merits of these three methods in the context of control charts.

Solution

Sample	1	2	3	4	5	6	7	8
mean	8.325	8.625	8.25	8.15	8.3	8.4	8.525	8.25
range	1.5	3.2	1.5	1.6	1.6	0.6	2.4	1.2

(a) mean range $= \dfrac{13.6}{8} = 1.7$

estimated standard deviation $= 0.4857 \times 1.7 = 0.826$

(b) chart for means

warning limits $9 \pm \dfrac{1.96 \times .826}{\sqrt{4}} \Rightarrow 8.19 - 9.81$

action limits $9 \pm \dfrac{3.09 \times 826}{\sqrt{4}} \Rightarrow 7.72 - 10.28$

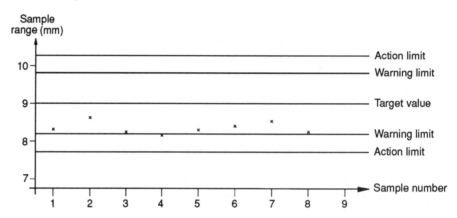

(c) chart for ranges

upper action limit	$5.309 \times 0.826 = 4.39$	
upper warning limit	$3.984 \times 0.826 = 3.29$	
lower warning limit	$0.595 \times 0.826 = 0.49$	
lower action limit	$0.199 \times 0.826 = 0.16$	

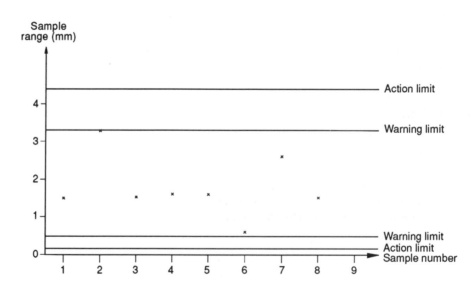

(d) All ranges are within warning limits. Variability appears to be under control. One mean below lower warning limit. This is not in itself a problem. Since 95% of sample means lie within the warning limits when the process is on target, 5% or 1 in 20 will lie outside warning limits if mean on target. However as all sample means are below target it appears that the machine needs resetting to increase the mean.

(e) (i) mean 9.475   range 1.3   no action

   (ii) mean 7.525   range 1.9   below action limit on mean chart.   Action needed to increase mean - probably resetting machine.

   (iii) mean 9.125   range 3.6   outside warning limit on range chart. Take another sample immediately. If still outside warning limit take action to reduce variability. Probably overhaul machine.

   (iv) mean 10.15   range 2.3   Outside warning limit on mean chart. Take another sample immediately. If still outside warning limit take action to increase mean.

   (v) mean 9.275   range 0.1 below lower action limit on range chart. Check data. If correct no action but investigate how variability has been reduced with a view to maintaining the improvement.

(f) An alternative method of estimating the standard deviation is to regard the 32 observations as a single sample and to estimate the standard deviation using the formula

$$\sqrt{\sum \frac{(x-\bar{x})^2}{(n-1)}}.$$ This would be a satisfactory method if the

mean had not changed while the eight samples were taken but would tend to overestimate the short term standard deviation if it had. In this case the eight plotted means suggest that the mean has remained constant (although below target).

Another alternative is to calculate the standard deviation separately for each sample. If these values are $\hat{\sigma}_1, \hat{\sigma}_2, ..., \hat{\sigma}_8$ the estimate of the standard deviation will be

$$\sqrt{\frac{\hat{\sigma}_1^2 + \hat{\sigma}_2^2 + ... + \hat{\sigma}_8^2}{8}}$$

another alternative is to use

$$\frac{\hat{\sigma}_1 + \hat{\sigma}_2 + ... + \sigma_8}{8}.$$

This method will be satisfactory even if the mean has changed and even if the data is not normally distributed.

Additional rules for taking action

When charts are plotted attention can be focused not only on the latest point but on the recent history of the process. A large number of consecutive points above (or below) the centre line on a chart for means may indicate that the mean is off target even though no single point has violated the action limits and no two consecutive points have violated the warning limits. Similarly an upward or downward trend on a chart may indicate the necessity for action even though no limits have been violated.

Rules such as, take action if eight successive points are on the same side of the target value, or, take action if seven consecutive points each exceed (or are less than) the previous point have been used. These additional rules will all increase the ability of the charts to detect a deviation from the target value but it should be borne in mind that they will also increase the number of false alarms.

Why will the number of false alarms be increased?

8.5 Tolerance limits

Many processes have tolerance limits within which the product must lie. The purpose of statistical process control is to ensure that a process functions as accurately and with as little variability as possible. Despite this the process may be unable to meet the tolerances consistently. Alternatively it may be able to meet the tolerances easily.

In the example of the drug potency the tolerances were 4.9 to 5.1. The standard deviation was estimated to be about 0.06. It is generally reasonable to assume that mass produced items will follow a normal distribution. If we also assume that the mean is exactly on target, i.e. 5.00, we can calculate the proportion outside the tolerances.

$$z_1 = \frac{(4.9 - 5.0)}{0.06} = -1.67$$

$$z_2 = \frac{(5.1 - 5.0)}{0.06} = 1.67$$

The proportion outside the tolerances is $2 \times (1 - 0.95254) = 0.095$. Hence even in the best possible case with the mean exactly on target about 10% of the tablets would be outside the tolerances.

This process cannot meet these tolerances however well statistical process control is applied. A better and almost certainly more expensive process is needed to meet these tolerances.

Almost all of a normal distribution lies within 3 standard deviations of the mean. So if the tolerance width exceeds 6 standard deviations the process should be able to meet the tolerances consistently, provided the mean is kept on target. In the drug example the tolerance width was $5.1 - 4.9 = 0.2$ which is only $\dfrac{0.2}{0.06} = 3.3$ standard deviations.

In some cases the tolerance width may greatly exceed 6 standard deviations and the tolerances will be easily met. It can be argued that in these cases statistical process control is unnecessary. However to produce a high quality product it is better to have the process exactly on target than just within the tolerances. A car door which is exactly the right width is likely to close more smoothly than one which is just within the acceptable tolerances.

Example 2

The copper content of bronze castings has a target value of 80%. The standard deviation, is known to be 4%. During the production process, samples of size 6 are taken at regular intervals and their copper content measured.

(a) Calculate upper and lower warning and action limits for control charts for
  (i)   means,
  (ii) standard deviations.

(b) The following results were obtained from samples on three separate occasions
  (i)   82.0 83.5 79.8 84.2 80.3 81.0
  (ii)   75.8 68.4 80.3 78.2 79.9 73.5
  (iii) 79.5 80.0 79.9 79.6 79.9 80.4

For each sample calculate the mean and standard deviation and recommend any necessary action.

(c) If the process currently has a mean of 76% with a standard deviation of 4%, what is the probability that the mean of the next sample will lie within the warning limits?

(d) The tolerance limits are 73% and 87%. A process capability index, C_p, is defined by
  (i)   Calculate $C_p = \dfrac{\text{tolerance width}}{6\sigma}$

  (ii) Explain why a C_p value less than 1 is regarded as unsatisfactory.

(iii) Explain why, if the mean is off target, a C_p value greater than 1 may still be unsatisfactory.

(e) In addition to using warning and action limits, action is sometimes recommended if eight consecutive means lie on the same side of the target value. What is the probability of the next eight means being on the same side of the target value if the process mean is exactly on target?

Solution

(a) Control chart for means

Warning limits $\quad 80 \pm 1.96 \times \dfrac{4}{\sqrt{6}} \quad \Rightarrow \quad 76.8 - 83.2$

Action limits $\quad\; 80 \pm 3.09 \times \dfrac{4}{\sqrt{6}} \quad \Rightarrow \quad 74.95 - 85.05$

Control chart for standard deviations

upper action limit	$2.03 \times 4 = 8.12$
upper warning limit	$1.60 \times 4 = 6.4$
lower warning limit	$0.41 \times 4 = 1.64$
lower action limit	$0.20 \times 4 = 0.8$

(b) (i) mean 81.8 s.d. 1.77 $\Rightarrow$ no action

(ii) mean 76.0 s.d. 4.53 $\Rightarrow$ mean below s.d. warning limit

You should take another sample immediately. If mean still outside warning limits, take action.

(iii) mean 79.9 s.d. 0.32 $\Rightarrow$ s.d. below action limit.

Variability has been reduced; try to find out why so that improvement may be maintained.

(c) $\quad z_1 = \dfrac{(76.8 - 76)}{\left(\dfrac{4}{\sqrt{6}}\right)} = 0.490$

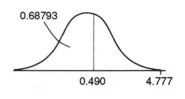

$\quad z_2 = \dfrac{(83.8 - 76)}{\left(\dfrac{4}{\sqrt{6}}\right)} = 4.777$

probability within warning limits $= 1 - 0.68793 = 0.312$

(d) (i) $C_p = \dfrac{(87-73)}{(6\times4)} = 0.583$

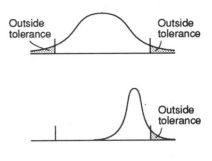

Outside tolerance · Outside tolerance

Outside tolerance

(ii) A C_p less than 1 indicates that the tolerance width is less than 6σ. Hence the process is unlikely to be able to meet the tolerances consistently even if the mean is exactly on target.

(iii) Even if the C_p is less than one the tolerances may not be consistently met if the mean is off target.

(e) Probability of next eight means being all on the same side of the target is

$$(0.5)^8 + (0.5)^8 \approx 0.0078$$

8.6 Control charts for proportion non-conforming or defective

Control charts may also be applied when instead of measuring a variable, such as weight or length, items are classified as **conforming** or **non-conforming** (defective and non-defective used to be more common terms but are now going out of use).

Samples of 100 components are taken from a production line at regular intervals and the number non-conforming counted. At a time when production was thought to be satisfactory 12 samples contained the following numbers of non-conforming items

10, 13, 12, 19, 8, 14, 17, 16, 10, 18, 9, 16

The total number of non-conforming items found is 162 out of 1200 components examined. This gives an estimate of p, the

proportion non-conforming, of $\dfrac{162}{1200} = 0.135$.

If p is constant the number non-conforming in the samples will follow a binomial distribution. As n is large (100) and np is reasonably large ($100\times0.135 = 13.5$) the binomial distribution may be approximated by a normal distribution with mean np and standard deviation $\sqrt{np(1-p)}$. Control charts may be set up in the usual way.

In this case warning limits for p are

$$0.135\pm1.96\sqrt{0.135\times\dfrac{0.865}{100}} \quad\Rightarrow\quad 0.068 - 0.202$$

action limits for p are

$$0.135 \pm 3.09 \sqrt{0.135 \times \frac{0.865}{100}} \quad \Rightarrow \quad 0.029 - 0.241$$

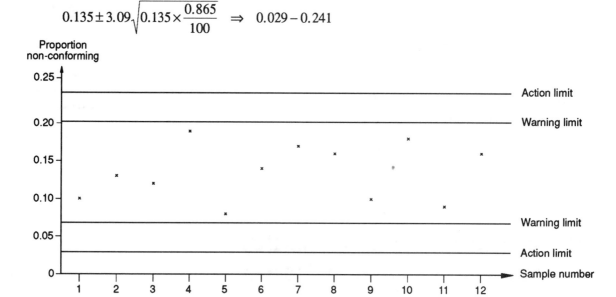

There are several points to note about this chart

1. Only one chart is necessary. The only way a signal can be given is if there are too many non-conforming items.

2. 0.135 is not the target value. The target value is zero. However in this case 0.135 is thought to be a reasonable level. The real purpose of these charts is to ensure that the proportion non-conforming does not rise above 0.135.

3. The lower limits are not needed but may be retained as a check on errors in the data or to indicate that an improvement has occurred.

4. Charts for the number non-conforming could be plotted as an alternative to the proportion non-conforming. There may be an advantage in plotting the proportion if the number of items inspected is likely to vary slightly from sample to sample.

5. Any variable such as weight or length may be treated in this way by defining limits outside which the item is classified as non-conforming. It is usually easier to decide whether an item lies within given limits or not rather than to make an exact measurement. However to get equivalent control of the process much larger samples are needed.

6. If the samples are too small the normal approximation will not be valid. It would be necessary to use exact binomial probabilities to calculate the limits. However as small samples do not give good control using proportion defective this problem is not likely to arise. Small values of p would also cause the normal approximation to be invalid. However good control cannot be maintained for small values of p. This problem can be overcome by tightening up the definition of non-conforming.

Example

At a factory making ball bearings, a scoop is used to take a sample at regular intervals. All the ball bearings in the scoop are classified as conforming or non-conforming according to whether or not they fit two gauges. This is a very quick and easy test to carry out.

Here is the data for ten samples

Sample	1	2	3	4	5	6	7	8	9	10
Number in scoop	95	99	115	120	84	107	97	119	92	112
Number non-conforming	16	6	11	10	11	5	13	14	10	13

(a) Use the data to estimate p, the proportion non-conforming, and n, the average number in a scoop. Use these estimated values of n and p to set up control charts for proportion non-conforming. Plot the 10 samples on the chart and comment.

(b) The following samples occurred on separate occasions when the chart was in operation,

   (i)   115 in scoop, 21 non-conforming

   (ii) 94 in scoop, 8 non-conforming

   (iii) 92 in scoop, 20 non-conforming

   (iv) 12 in scoop, 3 non-conforming

   (v) 104 in scoop, 1 non-conforming

For each of the samples comment on the current state of the process and on what action, if any, is necessary.   (AEB)

Solution

(a) The total number non-conforming observed is

$$16+6+11+10+11+5+13+14+10+13=109$$

the total number of ball bearings observed is

$$95+99+115+120+84+107+97+119+92+112=1040$$

$$\hat{n}=\frac{1040}{10}=104, \quad \hat{p}=\frac{109}{1040}=0.1048$$

This gives warning limits

$$0.1048\pm1.96\sqrt{0.1048\times\frac{0.8952}{104}}$$

$$\Rightarrow \quad 0.046-0.164$$

and action limits

$$0.1048 \pm 3.09 \sqrt{0.1048 \times \frac{0.8952}{104}}$$

$\Rightarrow \quad 0.012 - 0.198$

proportion non-conforming in samples

0.168, 0.061, 0.096, 0.083, 0.131, 0.047, 0.134, 0.118, 0.109, 0.116

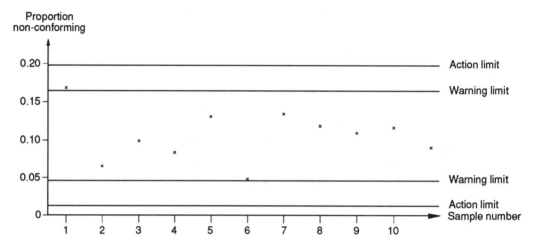

One point is just outside the warning limits. As one point in 20 is expected to lie outside the warning limits this is acceptable and does not cast doubt on the state of the process when these samples were taken. (If the process was unstable when the samples were taken they would be unsuitable for estimating a value of p for use in calculating limits for the chart. It would be necessary to take new samples when the process was running well and use these for estimating p.)

(b) (i) $\frac{21}{115} = 0.183 \Rightarrow$ above warning limit. Take another scoop immediately.

(ii) $\frac{8}{94} = 0.085 \Rightarrow$ production satisfactory.

(iii) $\frac{20}{92} = 0.217 \Rightarrow$ above action limit. Take action.

(iv) The limits on these charts depend on the sample size n. A small amount of variability in n will make little difference but they are unsuitable for use with samples as small as 12. Take another scoop and start again.

(v) $\frac{1}{104} = 0.010 \Rightarrow$ below action limits. Process has improved. Try to maintain the improvement.

8.7 Miscellaneous Exercises

1. A steel maker supplies sheet steel to a manufacturer whose machines are set on the assumption that the thickness is 750 (the units are thousandths of a mm). The supplier decides to set up control charts to ensure that the steel is as close to 750 as possible. 8 samples each of 5 measurements are taken when production is thought to be satisfactory. The sample means and ranges are as follows:

sample	1	2	3	4	5	6	7	8
mean	738	762	751	763	757	754	762	761
range	14	21	17	53	29	49	71	62

(a) Assuming the data are normally distributed estimate the standard deviation of the process.

(b) Using the target value as centre line draw a control chart for means showing 95% and 99.8% control lines. Plot the eight means.

(c) Draw a control chart for the range showing the upper action and warning limits. Plot the eight ranges.

(d) Comment on the patterns revealed by the charts and advise the producer how to proceed.

(e) In addition to using warning and action limits, action is sometimes recommended if seven consecutive points lie on the same side of the target value. What is the probability of this occurring if the process is exactly on target? (AEB)

2. Raw material used in a chemical process contains some impurity.

To ensure that the percentage impurity does not become too large samples of size 3 are tested at regular intervals. When the process is running satisfactorily the mean percentage impurity was found to be 16.7 with a standard deviation of 3.4.

(a) Set up control charts for means and for standard deviations.

(b) What action, if any, would you recommend if the next sample was

(i) 16.9,19.3,20.2   (ii) 24.2,25.6,22.0

(iii) 14.2,19.1,5.2   (iv) 22.7,19.3,23.1

(v) 9.3,12.2,8.1?

3. Reels of wire are wound automatically from a continuous source of wire. After each reel is wound the wire is cut and a new reel started. The target is to wind 10 m on each reel. The lengths of wire on ten samples each of four reels are measured with the following results.

The units are cm above 9 m 50 cm.

Sample										
1	2	3	4	5	6	7	8	9	10
42	64	53	62	26	27	16	17	48	41
57	76	7	31	54	37	54	44	72	59
36	52	41	17	62	69	32	46	76	80
8	40	56	44	51	61	48	49	64	68

(a) Use these samples to calculate limits for control charts for means and for standard deviations. Draw the charts and plot the points.

(b) What action, if any, would you take if the next sample was

(i) 54, 64, 70, 48,

(ii) 9, 99, 42, 58,

(iii) 84, 106, 99, 93?

(c) The tolerance for the length of wire on a reel is 50 ±70. Comment on the ability of the process to meet this.

(d) If the current mean is 55 and the standard deviation is 18 what is the probability that the next sample mean will be within

(i) the warning limits,

(ii) the action limits?

4. A biscuit factory produces cream crackers. Packets are sampled at hourly intervals and the weight, in grammes, of the contents measured. The results below are from seven samples each of size five taken at a time when production was thought to be satisfactory. The target value is 210 g.

sample						
1	2	3	4	5	6	7
209.0	214.5	204.5	217.5	211.0	224.0	210.0
211.0	210.0	209.0	216.0	198.0	220.0	208.0
213.5	212.0	198.5	217.0	209.5	224.0	210.0
205.0	203.5	203.0	214.0	213.5	218.5	220.0
210.0	214.0	213.5	209.5	213.5	210.0	211.0

(a) Estimate the standard deviation of the process.

(b) Calculate upper and lower warning and action limits for a control chart for
(i) means,
(ii) standard deviations.

(c) Draw the two control charts and plot the points. Comment on the current state of the process.

(d) What action, if any, would you recommend if the next sample was
(i) 196.0, 202.5, 189.0, 197.5, 197.0,

    (ii) 204.5, 214.0, 206.0, 207.0, 211.0,

    (iii) 188.5, 212.5, 220.0, 215.0, 208.0,

    (iv) 206.0, 214.5, 208.5, 209.0, 211.0?

(e) The upper specification limit (USL) is 220 g and the lower specification limit(LSL) is 200 g Estimate C_p where

$$C_p = \frac{(USL - LSL)}{6\sigma} \quad .$$

Comment on the ability of the process to meet this specification.

5. Lengths of cloth produced at a mill often have to be 'mended' by hand before being saleable. In sets of 50 the numbers needing mending were as follows;

    17, 14, 13, 16, 14, 16, 22, 19, 15, 16, 12

Set up control charts based on this data.

6. A manufacturer of fishing line takes samples of 60 lengths at regular intervals and counts the number that break when subjected to a strain of 38 newtons. During a period when production was satisfactory the results for ten samples were as follows:

sample	1	2	3	4	5	6	7	8	9	10
number breaking	14	9	7	15	10	8	13	12	6	7

(a) Draw a control chart for proportion defective showing approximate 95% and 99.8% control lines, and plotting the ten points.

(b) What action would you recommend if the number breaking in the next sample was

    (i) 18   (ii) 24   (iii) 1?

(c) List advantages and/or disadvantages of the manufacturer's method of control compared to measuring the actual breaking strength and setting up control charts for mean and range.

                         (AEB)

9 ACCEPTANCE SAMPLING

Objectives

After studying this chapter you should

- understand the operation of acceptance sampling schemes;
- be able to draw an operating characteristic for single sampling plans using attributes, double sampling plans using attributes, and single sampling plans for variables;
- be able to select appropriate plans to meet particular conditions.

9.0   Introduction

A large supermarket sells prepacked sandwiches in its food department. The sandwiches are bought in large batches from a catering firm. The supermarket manager wishes to test the sandwiches to make sure they are fresh and of good quality. She can test them only by unwrapping them and tasting them. After the test it will no longer be possible to sell them. She must therefore make a decision as to whether or not the batch is acceptable based on testing a relatively small sample of sandwiches. This is know as **acceptance sampling**.

Acceptance sampling may be applied where large quantities of similar items or large batches of material are being bought or are being transferred from one part of an organisation to another. Unlike statistical process control where the purpose is to check production as it proceeds, acceptance sampling is applied to large batches of goods which have already been produced.

The test on the sandwiches is called a **destructive test** because after the test has been carried out the sandwich is no longer saleable. Other reasons for applying acceptance sampling are that when buying large batches of components it may be too expensive or too time consuming to test them all. In other cases when dealing with a well established supplier the customer may be quite confident that the batch will be satisfactory but will still wish to test a small sample to make sure.

Activity 1

Think of three examples where testing would be destructive.
(Hint: tests involving measuring the lifetime of items are usually
destructive.)

9.1 Acceptance sampling attributes

In acceptance sampling by attributes each item tested is classified
as **conforming** or **non-conforming**. (Items used to be classified as
defective or non-defective but these days no self respecting
manufacturing firm will admit to making defective items.)

A sample is taken and if it contains too many non-conforming
items the batch is rejected, otherwise it is accepted.

For this method to be effective, batches containing some non-
conforming items must be acceptable. If the only acceptable
percentage of non-conforming items is zero this can only be
achieved by examing every item and removing any which are non-
conforming. This is known as **100% inspection** and is not
acceptance sampling. However the definition of non-conforming
may be chosen as required. For example, if the contents of jars of
jam are required to be between 453 g and 461 g, it would be
possible to define a jar with contents outside the range 455 g and
459 g as non-conforming. Batches containing up to, say 5% non-
conforming items, could then be accepted in the knowledge that,
unless there was something very unusual about the distribution,
this would ensure that virtually all jars in the batch contained
between 453 g and 461 g.

Operating characteristics

For any particular plan the **operating characteristic** is a graph of
the probability of accepting a batch against the proportion non-
conforming in the batch. Provided the sample is small compared
to the size of the batch and the sampling is random, the probability
of each member of the sample being non-conforming may be taken
to be constant. In this case the number of non-conforming items in
a batch will follow a binomial distribution.

One possible acceptance sampling plan is to take a sample of size
50 and to reject the batch if 3 or more non-conforming items are
found. If two or less non-conforming items are found the batch
will be accepted. This plan is often denoted by $n = 50$, $r = 3$. For
a batch containing a given proportion of non-conforming items the

probability of the sample containing two or less non-conforming items may be read directly from tables of the binomial distribution (or may be calculated). For example, if the batch contained 4% non-conforming items, the probability of any particular item in the sample being classified non-conforming is 0.04 and the probability of the batch containing two or less non-conforming items and therefore being accepted is 0.6767. The table below shows the probability of acceptance for a range of other cases.

Operating characteristics for $n = 50, r = 3$

Proportion non-conforming in batch	Probability of accepting
0.00	1.000
0.01	0.986
0.02	0.922
0.04	0.677
0.06	0.416
0.08	0.226
0.10	0.112
0.15	0.014
0.20	0.001

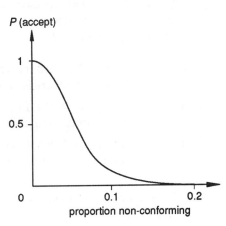

Ideally, if up to 4% non-conforming is accceptable, the probability of accepting a batch containing less than 4% non-conforming should be one and the probability of accepting a batch containing more than 4% non-conforming should be zero. If this were the case, the shape of the operating characteristic would be as shown opposite.

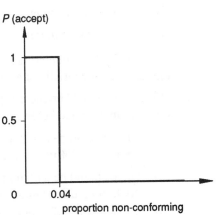

Activity 2

Draw the operating characteristic for $n = 50, r = 2$ (i.e. take a sample of size 50 and reject the batch if 2 or more non-conforming are found).

Draw on the same axes the operating characteristic for $n = 20, r = 1$. Show on your graph the ideal shape of the operating characteristic if up to 5% non-conforming items are acceptable.

What do you notice about the graphs?

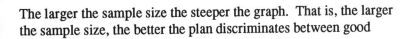

The larger the sample size the steeper the graph. That is, the larger the sample size, the better the plan discriminates between good batches (i.e. batches with a small proportion of non-conforming items) and bad batches (i.e. batches with a large proportion of non-conforming items). Note that, provided the batch is large enough for the binomial distribution to give a good approximation to the probabilities, it is the number of items inspected which determines how good the sampling plan is. The proportion of the batch inspected is not important. Provided the sampling is random it will be better to test say 100 items from a batch of 5000 than to test 10 items from a batch of 500.

Example

A manufacturer receives large batches of components daily and decides to institute an acceptance sampling scheme. Three possible plans are considered, each of which requires a sample of 30 components to be tested:

Plan A: Accept the batch if no non-conforming components are found, otherwise reject.

Plan B: Accept the batch if not more than one non-conforming component is found, otherwise reject.

Plan C: Accept the batch if two or fewer non-conforming components are found, otherwise reject.

(a)   For each plan, calculate the probability of accepting a batch containing

    (i)   2% non-conforming

    (ii) 8% non-conforming.

(b)   Without further calculation sketch on the same axes the operating characteristic of each plan.

(c)   Which plan would be most appropriate in each of the circumstances listed below?

    (i)   There should be a high probability of accepting batches containing 2% non-conforming.

    (ii) There should be a high probability of rejecting batches containing 8% non-conforming.

    (iii) A balance is required between the risk of accepting batches containing 8% defective and the risk of rejecting batches containing 2% non-conforming.

Solution

(a)   The probability may be calculated or be obtained directly from tables of the binomial distribution.

    For a batch containing 2% non-conforming, the probability of any member of the sample being a non-conforming component is 0.02. (Remember the batch is large so the fact that the sample will normally be drawn without replacement will have a negligible effect on the probabilities of the later members of the sample.) The probability of any member of the sample not being a non-conforming component is

$$1 - 0.02 = 0.98.$$

The probability of no non-conforming components in the sample is

$$0.98^{30} = 0.545$$

and this is the probability of the batch being accepted if **Plan A** is used.

If **Plan B** is used the batch will be accepted if the sample contains 0 or 1 non-conforming items and the probability of this is

$$0.98^{30} + 30 \times 0.02 \times 0.98^{29} = 0.879.$$

If **Plan C** is used the batch will be acepted if the sample contains 0, 1 or 2 non-conforming components. The probability of this is

$$0.98^{30} + 30 \times 0.02 \times 0.98^{29} + 435 \times 0.02^2 \times 0.98^{28} = 0.978.$$

Similar calculations may be carried out when the batch contains 8% non-conforming components, or the probabilities may be read directly from tables of the binomial distribution with $n = 30$, $p = 0.08$. This gives the following results for the probability of acceptance

Plan A: 0.082   **Plan B:** 0.296   **Plan C:** 0.565

(b) From part (a) we have two points on the operating characteristic for each plan. In addition, all operating characteristics go through the point (0, 1) because if the batch contains no non-conforming components, every sample will contain no non-conforming components and this must lead to the batch being accepted. Every operating characteristic will also pass through the point (1, 0). However this part of the curve is of no interest. It corresponds to batches which contain only non-conforming items. Acceptance sampling would not be used if there was any possibility of this occurring. The graphs may now be sketched as shown opposite.

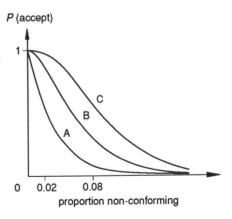

(c) (i) Plan C would be the most suitable as it has the highest probability (0.978) of accepting a batch containing 2% non- conforming.

(ii) Plan A has the lowest probability (0.082) of accepting a batch containing 8% non-conforming. Plan A is therefore the most suitable as the probability of rejecting a batch containing 8% non-conforming is $1 - 0.082 = 0.918$, and this is highest of the three plans.

(iii) Plan B would be the most suitable in this case. It can be seen from the graph that it has a lower probability than A of rejecting a batch containing 2% non-conforming and a lower probability than C of accepting a batch containing 8% non-conforming.

Example

(a) An acceptance sampling scheme consists of inspecting 25 items and rejecting the batch if two or more non-conforming items are found. Find the probability of accepting a batch containing 15% non-conforming. Find also the probability of accepting batches containing 2, 4, 6, 8, 10 and 20% non-conforming.

(b) The manufacturer requires a plan with a probability of not more than 0.05 of rejecting a batch containing 3% non-conforming. If the sample size remains 25, what should the criterion be for rejecting the batch if the manufacturer's risk is to be just met?

(c) It is decided to increase the number of items inspected to 50. What should the criterion be for accepting a batch if the consumer's risk of accepting a batch containing 15% non-conforming is to be as near as possible to 10%? Plot the operating characteristic for this plan on the same axes as the first. Does this plan satisfy the manufacturer's risk specified in (b)?

(d) Discuss the factors to be considered when deciding which of the plans to use.   (AEB)

Solution

(a) The batch will be accepted if 0 or 1 non-conforming items are found in a sample of 25 from a batch containing 15%. This may be calculated using the binomial distribution

$n = 25$, $p = 0.15$ or read from tables. The probability is

$$0.85^{25} + 25 \times 0.15 \times 0.85^{24} = 0.0931$$

You may wish to check the following figures

Proportion non-conforming	P(accept)
0.02	0.911
0.04	0.736
0.06	0.553
0.08	0.395
0.10	0.271
0.20	0.027

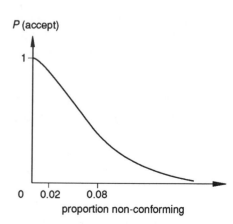

(b) For a batch containing 3% non-conforming the probability of r or less non-conforming items in a sample of 25 is given below.

r	P(r or less)
0	0.467
1	0.828
2	0.962
3	0.994

You may check these figures using the binomial distribution. The manufacturer requires a plan with a probability of not more than 0.05 of rejecting a batch containing 3% non-conforming. That is, a probability of at least 0.95 of accepting the batch. The table shows that the probability of the sample containing 2 or less is 0.962, thus $n = 25, r = 3$ will just meet this requirement. (Note accepting if 2 or less are found implies rejecting if 3 or more are found.)

(c) Binomial distribution $n = 50, p = 0.15$

r	P(r or less)
1	0.003
2	0.014
3	0.046
4	0.112
5	0.219

A consumer's risk of about 10% or 0.10 of accepting a batch containing 15% non-conforming is given by accepting batches if 4 or less non-conforming items are found. (As can be seen from the table above, the probability of finding 4 or less is 0.112.) This gives the plan $n = 50, r = 5$.

For this plan

proportion non-conforming	P(accept)
0.02	0.997
0.04	0.951
0.07	0.729
0.10	0.431
0.15	0.112
0.20	0.018

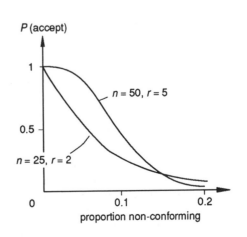

From the operating characteristic it can be seen that the probability of accepting a batch containing 3% or 0.03

non-conforming is about 0.98. Thus the probability of rejecting it is about 0.02 which is well below the 0.05 specified in (b). Hence it does meet the manufacturer's risk.

(d)   The plan requiring a sample of 50 will require more testing to be carried out and will thus be more expensive. As can be seen from the operating characteristics, it discriminates better between good and bad batches, giving a higher probability of accepting good (small proportion non-conforming) batches and a higher probability of rejecting bad (large proportion non-conforming) batches.

The cost of the extra sampling should be balanced against the cost of making wrong decisions, i.e. the waste involved in rejecting a good batch and the problems and frustrations caused by accepting a bad batch.

Note: This question was phrased in terms of manufacturer's risk and consumer's risk, the idea being that only the manufacturer was concerned if a good batch was rejected and only the consumer was concerned if a bad batch was accepted. These terms are rarely used these days as it is recognised that it is in no one's interest for mistakes to be made. If bad batches are accepted the manufacturer will be faced with customer complaints which are expensive to deal with and, in the long run, business will suffer. If good batches are rejected, the cost of unnecessarily replacing them - or at the least the cost of extensive extra testing - will eventually be borne by the consumer.

Exercise 9A

1.   An acceptance sampling scheme consists of taking a sample of 20 from a large batch of items and accepting the batch if the sample contains 2 or less non-conforming items. Draw the operating characteristic for this scheme.

2.   An engine component is defined to be defective if its length (in 0.001mm) is outside the range 19950 to 20050.

  (a) An acceptance sampling scheme consists of taking a sample of size 50 from each batch and accepting the batch if the sample contains 2 or fewer defectives. If the sample contains 3 or more defectives the batch is rejected.

   Find the probability of accepting batches containing 2%,5%,10% and 15% defective and draw the operating characteristic.

  (b) The customer complains that the plan in (a) has far too high a risk of accepting batches containing a large proportion of defectives. As far as she is concerned a batch containing 1 in 1000 defectives is bad but she will agree that a batch containing 1 in 10000 defectives is good.

  (i)   If lengths of components are normally distributed with mean 20000 and standard deviation 12.8, what proportion are defective?

  (ii) It is decided to define components outside the range 20000±k as non-conforming. Find the value of k to two significant figures which will give 5% non-conforming items for this distribution.

  (iii) If the distribution of lengths in a batch is normal with mean 20010 and standard deviation 12.8 about 1 component in 1000 will be defective. What proportion will be non-conforming? If the plan in (a) is applied to non-conforming instead of defective components find from your operating characteristic the probability of accepting this batch.

  (c) Explain why the plan in (b) (iii) should satisfy the customer.   (AEB)

9.2 Double sampling plans

The following is an example of a **double sampling plan**.

Take a sample of size 30. Accept the batch if 0 or 1 non-conforming items are found and reject the batch if 3 or more non-conforming items are found. If exactly 2 non-conforming items are found take a further sample of size 30. Accept the batch if a total of 4 or fewer (out of 60) are found, otherwise reject the batch. This plan is denoted

$$n = 30; \quad a = 1, r = 3,$$

$$n = 30; \quad a = 4, r = 5.$$

The acceptance number is a, i.e. the batch will be accepted if up to a non-conforming items are found. The rejection number is r, i.e. the batch will be rejected if r or more non-conforming items are found.

Note that the acceptance and rejection numbers refer to all items that have been inspected, not just to the most recent sample. There is no reason why the first and second sample need be of the same size, but in practice this is nearly always the case.

The idea behind double sampling plans is that a very good batch or a very bad batch may be detected with a relatively small sample but for an intermediate batch it is desirable to take a larger sample before deciding whether to accept or reject.

Example

A firm is to introduce an acceptance sampling scheme. Three alternative plans are considered.

Plan A   Take a sample of 50 and accept the batch if no non-conforming items are found, otherwise reject.

Plan B   Take a sample of 50 and accept the batch if 2 or fewer non-conforming items are found.

Plan C   Take a sample of 40 and accept the batch if no non-conforming items are found. Reject the batch if 2 or more are found. If one is found, then take a further sample of size 40. If a total of 2 or fewer (out of 80) is found, accept the batch, otherwise reject.

(a) Find the probability of acceptance for each of the plans A, B and C if batches are submitted containing

   (i)   1% non-conforming,

   (ii) 10% non-conforming.

(b) Without further calculation, sketch on the same axes the operating characteristic for plans A, B and C.

(c) Show that, for batches containing 1% non-conforming, the average number of items inspected when using plan C is similar to the number inspected when using plans A or B.

(AEB)

Solution

(a) **Plan A:** accept 0.

$$P(\text{accept}) = (1-p)^{50}.$$

For $p = 0.01$, $P(\text{accept}) = 0.99^{50} = 0.605$;

for $p = 0.1$, $P(\text{accept}) = 0.9^{50} = 0.005$.

Plan B: accept 0, 1 or 2.

$P(\text{accept})$

$$= (1-p)^{50} + 50 \times p \times (1-p)^{49} + \left(50 \times \frac{49}{2}\right) \times p^2 \times (1-p)48$$

for $p = 0.1$, $P(\text{accept}) = 0.986$; for $p = 0.1$, $P(\text{accept}) = 0.112$

Plan C: accept 0 in first sample (in which case no second sample will be taken) or 1 in first sample and 0 in second sample or 1 in first sample and 1 in second sample.

There are no other ways of accepting the batch - if 2 or more are found in the first sample the batch is immediately rejected and if 1 is found in the first sample and 2 or more in the second (giving a total of 3 or more) the batch is rejected.

The samples are of equal size and the batch is large so the probability of acceptance may be expressed as

$$P(0) + P(1) \times P(0) + P(1) \times P(1)$$

$$P(0) = (1-p)^{40} \qquad P(1) = 40 \times p \times (1-p)^{39}.$$

For $p = 0.01$ $P(0) = 0.669$ and $P(1) = 0.270$

$$P(\text{accept}) = 0.669 + 0.270 \times 0.669 + 0.270^2 = 0.923.$$

For $p = 0.1$ $\quad P(0) = 0.0148$, $P(1) = 0.0.0657$.

$$P(\text{accept}) = 0.0148 + 0.0657 \times 0.0148 + 0.0657^2 = 0.020.$$

(b) The operating characteristics are shown opposite.

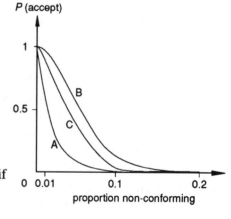

(c) For **Plan C**, if the first sample contains 0 or 2 or more non-conforming, a decision as to whether to accept or reject the batch is made immediately. A second sample is only taken if the first sample contains exactly 1 non-conforming item. The average number of items inspected is

$$40 + 40 \times P(1)$$

For batches containing 1% non-conforming the average number of items inspected is

$$40 + 40 \times 0.270 = 50.8.$$

Thus the average number inspected is similar to the 50 inspected in the single sample plans.

Note: This calculation only applies when $p = 0.01$. For other values of p you would have to make a further calculation. However it can be stated that if a single and a double sampling plan have similar operating characteristics (not the case here), the double sampling plan will, on average, require less items to be inspected than the single sampling plan. This will be true for any value of p. Against this, the double sampling plan is more complex to operate.

Activity 3

The three plans in the previous example are to be considered for use in a situation where it is expected that most batches submitted will contain about 1% non-conforming but that occasionally batches will contain about 10% non-conforming. Decide which of the three plans would be most suitable in each of the following cases:

(i) it is important that batches containing 1% non-conforming should be accepted as frequently as possible;

(ii) it is important that batches containing 10% non-conforming should be rejected as frequently as possible;

(iii) a balance should be struck between the risk of accepting batches containing 10% non-conforming and the risk of rejecting batches containing 1% non-conforming.

Example

The following acceptance sampling plans have similar operating characteristics.

Plan 1   Take a sample of size 80 and reject the batch if 6 or more non-conforming items are found.

Plan 2   Take a sample of size 50 and accept the batch if 2 or fewer non-conforming items are found. Reject the batch if 5 or more non-conforming items are found. If 3 or 4 non-conforming items are found take a further sample of size 50 and reject the batch if a total of 7 or more non-conforming items (out of 100) are found. Otherwise accept.

The following table gives the probability of obtaining r or less successes in n independent trials when the probability of success in a single trial is 0.04.

r	n = 50	n = 80
0	0.1299	0.0382
1	0.4005	0.1654
2	0.6767	0.3748
3	0.8609	0.6016
4	0.9510	0.7836
5	0.9856	0.8988
6	0.9964	0.9588
7	0.9992	0.9852

(a) Verify that both plans have similar probabilities of accepting batches containing 4% non-conforming.

(b) The cost of the sampling inspection is made up of the cost of obtaining the sample plus the cost of carrying out the inspection. A firm estimates that for a sample of size n the cost, in pence, of obtaining the sample is $400 + 4n$ and the cost of inspection is $24n$. For batches containing 4% non-conforming, compare the expected cost of the following three inspection procedures:

(i) Use **Plan 1**;

(ii) Use **Plan 2**, obtaining the second sample of 50 only if required to do so by the plan;

(iii) Use **Plan 2**, but obtain a sample of 100. Inspect the first 50, but only inspect the second 50 if required to do so by the plan. (AEB)

Solution

(a) For **Plan 1**, $n = 80, p = 0.04$; accept if 5 or less found

From table $P(\text{accept}) = 0.8988$.

For **Plan 2**, the batch can be accepted in the following ways

1st sample	2nd sample
0	
1	
2	
3	0
3	1
3	2
3	3
4	0
4	1
4	2

$$P(\text{accept}) = P(0) + P(1) + P(2) + P(3)P(0) + P(3)P(1) +$$
$$P(3)P(2) + P(3)P(3) + P(4)P(0) + P(4)P(1) + P(4)P(2)$$

This can be evaluated using the table given, noting that

$$P(r) = P(r \text{ or less}) - P(r-1 \text{ or less}).$$

Thus for example

$$P(4) = 0.9510 - 0.8609 = 0.0901$$

However, the evaluation can be speeded up by writing $P(\text{accept})$

$$= P(2 \text{ or less}) + P(3)P(3 \text{ or less}) + P(4)P(2 \text{ or less})$$
$$= 0.6767 + (0.8609 - 0.6767)0.8609 + 0.0901 \times 0.6767$$
$$= 0.896.$$

This probability is similar to the 0.899 obtained for **Plan 1**.

(b) (i) The cost for **Plan 1** is $400 + 4 \times 80 + 24 \times 80 = £26.40$.

(ii) In this case the second sample of 50 will be obtained only if the first sample contains 3 or 4 defectives. The probability of this occurring is

$$0.9510 - 0.6767 = 0.2743$$

The expected cost is the cost of obtaining and testing the first sample plus $0.2743 \times$ (the cost of obtaining and testing the second sample)

$$= 400 + 4 \times 50 + 24 \times 50 + 0.2743(400 + 4 \times 50 + 24 \times 50)$$

$$= £22.94$$

(iii) The expected cost is now the cost of obtaining a sample of 100 and testing 50 of these plus $0.2743 \times$ (the cost of testing a further 50)

$$= 400 + 4 \times 100 + 24 \times 50 + 0.2743 \times 24 \times 50$$
$$= £23.29$$

Hence the expected cost of the double sampling plan is less than that of the single sampling plan no matter whether two separate samples of 50 are taken as required, or a single sample of 100 is taken. This calculation, of course, applies only to the case where batches containing 4% non-conforming are submitted. However, the conclusion is probably true for all other possible batches. The double sampling plan is, however, more complex to operate.

Activity 4

For Plan 2 in the Example above, calculate the expected number of items inspected if the proportion non-conforming in the submitted batch is 0.00, 0.02, 0.04, 0.06, 0.08, 0.10 and 0.15. Draw a graph of this expected number against the proportion non-conforming.

Is this graph consistent with the statement that, for plans with similar operating characteristics, the expected number inspected will be less for a double sampling plan than for a single sampling plan?

Would it be possible to construct a triple sampling plan?

Exercise 9B

1. (i) An acceptance sampling scheme consists of taking a sample of size 20 and accepting the batch if no non-conforming items are found. If 2 or more non-conforming items are found the batch is rejected. If 1 non-conforming item is found a further sample of 20 is taken and the batch is accepted if a total of 2 or fewer (out of 40) non-conforming items are found. Otherwise it is rejected. This plan is denoted

$$n = 20, \ a = 0, \ r = 2$$

$$n = 20, \ a = 2, \ r = 3.$$

Find the probability of accepting a batch containing 4% non-conforming.

(ii) Find the probability of accepting a batch containing 3% non-conforming for the plan

$$n = 40, \ a = 0, \ r = 3$$

$$n = 40, \ a = 2, \ r = 3$$

(iii) Find the probability of accepting a batch containing 5% non-conforming for the plan

$$n = 30, \ a = 0, \ r = 3$$

$$n = 30, \ a = 3, \ r = 4$$

2. When checking large batches of goods the following acceptance sampling plans have similar operating characteristics.

Plan 1: Take a sample of size 50 and accept the batch if 3 or fewer non-conforming items are found, otherwise reject it.

Plan 2: Take a sample of size 30, accept the batch if zero or one non-conforming items are found and reject the batch if 3 or more are found. If exactly 2 are found, take a further sample of size 30. Accept the batch if a total of 4 or fewer (out of 60) are found, otherwise reject it.

(a) Using the following table, verify that the two plans have similar probabilities of accepting a batch containing 5% non-conforming. The table gives the probability of obtaining r or more successes in n independent trials when the probability of a success in a single trial is 0.05.

r	$n = 30$	$n = 50$
0	1.0000	1.0000
1	0.7854	0.9231
2	0.4465	0.7206
3	0.1878	0.4595
4	0.0608	0.2396

(b) For the second plan, evaluate the expected number of items inspected each time the plan is used when the proportion non-conforming in the batch is 0, 0.02, 0.05, 0.10 and 1.00. Sketch a graph of the expected number of items inspected against the proportion non-conforming in the batch.

(c) What factors should be considered when deciding which of the two plans is to be used?

9.3 Acceptance sampling by variable

Acceptance sampling can be carried out by measuring a variable rather than classifying an item as conforming or non-conforming. Variables such as thickness, strength or weight might be measured. A typical plan would be to take a sample of size n and reject the batch if the mean measurement, $\bar{x}$, is less than k. This would be appropriate for, say, the strength of a batch of climbing ropes where a large value is desirable. If the variable was, say, percentage of impurity in raw material,where a small value was desirable, the plan would be of the form - take a sample of size n and reject the batch if the mean measurement, $\bar{x}$, is greater than k.

Usually it is easier and quicker to classify an item as conforming or non-conforming than to make an exact measurement. However, the information gained from an exact measurement is greater and so smaller sample sizes are required. A decision as to whether to use attributes or variables will depend on the particular circumstances of each case.

Operating characteristic

A component for use in the manufacture of office machinery will fail to function if the temperature becomes too high. A batch of these components has a mean failure temperature of 95.6°C. The standard deviation is 2.4°C. The company receiving this batch operates the following acceptance sampling scheme - test a sample of size 16 and reject the batch if the mean failure temperature is less than 95.0°C.

It is reasonable to assume normal distribution since we are concerned with the mean of a reasonably large sample. The batch will be accepted if the sample mean exceeds 95.0°C.

$$z = \frac{95 - 95.6}{\left(\dfrac{2.4}{\sqrt{16}}\right)} = -1$$

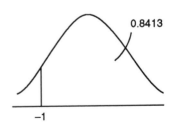

The probability of the batch being accepted is 0.841.

The operating characteristic can be constructed by carrying out this calculation for batches with different means (assuming the standard deviation remains at 2.4°C). The calculations can be put in a table as shown on the next page. (Be careful to use the correct tail of the normal distribution, this will depend on the sign of z and will change when this changes).

μ	$(k-\mu)/\left(\dfrac{\sigma}{\sqrt{n}}\right)$	P(accept)
93.2	3.0	0.001
93.8	2.0	0.023
94.4	1.0	0.159
94.7	0.5	0.308
95.0	0.0	0.500
95.3	−0.5	0.691
95.6	−1.0	0.841
96.2	−2.0	0.977
96.8	−3.0	0.999

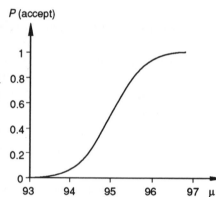

Note that the shape of the operating characteristic is a reflection in a vertical line of the typical shape for an attributes scheme. This is because, in this case, the good batches have large mean values whereas for attributes good batches have small proportions of non-conforming items.

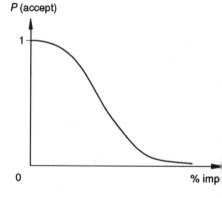

An operating characteristic for percentage impurity, where a good batch has a low mean, would have shape shown opposite.

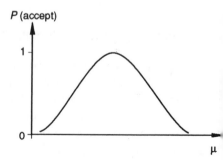

In other cases, such as the diameter of screw caps for bottles of vinegar, the mean of a good batch must be neither too big nor too small and the shape of the operating characteristic would be as shown in the diagram on the right.

Is it possible for P(accept) to equal one in an acceptance sampling by variables scheme?

Activity 5

Think of an example where acceptance sampling by variables could be applied and the value of the variable should be

(i) as large as possible,

(ii) as small as possible,

(iii) neither too large nor too small.

Example

(a) Before cement is delivered to a civil engineering site, a number of small bricks are made from it. Five are chosen at random and measured for compressive strength (measured in $N m^{-2} \times 10^9$). This is known to be normally distributed with standard deviation 5.5. The batch of cement is accepted for delivery if the mean compressive strength of the five bricks is greater than 51. Draw the operating characteristic for this plan.

(b) It is decided to redesign the plan. The customer requires that the probability of accepting a batch with a mean strength of 47 or less should be less than 0.1. The manufacturer requires that the probability of rejecting a batch with a mean strength of 52.5 or more should be less than 0.05. By consulting your operating characteristic which, if either, of these criteria are satisfied by the current plan.

(c) If n is the sample size and k is the compressive strength which must be exceeded by the sample mean for the batch to be accepted, find the minimum value of n to satisfy the manufacturer's requirements if k remains at 51.

(d) If k is changed to 49.4, find the minimum value of n to satisfy the customer's requirements. Verify that using this value of n the manufacturer's requirements will also be met.

(AEB)

Solution

(a) The operating characteristic is a graph of probability of acceptance against mean strength of bricks from the batch of cement. First, suitable values of this mean strength must be chosen so that the probability of acceptance can be calculated and the graph drawn. The standard deviation is 5.5. Since samples of size five are being taken, the standard error is

$\frac{5.5}{\sqrt{5}} = 2.46$. For most purposes a graph which extends

between 2 and 3 standard errors either side of k will be adequate. In this case, say, 44 to 58. Steps of 2 will give 8 points and this will usually be adequate. If a more detailed graph is required, further points can be interpolated and the range can be extended.

μ	$(51-\mu)/\left(\dfrac{5.5}{\sqrt{5}}\right)$	P(accept)
44	2.846	0.002
46	2.033	0.021
48	1.220	0.111
50	0.407	0.342
52	−0.407	0.658
54	−1.220	0.889
56	−2.033	0.979
58	−2.846	0.998

Note: Interpolation was used in reading from tables of the normal distribution. However to find P(accept) to 3 decimal places this only affected the result for the middle two points and then only by 0.001.

(b) From the graph the probability of accepting a batch with a mean strength of 47 is approximately 0.05. This is less than 0.1 and so satisfies the customer's requirement.

The probability of accepting a batch with a mean strength of 52.5 is approximately 0.73. Hence the probability of rejecting it is approximately 0.27. This is much larger than 0.05 and so does not meet the manufacturer's requirement.

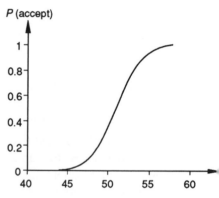

(c) To satisfy the manufacturer's requirement

$$z = \frac{(51 - 52.5)}{\left(\dfrac{5.5}{\sqrt{n}}\right)} < -1.645$$

$$-0.2727\sqrt{n} < -1.645$$

$$\sqrt{n} > 6.032$$

$$n > 36.4$$

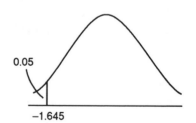

The minimum value of n to satisfy the manufacturer's requirement is 37.

(d) To satisfy the customer's requirement

$$z = \frac{(49.4 - 47)}{\left(\frac{5.5}{\sqrt{n}}\right)} > 1.282$$

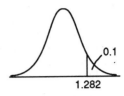

$$0.4364\sqrt{n} > 1.282$$

$$\sqrt{n} > 2.94$$

$$n > 8.63$$

The minimum value of n to satisfy the customer's requirement is 9.

To calculate the manufacturer's risk if $n = 9$

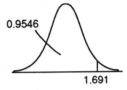

$$z = \frac{(52.5 - 49.4)}{\left(\frac{5.5}{\sqrt{9}}\right)} = 1.691$$

Probability of accepting the batch is 0.955. Probability of rejecting is $1 - 0.955 = 0.045$. This is less than 0.05 and so satisfies the manufacturer's risk.

Exercise 7C

1. An acceptance sampling plan consists of weighing a sample of 6 loaves of bread and accepting the batch if the sample mean is greater than 900g. Draw the operating characteristic if the standard deviation is known from past experience to be 12g.

2. An acceptance sampling plan consists of measuring the percentage of fat in a sample of 8 prepackaged portions of boiled ham. The batch is rejected if the mean proportion exceeds 42%. If the standard deviation is estimated to be 3%, draw the operating characteristic.

3. The quality of a certain chemical is measured by the time it takes to react. (The shorter the time, the better the quality). This time is known to be normally distributed with a standard deviation of 8 seconds. Nine samples are taken from each batch and the batch accepted if the mean reaction time is less than 33.5 seconds.

(a) Draw the operating characteristic for this plan.

(b) The manufacturer requires a plan which has a probability of rejection of less than 0.05 if the mean reaction time of the batch is 30 seconds. The customer requires a plan that has a probability of acceptance of less than 0.10 if the mean reaction time of the batch is 35 seconds. Use your operating characteristic to find which, if either, of these conditions this plan will meet.

(c) If the criterion for acceptance remains unchanged, find the smallest sample size that would enable the plan to satisfy the customer's requirement.

(d) If the criterion for acceptance is for the sample to be accepted if the mean is less than 32.8 seconds, find the smallest sample size that would enable the plan to satisfy the manufacturer's requirement. Verify that this plan would also satisfy the customer's requirement.

9.4 Miscellaneous Exercises

1. (a) A manufacturer will accept a risk of not more than 10% of a batch of items containing 2% non-conforming being rejected. If a decision is to be made by examining a sample of 50 items, find the appropriate decision procedure.

   (b) Draw the operating characteristic for the above plan and indicate on the graph the ideal shape of the operating characteristics if batches containing up to 5% non-conforming are acceptable.

   (c) Would this plan satisfy a customer who specified a risk of not more than 5% of a batch containing 11% non-conforming being accepted?

2. (a) Large batches of wrappers for sliced loaves are to be checked by examining a random sample of 50. If the customer will accept a risk of not more than 5% of a batch containing 10% non-conforming wrappers being accepted, what should the criterion be for rejecting the batch?

   (b) A double sampling plan is specified by

   $$n = 20, \quad a = 0, \quad r = 2$$
   $$n = 20, \quad a = 2, \quad r = 3$$

   (i) What is the probability of a batch containing 10% non-conforming being accepted?

   (ii) What is the average number of items inspected when batches containing 10% non-conforming are submitted?

3. A random sample of 20 from a large batch of components is to be tested, and by counting the number non-conforming, a decision is to be made as to whether the batch should be accepted or rejected by the customer. If the producer is willing to accept the risk of not more than 2% of a batch containing 1% or less non-conforming being rejected, what should be the criterion for rejecting batches? Using tables, plot on graph paper the operating characteristic for this scheme. If the sample size is increased to 50 but the producer's risk is unchanged, plot the operating characteristic of this new scheme on the same graph paper.

   Compare the risk of accepting a batch containing 9% non-conforming components for the two schemes. Sketch, on the same graph paper, the ideal shape of the operating characteristic if a batch containing up to 4% non-conforming is mutually acceptable to both the producer and the customer.

4. A wholesaler packs sugar into bags of nominal weight 1000 g with an automatic machine. It is known from previous experience with the machine that the weights of bags are normally distributed with standard deviation 5 g.

   A retailer, considering the purchase of a large batch, does not want too many bags to be noticeably underweight: he states that an acceptable sampling scheme must be such that if the mean weight per bag is 1000 g, the probability of the batch being accepted must be no more than 0.10.

   The wholesaler, who wishes to avoid repacking the bags, states that if the mean weight per bag is 1005 g, the probability of rejection must be no more than 0.05.

   (a) Design a sampling and decision procedure to satisfy both the wholesaler and retailer.

   (b) Plot the operating characteristic for this sampling scheme.

5. (a) An acceptance sampling scheme consists of taking a sample of 25 from a large batch of components and rejecting the batch if 3 or more non-conforming items are found. What is the probability of accepting batches containing 2%, 4%, 6%, 10%, 15% and 20% non-conforming?

   Use your results to draw an operating characteristic.

   From your operating characteristic, estimate

   (i) the probability of accepting a batch containing 11% non-conforming,

   (ii) the proportion non-conforming in a batch that has a probability of 0.6 of being rejected.

   (b) An alternative plan requires a sample of 40 to be taken from the batch and the batch to be rejected if four or more non-conforming are found. Verify that both plans have similar probabilities of of rejecting batches containing 4% non-conforming, and comment on the advantages and disadvantages of the second plan compared to the first.

   (c) If more than one out of eight successive batches from a particular supplier are rejected, a more stringent form of inspection is introduced. What is the probability of more than one out of the next eight batches being rejected if all batches contain 4% non-conforming?

   (d) The more stringent inspection requires samples of 100 from each batch. The original form of inspection is reinstated if a sample contains no non-conforming items. What is the proportion non-conforming in the batch if the probability of no defectives in a sample of 100 is 0.5?   (AEB)

6. (a) A hotel group buys large quantities of towels for use by guests. When a batch is received, a sample of 25 towels is subjected to a test of water absorption. If no more than one towel fails the test the batch is accepted. If two or three towels fail, a further sample of 25 towels is tested. The batch is then accepted if a total of no more than three (out of 50) fail the test. Otherwise it is rejected. If a batch of towels, containing 7% which would fail the test, is submitted what is

   (i) the probability of its being rejected,

   (ii) the expected number of towels inspected?

   (b) In another test, the towels are checked for visual defects. If the defects are distributed at random with a mean of 2 defects per towel, how many defects would be exceeded (on a particular towel) with a probability of just over 5%?

   (c) In a final check, the lengths of 25 towels are measured and the batch rejected if the mean length is less than a specified value k. What should be the value of k to give a probability of 0.99 of accepting a batch with mean length 106 mm and standard deviation 6 mm?

   (d) For towels from a particular supplier, the probabilities of a batch failing these tests are p_1, p_2 and p_3, respectively. Write down an expression for the probability of the batch passing all three tests, stating any assumption you have needed to make.

$\qquad\qquad\qquad\qquad\qquad$ (AEB)

APPENDIX

TABLE 1   2500 RANDOM DIGITS

```
38956   29927   66187   80784   37542   62446   13481   72730   48511   42315
94451   62506   22780   30720   79338   68358   62765   33401   82758   42929
01323   83752   10664   12193   88766   76763   90977   46881   59089   39648
81916   75703   27522   79504   06662   25468   92407   19626   61173   52793
83727   99617   59120   33554   32904   95312   61763   68868   94179   73442
51966   17490   64900   12690   95474   53849   64791   35843   44832   01296
27355   02384   16680   76637   42437   27994   24718   09566   43821   89315
78802   44031   51668   85907   22683   06119   25360   35480   91334   01522
46134   94058   36466   99717   57651   02512   98785   86491   76812   10324
57217   88783   77127   95783   40666   82539   84224   94354   41979   32823
67895   33380   47444   02936   57303   31458   28669   22538   66884   38370
99108   95198   41684   89066   17963   39042   50791   44683   15134   19909
79310   03183   62706   65531   47767   42347   51899   33582   28098   43168
34447   26623   00550   52329   90292   37508   97310   92049   47365   80242
02737   57929   14290   08118   95473   91586   58953   74998   73950   54662
15269   49103   92150   78211   27762   18135   43479   61698   77768   00223
96198   98634   31870   56839   60478   62129   87149   60240   09079   38567
75823   90593   76248   60379   98204   59254   51616   41091   11818   11001
19611   68604   90298   38595   52048   95137   73363   53307   37914   27903
32205   72711   43441   87108   82155   43650   81967   56348   19878   75813
74513   08193   05302   11352   48369   55731   81158   21037   29534   98074
39851   74829   51695   51682   97660   97110   69540   69776   22736   54635
10349   25900   81265   25339   43875   38563   43530   36289   78810   18959
39871   42417   50106   24752   94664   11611   05720   77091   96338   68507
51268   32291   57653   42135   36440   79427   11660   15666   55682   25449
07468   24096   57419   35611   91179   51464   94284   92449   97347   22184
34454   50344   22824   09193   98771   30963   02876   97671   56397   91677
41503   76672   52872   48610   31314   21545   23601   18278   93530   02142
47261   50385   70112   26897   00077   04803   98326   88933   17710   75750
14852   64222   95920   80534   55090   04105   01415   11376   20709   78887
51198   11602   06891   07924   42959   73124   36830   70559   55739   73191
20818   87962   92071   13405   05057   85947   73043   94208   52829   88272
77297   41595   07611   36646   70863   57797   82033   19236   74608   14324
64648   34917   58038   47230   38817   70605   62771   02851   23195   20204
49898   50622   76133   54065   34055   13961   07604   30260   92240   40736
95060   14422   58282   73673   04535   03557   40036   85475   16021   77173
74300   48254   71043   44942   12252   59557   53013   26170   21980   18582
62710   59322   65251   84379   05985   45765   38349   68661   18129   29338
01352   04224   19593   72554   54239   44870   38726   51297   82412   65799
95076   17264   41154   16019   70481   97716   53185   53901   89036   01253
62445   09632   07182   78111   19253   12414   73496   24090   54974   48941
86267   54282   74626   40866   91371   44589   31478   58842   71961   38487
69681   80207   43497   37079   53974   20241   62576   15660   68405   57982
51884   93899   94309   56732   59858   28457   74546   45424   92496   71035
80038   46869   52284   00000   42554   58770   83458   58425   60956   21595
25342   61693   10160   27212   91407   61420   55196   32064   99083   45348
87696   88047   21252   52768   88011   96661   77691   78801   05384   92340
25749   27087   84246   04208   37579   54270   94698   86310   06727   88176
15251   34691   89127   51214   38276   27601   02422   77625   02017   13801
64230   48467   55548   84036   63668   20271   26235   76671   51372   35552
```

Cumulative Binomial Distribution Function

TABLE 2

These tables give the probability of obtaining at most x successes in n independent trials, when the probability of success for each trial is p.

p	0.01	0.02	0.03	0.04	0.05	0.06	0.07	0.08	0.09	0.10	0.15	0.20	0.25	0.30	0.35	0.40	0.45	0.50	
x	n=5																		
0	0.9510	0.9039	0.8587	0.8154	0.7738	0.7339	0.6957	0.6591	0.6240	0.5905	0.4437	0.3277	0.2373	0.1681	0.1160	0.0778	0.0503	0.0313	0
1	0.9990	0.9962	0.9915	0.9852	0.9774	0.9681	0.9575	0.9456	0.9326	0.9185	0.8352	0.7373	0.6328	0.5282	0.4284	0.3370	0.2562	0.1875	1
2	1.0000	0.9999	0.9997	0.9994	0.9988	0.9980	0.9969	0.9955	0.9937	0.9914	0.9734	0.9421	0.8965	0.8369	0.7648	0.6826	0.5931	0.5000	2
3	1.0000	1.0000	1.0000	1.0000	1.0000	0.9999	0.9999	0.9998	0.9997	0.9995	0.9978	0.9933	0.9844	0.9692	0.9460	0.9130	0.8688	0.8125	3
4	1.0000	1.0000	1.0000	1.0000	1.0000	1.0000	1.0000	1.0000	1.0000	1.0000	0.9999	0.9997	0.9990	0.9976	0.9947	0.9898	0.9815	0.9688	4
5	1.0000	1.0000	1.0000	1.0000	1.0000	1.0000	1.0000	1.0000	1.0000	1.0000	1.0000	1.0000	1.0000	1.0000	1.0000	1.0000	1.0000	1.0000	5
	n=6																		
0	0.9415	0.8858	0.8330	0.7828	0.7351	0.6899	0.6470	0.6064	0.5679	0.5314	0.3771	0.2621	0.1780	0.1176	0.0754	0.0467	0.0277	0.0156	0
1	0.9985	0.9943	0.9875	0.9784	0.9672	0.9541	0.9392	0.9227	0.9048	0.8857	0.7765	0.6554	0.5339	0.4202	0.3191	0.2333	0.1636	0.1094	1
2	1.0000	0.9998	0.9995	0.9988	0.9978	0.9962	0.9942	0.9915	0.9882	0.9842	0.9527	0.9011	0.8306	0.7443	0.6471	0.5443	0.4415	0.3438	2
3	1.0000	1.0000	1.0000	1.0000	0.9999	0.9998	0.9997	0.9995	0.9992	0.9987	0.9941	0.9830	0.9624	0.9295	0.8826	0.8208	0.7447	0.6563	3
4	1.0000	1.0000	1.0000	1.0000	1.0000	1.0000	1.0000	1.0000	1.0000	0.9999	0.9996	0.9984	0.9954	0.9891	0.9777	0.9590	0.9308	0.8906	4
5	1.0000	1.0000	1.0000	1.0000	1.0000	1.0000	1.0000	1.0000	1.0000	1.0000	1.0000	0.9999	0.9998	0.9993	0.9982	0.9959	0.9917	0.9844	5
6	1.0000	1.0000	1.0000	1.0000	1.0000	1.0000	1.0000	1.0000	1.0000	1.0000	1.0000	1.0000	1.0000	1.0000	1.0000	1.0000	1.0000	1.0000	6
	n=8																		
0	0.9227	0.8508	0.7837	0.7214	0.6634	0.6096	0.5596	0.5132	0.4703	0.4305	0.2725	0.1678	0.1001	0.0576	0.0319	0.0168	0.0084	0.0039	0
1	0.9973	0.9897	0.9777	0.9619	0.9428	0.9208	0.8965	0.8702	0.8423	0.8131	0.6572	0.5033	0.3671	0.2553	0.1691	0.1064	0.0632	0.0352	1
2	0.9999	0.9996	0.9987	0.9969	0.9942	0.9904	0.9853	0.9789	0.9711	0.9619	0.8948	0.7969	0.6785	0.5518	0.4278	0.3154	0.2201	0.1445	2
3	1.0000	1.0000	0.9999	0.9998	0.9996	0.9993	0.9987	0.9978	0.9966	0.9950	0.9786	0.9437	0.8862	0.8059	0.7064	0.5941	0.4770	0.3633	3
4	1.0000	1.0000	1.0000	1.0000	1.0000	1.0000	0.9999	0.9999	0.9997	0.9996	0.9971	0.9896	0.9727	0.9420	0.8939	0.8263	0.7396	0.6367	4
5	1.0000	1.0000	1.0000	1.0000	1.0000	1.0000	1.0000	1.0000	1.0000	1.0000	0.9998	0.9988	0.9958	0.9887	0.9747	0.9502	0.9115	0.8555	5
6	1.0000	1.0000	1.0000	1.0000	1.0000	1.0000	1.0000	1.0000	1.0000	1.0000	1.0000	0.9999	0.9996	0.9987	0.9964	0.9915	0.9819	0.9648	6
7	1.0000	1.0000	1.0000	1.0000	1.0000	1.0000	1.0000	1.0000	1.0000	1.0000	1.0000	1.0000	1.0000	0.9999	0.9998	0.9993	0.9983	0.9961	7
8	1.0000	1.0000	1.0000	1.0000	1.0000	1.0000	1.0000	1.0000	1.0000	1.0000	1.0000	1.0000	1.0000	1.0000	1.0000	1.0000	1.0000	1.0000	8
	n=10																		
0	0.9044	0.8171	0.7374	0.6648	0.5987	0.5386	0.4840	0.4344	0.3894	0.3487	0.1969	0.1074	0.0563	0.0282	0.0135	0.0060	0.0025	0.0010	0
1	0.9957	0.9838	0.9655	0.9418	0.9139	0.8824	0.8483	0.8121	0.7746	0.7361	0.5443	0.3758	0.2440	0.1493	0.0860	0.0464	0.0233	0.0107	1
2	0.9999	0.9991	0.9972	0.9938	0.9885	0.9812	0.9717	0.9599	0.9460	0.9298	0.8202	0.6778	0.5256	0.3828	0.2616	0.1673	0.0996	0.0547	2
3	1.0000	1.0000	0.9999	0.9996	0.9990	0.9980	0.9964	0.9942	0.9912	0.9872	0.9500	0.8791	0.7759	0.6496	0.5138	0.3823	0.2660	0.1719	3
4	1.0000	1.0000	1.0000	1.0000	0.9999	0.9998	0.9997	0.9994	0.9990	0.9984	0.9901	0.9672	0.9219	0.8497	0.7515	0.6331	0.5044	0.3770	4
5	1.0000	1.0000	1.0000	1.0000	1.0000	1.0000	1.0000	1.0000	0.9999	0.9999	0.9986	0.9936	0.9803	0.9527	0.9051	0.8338	0.7384	0.6230	5
6	1.0000	1.0000	1.0000	1.0000	1.0000	1.0000	1.0000	1.0000	1.0000	1.0000	0.9999	0.9991	0.9965	0.9894	0.9740	0.9452	0.8980	0.8281	6
7	1.0000	1.0000	1.0000	1.0000	1.0000	1.0000	1.0000	1.0000	1.0000	1.0000	1.0000	0.9999	0.9996	0.9984	0.9952	0.9877	0.9726	0.9453	7
8	1.0000	1.0000	1.0000	1.0000	1.0000	1.0000	1.0000	1.0000	1.0000	1.0000	1.0000	1.0000	1.0000	0.9999	0.9995	0.9983	0.9955	0.9893	8
9	1.0000	1.0000	1.0000	1.0000	1.0000	1.0000	1.0000	1.0000	1.0000	1.0000	1.0000	1.0000	1.0000	1.0000	0.9999	0.9997	0.9990	9	
10	1.0000	1.0000	1.0000	1.0000	1.0000	1.0000	1.0000	1.0000	1.0000	1.0000	1.0000	1.0000	1.0000	1.0000	1.0000	1.0000	1.0000	1.0000	10

Cumulative Binomial Distribution Function

p	0.01	0.02	0.03	0.04	0.05	0.06	0.07	0.08	0.09	0.10	0.15	0.20	0.25	0.30	0.35	0.40	0.45	0.50
x	n =20																	
0	0.8179	0.6676	0.5438	0.4420	0.3585	0.2901	0.2342	0.1887	0.1516	0.1216	0.0388	0.0115	0.0032	0.0008	0.0002	0.0000	0.0000	0.0000
1	0.9831	0.9401	0.8802	0.8103	0.7358	0.6605	0.5869	0.5169	0.4516	0.3917	0.1756	0.0692	0.0243	0.0076	0.0021	0.0005	0.0001	0.0000
2	0.9990	0.9929	0.9790	0.9561	0.9245	0.8850	0.8390	0.7879	0.7334	0.6769	0.4049	0.2061	0.0913	0.0355	0.0121	0.0036	0.0009	0.0002
3	1.0000	0.9994	0.9973	0.9926	0.9841	0.9710	0.9529	0.9294	0.9007	0.8670	0.6477	0.4114	0.2252	0.1071	0.0444	0.0160	0.0049	0.0013
4	1.0000	1.0000	0.9997	0.9990	0.9974	0.9944	0.9893	0.9817	0.9710	0.9568	0.8298	0.6296	0.4148	0.2375	0.1182	0.0510	0.0189	0.0059
5	1.0000	1.0000	1.0000	0.9999	0.9997	0.9991	0.9981	0.9962	0.9932	0.9887	0.9327	0.8042	0.6172	0.4164	0.2454	0.1256	0.0553	0.0207
6	1.0000	1.0000	1.0000	1.0000	1.0000	0.9999	0.9997	0.9994	0.9987	0.9976	0.9781	0.9133	0.7858	0.6080	0.4166	0.2500	0.1299	0.0577
7	1.0000	1.0000	1.0000	1.0000	1.0000	1.0000	1.0000	0.9999	0.9998	0.9996	0.9941	0.9679	0.8982	0.7723	0.6010	0.4159	0.2520	0.1316
8	1.0000	1.0000	1.0000	1.0000	1.0000	1.0000	1.0000	1.0000	1.0000	0.9999	0.9987	0.9900	0.9591	0.8867	0.7624	0.5956	0.4143	0.2517
9	1.0000	1.0000	1.0000	1.0000	1.0000	1.0000	1.0000	1.0000	1.0000	1.0000	0.9998	0.9974	0.9861	0.9520	0.8782	0.7553	0.5914	0.4119
10	1.0000	1.0000	1.0000	1.0000	1.0000	1.0000	1.0000	1.0000	1.0000	1.0000	1.0000	0.9994	0.9961	0.9829	0.9468	0.8725	0.7507	0.5881
11	1.0000	1.0000	1.0000	1.0000	1.0000	1.0000	1.0000	1.0000	1.0000	1.0000	1.0000	0.9999	0.9991	0.9949	0.9804	0.9435	0.8692	0.7483
12	1.0000	1.0000	1.0000	1.0000	1.0000	1.0000	1.0000	1.0000	1.0000	1.0000	1.0000	1.0000	0.9998	0.9987	0.9940	0.9790	0.9420	0.8684
13	1.0000	1.0000	1.0000	1.0000	1.0000	1.0000	1.0000	1.0000	1.0000	1.0000	1.0000	1.0000	1.0000	0.9997	0.9985	0.9935	0.9786	0.9423
14	1.0000	1.0000	1.0000	1.0000	1.0000	1.0000	1.0000	1.0000	1.0000	1.0000	1.0000	1.0000	1.0000	1.0000	0.9997	0.9984	0.9936	0.9793
15	1.0000	1.0000	1.0000	1.0000	1.0000	1.0000	1.0000	1.0000	1.0000	1.0000	1.0000	1.0000	1.0000	1.0000	1.0000	0.9997	0.9985	0.9941
16	1.0000	1.0000	1.0000	1.0000	1.0000	1.0000	1.0000	1.0000	1.0000	1.0000	1.0000	1.0000	1.0000	1.0000	1.0000	1.0000	0.9997	0.9987
17	1.0000	1.0000	1.0000	1.0000	1.0000	1.0000	1.0000	1.0000	1.0000	1.0000	1.0000	1.0000	1.0000	1.0000	1.0000	1.0000	1.0000	0.9998
18	1.0000	1.0000	1.0000	1.0000	1.0000	1.0000	1.0000	1.0000	1.0000	1.0000	1.0000	1.0000	1.0000	1.0000	1.0000	1.0000	1.0000	1.0000
19	1.0000	1.0000	1.0000	1.0000	1.0000	1.0000	1.0000	1.0000	1.0000	1.0000	1.0000	1.0000	1.0000	1.0000	1.0000	1.0000	1.0000	1.0000
20	1.0000	1.0000	1.0000	1.0000	1.0000	1.0000	1.0000	1.0000	1.0000	1.0000	1.0000	1.0000	1.0000	1.0000	1.0000	1.0000	1.0000	1.0000

Cumulative Binomial Distribution Function

	0.01	0.02	0.03	0.04	0.05	0.06	0.07	0.08	0.09	0.10	0.15	0.20	0.25	0.30	0.35	0.40	0.45	0.50	
x	n=25																		
0	0.7778	0.6035	0.4670	0.3604	0.2774	0.2129	0.1630	0.1244	0.0946	0.0718	0.0172	0.0038	0.0008	0.0001	0.0000	0.0000	0.0000	0.0000	0
1	0.9742	0.9114	0.8280	0.7358	0.6424	0.5527	0.4696	0.3947	0.3286	0.2712	0.0931	0.0274	0.0070	0.0016	0.0003	0.0001	0.0000	0.0000	1
2	0.9980	0.9868	0.9620	0.9235	0.8729	0.8129	0.7466	0.6768	0.6063	0.5371	0.2537	0.0982	0.0321	0.0090	0.0021	0.0004	0.0001	0.0000	2
3	0.9999	0.9986	0.9938	0.9835	0.9659	0.9402	0.9064	0.8649	0.8169	0.7636	0.4711	0.2340	0.0962	0.0332	0.0097	0.0024	0.0005	0.0001	3
4	1.0000	0.9999	0.9992	0.9972	0.9928	0.9850	0.9726	0.9549	0.9314	0.9020	0.6821	0.4207	0.2137	0.0905	0.0320	0.0095	0.0023	0.0005	4
5	1.0000	1.0000	0.9999	0.9996	0.9988	0.9969	0.9935	0.9877	0.9790	0.9666	0.8385	0.6167	0.3783	0.1935	0.0826	0.0294	0.0086	0.0020	5
6	1.0000	1.0000	1.0000	1.0000	0.9998	0.9995	0.9987	0.9972	0.9946	0.9905	0.9305	0.7800	0.5611	0.3407	0.1734	0.0736	0.0258	0.0073	6
7	1.0000	1.0000	1.0000	1.0000	1.0000	0.9999	0.9998	0.9995	0.9989	0.9977	0.9745	0.8909	0.7265	0.5118	0.3061	0.1536	0.0639	0.0216	7
8	1.0000	1.0000	1.0000	1.0000	1.0000	1.0000	1.0000	0.9999	0.9998	0.9995	0.9920	0.9532	0.8506	0.6769	0.4668	0.2735	0.1340	0.0539	8
9	1.0000	1.0000	1.0000	1.0000	1.0000	1.0000	1.0000	1.0000	1.0000	0.9999	0.9979	0.9827	0.9287	0.8106	0.6303	0.4246	0.2424	0.1148	9
10	1.0000	1.0000	1.0000	1.0000	1.0000	1.0000	1.0000	1.0000	1.0000	1.0000	0.9995	0.9944	0.9703	0.9022	0.7712	0.5858	0.3843	0.2122	10
11	1.0000	1.0000	1.0000	1.0000	1.0000	1.0000	1.0000	1.0000	1.0000	1.0000	0.9999	0.9985	0.9893	0.9558	0.8746	0.7323	0.5426	0.3450	11
12	1.0000	1.0000	1.0000	1.0000	1.0000	1.0000	1.0000	1.0000	1.0000	1.0000	1.0000	0.9996	0.9966	0.9825	0.9396	0.8462	0.6937	0.5000	12
13	1.0000	1.0000	1.0000	1.0000	1.0000	1.0000	1.0000	1.0000	1.0000	1.0000	1.0000	0.9999	0.9991	0.9940	0.9745	0.9222	0.8173	0.6550	13
14	1.0000	1.0000	1.0000	1.0000	1.0000	1.0000	1.0000	1.0000	1.0000	1.0000	1.0000	1.0000	0.9998	0.9982	0.9907	0.9656	0.9040	0.7878	14
15	1.0000	1.0000	1.0000	1.0000	1.0000	1.0000	1.0000	1.0000	1.0000	1.0000	1.0000	1.0000	1.0000	0.9995	0.9971	0.9868	0.9560	0.8852	15
16	1.0000	1.0000	1.0000	1.0000	1.0000	1.0000	1.0000	1.0000	1.0000	1.0000	1.0000	1.0000	1.0000	0.9999	0.9992	0.9957	0.9826	0.9461	16
17	1.0000	1.0000	1.0000	1.0000	1.0000	1.0000	1.0000	1.0000	1.0000	1.0000	1.0000	1.0000	1.0000	1.0000	0.9998	0.9988	0.9942	0.9784	17
18	1.0000	1.0000	1.0000	1.0000	1.0000	1.0000	1.0000	1.0000	1.0000	1.0000	1.0000	1.0000	1.0000	1.0000	1.0000	0.9997	0.9984	0.9927	18
19	1.0000	1.0000	1.0000	1.0000	1.0000	1.0000	1.0000	1.0000	1.0000	1.0000	1.0000	1.0000	1.0000	1.0000	1.0000	0.9999	0.9996	0.9980	19
20	1.0000	1.0000	1.0000	1.0000	1.0000	1.0000	1.0000	1.0000	1.0000	1.0000	1.0000	1.0000	1.0000	1.0000	1.0000	1.0000	0.9999	0.9995	20
21	1.0000	1.0000	1.0000	1.0000	1.0000	1.0000	1.0000	1.0000	1.0000	1.0000	1.0000	1.0000	1.0000	1.0000	1.0000	1.0000	1.0000	0.9999	21
22	1.0000	1.0000	1.0000	1.0000	1.0000	1.0000	1.0000	1.0000	1.0000	1.0000	1.0000	1.0000	1.0000	1.0000	1.0000	1.0000	1.0000	1.0000	22
23	1.0000	1.0000	1.0000	1.0000	1.0000	1.0000	1.0000	1.0000	1.0000	1.0000	1.0000	1.0000	1.0000	1.0000	1.0000	1.0000	1.0000	1.0000	23
24	1.0000	1.0000	1.0000	1.0000	1.0000	1.0000	1.0000	1.0000	1.0000	1.0000	1.0000	1.0000	1.0000	1.0000	1.0000	1.0000	1.0000	1.0000	24
25	1.0000	1.0000	1.0000	1.0000	1.0000	1.0000	1.0000	1.0000	1.0000	1.0000	1.0000	1.0000	1.0000	1.0000	1.0000	1.0000	1.0000	1.0000	25

Cumulative Binomial Distribution Function

p x	0.01	0.02	0.03	0.04	0.05	0.06	0.07	0.08	0.09	0.10	0.15	0.20	0.25	0.30	0.35	0.40	0.45	0.50
n=30																		
0	0.7397	0.5455	0.4010	0.2939	0.2146	0.1563	0.1134	0.0820	0.0591	0.0424	0.0076	0.0012	0.0002	0.0000	0.0000	0.0000	0.0000	0.0000
1	0.9639	0.8795	0.7731	0.6612	0.5535	0.4555	0.3694	0.2958	0.2343	0.1837	0.0480	0.0105	0.0020	0.0003	0.0000	0.0000	0.0000	0.0000
2	0.9967	0.9783	0.9399	0.8831	0.8122	0.7324	0.6487	0.5654	0.4855	0.4114	0.1514	0.0442	0.0106	0.0021	0.0003	0.0000	0.0000	0.0000
3	0.9998	0.9971	0.9881	0.9694	0.9392	0.8974	0.8450	0.7842	0.7175	0.6474	0.3217	0.1227	0.0374	0.0093	0.0019	0.0003	0.0000	0.0000
4	1.0000	0.9997	0.9982	0.9937	0.9844	0.9685	0.9447	0.9126	0.8723	0.8245	0.5245	0.2552	0.0979	0.0302	0.0075	0.0015	0.0002	0.0000
5	1.0000	1.0000	0.9998	0.9989	0.9967	0.9921	0.9838	0.9707	0.9519	0.9268	0.7106	0.4275	0.2026	0.0766	0.0233	0.0057	0.0011	0.0002
6	1.0000	1.0000	1.0000	0.9999	0.9994	0.9983	0.9960	0.9918	0.9848	0.9742	0.8474	0.6070	0.3481	0.1595	0.0586	0.0172	0.0040	0.0007
7	1.0000	1.0000	1.0000	1.0000	0.9999	0.9997	0.9992	0.9980	0.9959	0.9922	0.9302	0.7608	0.5143	0.2814	0.1238	0.0435	0.0121	0.0026
8	1.0000	1.0000	1.0000	1.0000	1.0000	1.0000	0.9999	0.9996	0.9990	0.9980	0.9722	0.8713	0.6736	0.4315	0.2247	0.0940	0.0312	0.0081
9	1.0000	1.0000	1.0000	1.0000	1.0000	1.0000	1.0000	0.9999	0.9998	0.9995	0.9903	0.9389	0.8034	0.5888	0.3575	0.1763	0.0694	0.0214
10	1.0000	1.0000	1.0000	1.0000	1.0000	1.0000	1.0000	1.0000	1.0000	0.9999	0.9971	0.9744	0.8943	0.7304	0.5078	0.2915	0.1350	0.0494
11	1.0000	1.0000	1.0000	1.0000	1.0000	1.0000	1.0000	1.0000	1.0000	1.0000	0.9992	0.9905	0.9493	0.8407	0.6548	0.4311	0.2327	0.1002
12	1.0000	1.0000	1.0000	1.0000	1.0000	1.0000	1.0000	1.0000	1.0000	1.0000	0.9998	0.9969	0.9784	0.9155	0.7802	0.5785	0.3592	0.1808
13	1.0000	1.0000	1.0000	1.0000	1.0000	1.0000	1.0000	1.0000	1.0000	1.0000	1.0000	0.9991	0.9918	0.9599	0.8737	0.7145	0.5025	0.2923
14	1.0000	1.0000	1.0000	1.0000	1.0000	1.0000	1.0000	1.0000	1.0000	1.0000	1.0000	0.9998	0.9973	0.9831	0.9348	0.8246	0.6448	0.4278
15	1.0000	1.0000	1.0000	1.0000	1.0000	1.0000	1.0000	1.0000	1.0000	1.0000	1.0000	0.9999	0.9992	0.9936	0.9699	0.9029	0.7691	0.5722
16	1.0000	1.0000	1.0000	1.0000	1.0000	1.0000	1.0000	1.0000	1.0000	1.0000	1.0000	1.0000	0.9998	0.9979	0.9876	0.9519	0.8644	0.7077
17	1.0000	1.0000	1.0000	1.0000	1.0000	1.0000	1.0000	1.0000	1.0000	1.0000	1.0000	1.0000	0.9999	0.9994	0.9955	0.9788	0.9286	0.8192
18	1.0000	1.0000	1.0000	1.0000	1.0000	1.0000	1.0000	1.0000	1.0000	1.0000	1.0000	1.0000	1.0000	0.9998	0.9986	0.9917	0.9666	0.8998
19	1.0000	1.0000	1.0000	1.0000	1.0000	1.0000	1.0000	1.0000	1.0000	1.0000	1.0000	1.0000	1.0000	1.0000	0.9996	0.9971	0.9862	0.9506
20	1.0000	1.0000	1.0000	1.0000	1.0000	1.0000	1.0000	1.0000	1.0000	1.0000	1.0000	1.0000	1.0000	1.0000	0.9999	0.9991	0.9950	0.9786
21	1.0000	1.0000	1.0000	1.0000	1.0000	1.0000	1.0000	1.0000	1.0000	1.0000	1.0000	1.0000	1.0000	1.0000	1.0000	0.9998	0.9984	0.9919
22	1.0000	1.0000	1.0000	1.0000	1.0000	1.0000	1.0000	1.0000	1.0000	1.0000	1.0000	1.0000	1.0000	1.0000	1.0000	1.0000	0.9996	0.9974
23	1.0000	1.0000	1.0000	1.0000	1.0000	1.0000	1.0000	1.0000	1.0000	1.0000	1.0000	1.0000	1.0000	1.0000	1.0000	0.9999	0.9999	0.9993
24	1.0000	1.0000	1.0000	1.0000	1.0000	1.0000	1.0000	1.0000	1.0000	1.0000	1.0000	1.0000	1.0000	1.0000	1.0000	1.0000	1.0000	0.9998
25	1.0000	1.0000	1.0000	1.0000	1.0000	1.0000	1.0000	1.0000	1.0000	1.0000	1.0000	1.0000	1.0000	1.0000	1.0000	1.0000	1.0000	1.0000

Cumulative Binomial Distribution Function

p	0.01	0.02	0.03	0.04	0.05	0.06	0.07	0.08	0.09	0.10	0.15	0.20	0.25	0.30	0.35	0.40	0.45	0.50	
x	**n =40**																		
0	0.6690	0.4457	0.2957	0.1954	0.1285	0.0842	0.0549	0.0356	0.0230	0.0148	0.0015	0.0001	0.0000	0.0000	0.0000	0.0000	0.0000	0.0000	0
1	0.9393	0.8095	0.6615	0.5210	0.3991	0.2990	0.2201	0.1594	0.1140	0.0805	0.0121	0.0015	0.0001	0.0000	0.0000	0.0000	0.0000	0.0000	1
2	0.9925	0.9543	0.8822	0.7855	0.6767	0.5665	0.4625	0.3694	0.2894	0.2228	0.0486	0.0079	0.0010	0.0001	0.0000	0.0000	0.0000	0.0000	2
3	0.9993	0.9918	0.9686	0.9252	0.8619	0.7827	0.6937	0.6007	0.5092	0.4231	0.1302	0.0285	0.0047	0.0006	0.0001	0.0000	0.0000	0.0000	3
4	1.0000	0.9988	0.9933	0.9790	0.9520	0.9104	0.8546	0.7868	0.7103	0.6290	0.2633	0.0759	0.0160	0.0026	0.0003	0.0000	0.0000	0.0000	4
5	1.0000	0.9999	0.9988	0.9951	0.9861	0.9691	0.9419	0.9033	0.8535	0.7937	0.4325	0.1613	0.0433	0.0086	0.0013	0.0001	0.0000	0.0000	5
6	1.0000	1.0000	0.9998	0.9990	0.9966	0.9909	0.9801	0.9624	0.9361	0.9005	0.6067	0.2859	0.0962	0.0238	0.0044	0.0006	0.0001	0.0000	6
7	1.0000	1.0000	1.0000	0.9998	0.9993	0.9977	0.9942	0.9873	0.9758	0.9581	0.7559	0.4371	0.1820	0.0553	0.0124	0.0021	0.0002	0.0001	7
8	1.0000	1.0000	1.0000	1.0000	0.9999	0.9995	0.9985	0.9963	0.9919	0.9845	0.8646	0.5931	0.2998	0.1110	0.0303	0.0061	0.0009	0.0001	8
9	1.0000	1.0000	1.0000	1.0000	1.0000	0.9999	0.9997	0.9990	0.9976	0.9949	0.9328	0.7318	0.4395	0.1959	0.0644	0.0156	0.0027	0.0003	9
10	1.0000	1.0000	1.0000	1.0000	1.0000	1.0000	0.9999	0.9998	0.9994	0.9985	0.9701	0.8392	0.5839	0.3087	0.1215	0.0352	0.0074	0.0011	10
11	1.0000	1.0000	1.0000	1.0000	1.0000	1.0000	1.0000	1.0000	0.9999	0.9996	0.9880	0.9125	0.7151	0.4406	0.2053	0.0709	0.0179	0.0032	11
12	1.0000	1.0000	1.0000	1.0000	1.0000	1.0000	1.0000	1.0000	1.0000	0.9999	0.9957	0.9568	0.8209	0.5772	0.3143	0.1285	0.0386	0.0083	12
13	1.0000	1.0000	1.0000	1.0000	1.0000	1.0000	1.0000	1.0000	1.0000	1.0000	0.9986	0.9806	0.8968	0.7032	0.4408	0.2112	0.0751	0.0192	13
14	1.0000	1.0000	1.0000	1.0000	1.0000	1.0000	1.0000	1.0000	1.0000	1.0000	0.9996	0.9921	0.9456	0.8074	0.5721	0.3174	0.1326	0.0403	14
15	1.0000	1.0000	1.0000	1.0000	1.0000	1.0000	1.0000	1.0000	1.0000	1.0000	0.9999	0.9971	0.9738	0.8849	0.6946	0.4402	0.2142	0.0769	15
16	1.0000	1.0000	1.0000	1.0000	1.0000	1.0000	1.0000	1.0000	1.0000	1.0000	1.0000	0.9990	0.9884	0.9367	0.7978	0.5681	0.3185	0.1341	16
17	1.0000	1.0000	1.0000	1.0000	1.0000	1.0000	1.0000	1.0000	1.0000	1.0000	1.0000	0.9997	0.9953	0.9680	0.8761	0.6885	0.4391	0.2148	17
18	1.0000	1.0000	1.0000	1.0000	1.0000	1.0000	1.0000	1.0000	1.0000	1.0000	1.0000	0.9999	0.9983	0.9852	0.9301	0.7911	0.5651	0.3179	18
19	1.0000	1.0000	1.0000	1.0000	1.0000	1.0000	1.0000	1.0000	1.0000	1.0000	1.0000	1.0000	0.9994	0.9937	0.9637	0.8702	0.6844	0.4373	19
20	1.0000	1.0000	1.0000	1.0000	1.0000	1.0000	1.0000	1.0000	1.0000	1.0000	1.0000	1.0000	0.9998	0.9976	0.9827	0.9256	0.7870	0.5627	20
21	1.0000	1.0000	1.0000	1.0000	1.0000	1.0000	1.0000	1.0000	1.0000	1.0000	1.0000	1.0000	1.0000	0.9991	0.9925	0.9608	0.8669	0.6821	21
22	1.0000	1.0000	1.0000	1.0000	1.0000	1.0000	1.0000	1.0000	1.0000	1.0000	1.0000	1.0000	1.0000	0.9997	0.9970	0.9811	0.9233	0.7852	22
23	1.0000	1.0000	1.0000	1.0000	1.0000	1.0000	1.0000	1.0000	1.0000	1.0000	1.0000	1.0000	1.0000	0.9999	0.9989	0.9917	0.9595	0.8659	23
24	1.0000	1.0000	1.0000	1.0000	1.0000	1.0000	1.0000	1.0000	1.0000	1.0000	1.0000	1.0000	1.0000	1.0000	0.9996	0.9966	0.9804	0.9231	24
25	1.0000	1.0000	1.0000	1.0000	1.0000	1.0000	1.0000	1.0000	1.0000	1.0000	1.0000	1.0000	1.0000	1.0000	0.9999	0.9988	0.9914	0.9597	25
26	1.0000	1.0000	1.0000	1.0000	1.0000	1.0000	1.0000	1.0000	1.0000	1.0000	1.0000	1.0000	1.0000	1.0000	1.0000	0.9996	0.9966	0.9808	26
27	1.0000	1.0000	1.0000	1.0000	1.0000	1.0000	1.0000	1.0000	1.0000	1.0000	1.0000	1.0000	1.0000	1.0000	1.0000	0.9999	0.9988	0.9917	27
28	1.0000	1.0000	1.0000	1.0000	1.0000	1.0000	1.0000	1.0000	1.0000	1.0000	1.0000	1.0000	1.0000	1.0000	1.0000	1.0000	0.9996	0.9968	28
29	1.0000	1.0000	1.0000	1.0000	1.0000	1.0000	1.0000	1.0000	1.0000	1.0000	1.0000	1.0000	1.0000	1.0000	1.0000	1.0000	0.9999	0.9989	29
30	1.0000	1.0000	1.0000	1.0000	1.0000	1.0000	1.0000	1.0000	1.0000	1.0000	1.0000	1.0000	1.0000	1.0000	1.0000	1.0000	1.0000	0.9997	30
31	1.0000	1.0000	1.0000	1.0000	1.0000	1.0000	1.0000	1.0000	1.0000	1.0000	1.0000	1.0000	1.0000	1.0000	1.0000	1.0000	1.0000	0.9999	31
32	1.0000	1.0000	1.0000	1.0000	1.0000	1.0000	1.0000	1.0000	1.0000	1.0000	1.0000	1.0000	1.0000	1.0000	1.0000	1.0000	1.0000	1.0000	32

Cumulative Binomial Distribution Function

x	0.01	0.02	0.03	0.04	0.05	0.06	0.07	0.08	0.09	0.10	0.15	0.20	0.25	0.30	0.35	0.40	0.45	0.50
	n=50																	
0	0.6050	0.3642	0.2181	0.1299	0.0769	0.0453	0.0266	0.0155	0.0090	0.0052	0.0003	0.0000	0.0000	0.0000	0.0000	0.0000	0.0000	0.0000
1	0.9106	0.7358	0.5553	0.4005	0.2794	0.1900	0.1265	0.0827	0.0532	0.0338	0.0029	0.0002	0.0000	0.0000	0.0000	0.0000	0.0000	0.0000
2	0.9862	0.9216	0.8108	0.6767	0.5405	0.4162	0.3108	0.2260	0.1605	0.1117	0.0142	0.0013	0.0001	0.0000	0.0000	0.0000	0.0000	0.0000
3	0.9984	0.9822	0.9372	0.8609	0.7604	0.6473	0.5327	0.4253	0.3303	0.2503	0.0460	0.0057	0.0005	0.0000	0.0000	0.0000	0.0000	0.0000
4	0.9999	0.9968	0.9832	0.9510	0.8964	0.8206	0.7290	0.6290	0.5277	0.4312	0.1121	0.0185	0.0021	0.0002	0.0000	0.0000	0.0000	0.0000
5	1.0000	0.9995	0.9963	0.9856	0.9622	0.9224	0.8650	0.7919	0.7072	0.6161	0.2194	0.0480	0.0070	0.0007	0.0001	0.0000	0.0000	0.0000
6	1.0000	0.9999	0.9993	0.9964	0.9882	0.9711	0.9417	0.8981	0.8404	0.7702	0.3613	0.1034	0.0194	0.0025	0.0002	0.0000	0.0000	0.0000
7	1.0000	1.0000	0.9999	0.9992	0.9968	0.9906	0.9780	0.9562	0.9232	0.8779	0.5188	0.1904	0.0453	0.0073	0.0008	0.0001	0.0000	0.0000
8	1.0000	1.0000	1.0000	0.9999	0.9992	0.9973	0.9927	0.9833	0.9672	0.9421	0.6681	0.3073	0.0916	0.0183	0.0025	0.0002	0.0000	0.0000
9	1.0000	1.0000	1.0000	1.0000	0.9998	0.9993	0.9978	0.9944	0.9875	0.9755	0.7911	0.4437	0.1637	0.0402	0.0067	0.0008	0.0001	0.0000
10	1.0000	1.0000	1.0000	1.0000	1.0000	0.9998	0.9994	0.9983	0.9957	0.9906	0.8801	0.5836	0.2622	0.0789	0.0160	0.0022	0.0002	0.0000
11	1.0000	1.0000	1.0000	1.0000	1.0000	1.0000	0.9999	0.9995	0.9987	0.9968	0.9372	0.7107	0.3816	0.1390	0.0342	0.0057	0.0006	0.0000
12	1.0000	1.0000	1.0000	1.0000	1.0000	1.0000	1.0000	0.9999	0.9996	0.9990	0.9699	0.8139	0.5110	0.2229	0.0661	0.0133	0.0018	0.0002
13	1.0000	1.0000	1.0000	1.0000	1.0000	1.0000	1.0000	1.0000	0.9999	0.9997	0.9868	0.8894	0.6370	0.3279	0.1163	0.0280	0.0045	0.0005
14	1.0000	1.0000	1.0000	1.0000	1.0000	1.0000	1.0000	1.0000	1.0000	0.9999	0.9947	0.9393	0.7481	0.4468	0.1878	0.0540	0.0104	0.0013
15	1.0000	1.0000	1.0000	1.0000	1.0000	1.0000	1.0000	1.0000	1.0000	1.0000	0.9981	0.9692	0.8369	0.5692	0.2801	0.0955	0.0220	0.0033
16	1.0000	1.0000	1.0000	1.0000	1.0000	1.0000	1.0000	1.0000	1.0000	1.0000	0.9993	0.9856	0.9017	0.6839	0.3889	0.1561	0.0427	0.0077
17	1.0000	1.0000	1.0000	1.0000	1.0000	1.0000	1.0000	1.0000	1.0000	1.0000	0.9998	0.9937	0.9449	0.7822	0.5060	0.2369	0.0765	0.0164
18	1.0000	1.0000	1.0000	1.0000	1.0000	1.0000	1.0000	1.0000	1.0000	1.0000	0.9999	0.9975	0.9713	0.8594	0.6216	0.3356	0.1273	0.0325
19	1.0000	1.0000	1.0000	1.0000	1.0000	1.0000	1.0000	1.0000	1.0000	1.0000	1.0000	0.9991	0.9861	0.9152	0.7264	0.4465	0.1974	0.0595
20	1.0000	1.0000	1.0000	1.0000	1.0000	1.0000	1.0000	1.0000	1.0000	1.0000	1.0000	0.9997	0.9937	0.9522	0.8139	0.5610	0.2862	0.1013
21	1.0000	1.0000	1.0000	1.0000	1.0000	1.0000	1.0000	1.0000	1.0000	1.0000	1.0000	0.9999	0.9974	0.9749	0.8813	0.6701	0.3900	0.1611
22	1.0000	1.0000	1.0000	1.0000	1.0000	1.0000	1.0000	1.0000	1.0000	1.0000	1.0000	1.0000	0.9990	0.9877	0.9290	0.7660	0.5019	0.2399
23	1.0000	1.0000	1.0000	1.0000	1.0000	1.0000	1.0000	1.0000	1.0000	1.0000	1.0000	1.0000	0.9996	0.9944	0.9604	0.8438	0.6134	0.3359
24	1.0000	1.0000	1.0000	1.0000	1.0000	1.0000	1.0000	1.0000	1.0000	1.0000	1.0000	1.0000	0.9999	0.9976	0.9793	0.9022	0.7160	0.4439
25	1.0000	1.0000	1.0000	1.0000	1.0000	1.0000	1.0000	1.0000	1.0000	1.0000	1.0000	1.0000	1.0000	0.9991	0.9900	0.9427	0.8034	0.5561
26	1.0000	1.0000	1.0000	1.0000	1.0000	1.0000	1.0000	1.0000	1.0000	1.0000	1.0000	1.0000	1.0000	0.9997	0.9955	0.9686	0.8721	0.6641
27	1.0000	1.0000	1.0000	1.0000	1.0000	1.0000	1.0000	1.0000	1.0000	1.0000	1.0000	1.0000	1.0000	0.9999	0.9981	0.9840	0.9220	0.7601
28	1.0000	1.0000	1.0000	1.0000	1.0000	1.0000	1.0000	1.0000	1.0000	1.0000	1.0000	1.0000	1.0000	1.0000	0.9993	0.9924	0.9556	0.8389
29	1.0000	1.0000	1.0000	1.0000	1.0000	1.0000	1.0000	1.0000	1.0000	1.0000	1.0000	1.0000	1.0000	1.0000	0.9997	0.9966	0.9765	0.8987
30	1.0000	1.0000	1.0000	1.0000	1.0000	1.0000	1.0000	1.0000	1.0000	1.0000	1.0000	1.0000	1.0000	1.0000	0.9999	0.9986	0.9884	0.9405
31	1.0000	1.0000	1.0000	1.0000	1.0000	1.0000	1.0000	1.0000	1.0000	1.0000	1.0000	1.0000	1.0000	1.0000	1.0000	0.9995	0.9947	0.9675
32	1.0000	1.0000	1.0000	1.0000	1.0000	1.0000	1.0000	1.0000	1.0000	1.0000	1.0000	1.0000	1.0000	1.0000	1.0000	0.9998	0.9978	0.9836
33	1.0000	1.0000	1.0000	1.0000	1.0000	1.0000	1.0000	1.0000	1.0000	1.0000	1.0000	1.0000	1.0000	1.0000	1.0000	0.9999	0.9991	0.9923
34	1.0000	1.0000	1.0000	1.0000	1.0000	1.0000	1.0000	1.0000	1.0000	1.0000	1.0000	1.0000	1.0000	1.0000	1.0000	1.0000	0.9997	0.9967
35	1.0000	1.0000	1.0000	1.0000	1.0000	1.0000	1.0000	1.0000	1.0000	1.0000	1.0000	1.0000	1.0000	1.0000	1.0000	1.0000	0.9999	0.9987
36	1.0000	1.0000	1.0000	1.0000	1.0000	1.0000	1.0000	1.0000	1.0000	1.0000	1.0000	1.0000	1.0000	1.0000	1.0000	1.0000	1.0000	0.9995
37	1.0000	1.0000	1.0000	1.0000	1.0000	1.0000	1.0000	1.0000	1.0000	1.0000	1.0000	1.0000	1.0000	1.0000	1.0000	1.0000	1.0000	0.9998
38	1.0000	1.0000	1.0000	1.0000	1.0000	1.0000	1.0000	1.0000	1.0000	1.0000	1.0000	1.0000	1.0000	1.0000	1.0000	1.0000	1.0000	1.0000

TABLE 3

Cumulative Poisson Distribution Function

These tables give the probability of a random variable, which has a Poisson distribution with mean λ, having integer values less than or equal to x.

λ	0.10	0.20	0.30	0.40	0.50	0.60	0.70	0.80	0.90	1.00	1.20	1.40	1.60	1.80	
x															
0	0.9048	0.8187	0.7408	0.6703	0.6065	0.5488	0.4966	0.4493	0.4066	0.3679	0.3012	0.2466	0.2019	0.1653	0
1	0.9953	0.9825	0.9631	0.9384	0.9098	0.8781	0.8442	0.8088	0.7725	0.7358	0.6626	0.5918	0.5249	0.4628	1
2	0.9998	0.9989	0.9964	0.9921	0.9856	0.9769	0.9659	0.9526	0.9371	0.9197	0.8795	0.8335	0.7834	0.7306	2
3	1.0000	0.9999	0.9997	0.9992	0.9982	0.9966	0.9942	0.9909	0.9865	0.9810	0.9662	0.9463	0.9212	0.8913	3
4	1.0000	1.0000	1.0000	0.9999	0.9998	0.9996	0.9992	0.9986	0.9977	0.9963	0.9923	0.9857	0.9763	0.9636	4
5	1.0000	1.0000	1.0000	1.0000	1.0000	1.0000	0.9999	0.9998	0.9997	0.9994	0.9985	0.9968	0.9940	0.9896	5
6	1.0000	1.0000	1.0000	1.0000	1.0000	1.0000	1.0000	1.0000	1.0000	0.9999	0.9997	0.9994	0.9987	0.9974	6
7	1.0000	1.0000	1.0000	1.0000	1.0000	1.0000	1.0000	1.0000	1.0000	1.0000	1.0000	0.9999	0.9997	0.9994	7
8	1.0000	1.0000	1.0000	1.0000	1.0000	1.0000	1.0000	1.0000	1.0000	1.0000	1.0000	1.0000	1.0000	0.9999	8
9	1.0000	1.0000	1.0000	1.0000	1.0000	1.0000	1.0000	1.0000	1.0000	1.0000	1.0000	1.0000	1.0000	1.0000	9

λ	2.00	2.20	2.40	2.60	2.80	3.00	3.20	3.40	3.60	3.80	4.00	4.50	5.00	5.50	
x															
0	0.1353	0.1108	0.0907	0.0743	0.0608	0.0498	0.0408	0.0334	0.0273	0.0224	0.0183	0.0111	0.0067	0.0041	0
1	0.4060	0.3546	0.3084	0.2674	0.2311	0.1991	0.1712	0.1468	0.1257	0.1074	0.0916	0.0611	0.0404	0.0266	1
2	0.6767	0.6227	0.5697	0.5184	0.4695	0.4232	0.3799	0.3397	0.3027	0.2689	0.2381	0.1736	0.1247	0.0884	2
3	0.8571	0.8194	0.7787	0.7360	0.6919	0.6472	0.6025	0.5584	0.5152	0.4735	0.4335	0.3423	0.2650	0.2017	3
4	0.9473	0.9275	0.9041	0.8774	0.8477	0.8153	0.7806	0.7442	0.7064	0.6678	0.6288	0.5321	0.4405	0.3575	4
5	0.9834	0.9751	0.9643	0.9510	0.9349	0.9161	0.8946	0.8705	0.8441	0.8156	0.7851	0.7029	0.6160	0.5289	5
6	0.9955	0.9925	0.9884	0.9828	0.9756	0.9665	0.9554	0.9421	0.9267	0.9091	0.8893	0.8311	0.7622	0.6860	6
7	0.9989	0.9980	0.9967	0.9947	0.9919	0.9881	0.9832	0.9769	0.9692	0.9599	0.9489	0.9134	0.8666	0.8095	7
8	0.9998	0.9995	0.9991	0.9985	0.9976	0.9962	0.9943	0.9917	0.9883	0.9840	0.9786	0.9597	0.9319	0.8944	8
9	1.0000	0.9999	0.9998	0.9996	0.9993	0.9989	0.9982	0.9973	0.9960	0.9942	0.9919	0.9829	0.9682	0.9462	9
10	1.0000	1.0000	1.0000	0.9999	0.9998	0.9997	0.9995	0.9992	0.9987	0.9981	0.9972	0.9933	0.9863	0.9747	10
11	1.0000	1.0000	1.0000	1.0000	1.0000	0.9999	0.9999	0.9998	0.9996	0.9994	0.9991	0.9976	0.9945	0.9890	11
12	1.0000	1.0000	1.0000	1.0000	1.0000	1.0000	1.0000	0.9999	0.9999	0.9998	0.9997	0.9992	0.9980	0.9955	12
13	1.0000	1.0000	1.0000	1.0000	1.0000	1.0000	1.0000	1.0000	1.0000	1.0000	0.9999	0.9997	0.9993	0.9983	13
14	1.0000	1.0000	1.0000	1.0000	1.0000	1.0000	1.0000	1.0000	1.0000	1.0000	1.0000	0.9999	0.9998	0.9994	14
15	1.0000	1.0000	1.0000	1.0000	1.0000	1.0000	1.0000	1.0000	1.0000	1.0000	1.0000	1.0000	0.9999	0.9998	15
16	1.0000	1.0000	1.0000	1.0000	1.0000	1.0000	1.0000	1.0000	1.0000	1.0000	1.0000	1.0000	1.0000	0.9999	16
17	1.0000	1.0000	1.0000	1.0000	1.0000	1.0000	1.0000	1.0000	1.0000	1.0000	1.0000	1.0000	1.0000	1.0000	17
18	1.0000	1.0000	1.0000	1.0000	1.0000	1.0000	1.0000	1.0000	1.0000	1.0000	1.0000	1.0000	1.0000	1.0000	18
19	1.0000	1.0000	1.0000	1.0000	1.0000	1.0000	1.0000	1.0000	1.0000	1.0000	1.0000	1.0000	1.0000	1.0000	19
20	1.0000	1.0000	1.0000	1.0000	1.0000	1.0000	1.0000	1.0000	1.0000	1.0000	1.0000	1.0000	1.0000	1.0000	20

Cumulative Poisson Distribution Function

These tables give the probability of a random variable, which has a Poisson distribution with mean λ, having integer values less than or equal to x.

λ / x	6.0	6.5	7.0	7.5	8.0	8.5	9.0	9.5	10.0	11.0	12.0	13.0	14.0	15.0	
0	0.0025	0.0015	0.0009	0.0006	0.0003	0.0002	0.0001	0.0001	0.0000	0.0000	0.0000	0.0000	0.0000	0.0000	0
1	0.0174	0.0113	0.0073	0.0047	0.0030	0.0019	0.0012	0.0008	0.0005	0.0002	0.0001	0.0000	0.0000	0.0000	1
2	0.0620	0.0430	0.0296	0.0203	0.0138	0.0093	0.0062	0.0042	0.0028	0.0012	0.0005	0.0002	0.0001	0.0000	2
3	0.1512	0.1118	0.0818	0.0591	0.0424	0.0301	0.0212	0.0149	0.0103	0.0049	0.0023	0.0011	0.0005	0.0002	3
4	0.2851	0.2237	0.1730	0.1321	0.0996	0.0744	0.0550	0.0403	0.0293	0.0151	0.0076	0.0037	0.0018	0.0009	4
5	0.4457	0.3690	0.3007	0.2414	0.1912	0.1496	0.1157	0.0885	0.0671	0.0375	0.0203	0.0107	0.0055	0.0028	5
6	0.6063	0.5265	0.4497	0.3782	0.3134	0.2562	0.2068	0.1649	0.1301	0.0786	0.0458	0.0259	0.0142	0.0076	6
7	0.7440	0.6728	0.5987	0.5246	0.4530	0.3856	0.3239	0.2687	0.2202	0.1432	0.0895	0.0540	0.0316	0.0180	7
8	0.8472	0.7916	0.7291	0.6620	0.5925	0.5231	0.4557	0.3918	0.3328	0.2320	0.1550	0.0998	0.0621	0.0374	8
9	0.9161	0.8774	0.8305	0.7764	0.7166	0.6530	0.5874	0.5218	0.4579	0.3405	0.2424	0.1658	0.1094	0.0699	9
10	0.9574	0.9332	0.9015	0.8622	0.8159	0.7634	0.7060	0.6453	0.5830	0.4599	0.3472	0.2517	0.1757	0.1185	10
11	0.9799	0.9661	0.9467	0.9208	0.8881	0.8487	0.8030	0.7520	0.6968	0.5793	0.4616	0.3532	0.2600	0.1848	11
12	0.9912	0.9840	0.9730	0.9573	0.9362	0.9091	0.8758	0.8364	0.7916	0.6887	0.5760	0.4631	0.3585	0.2676	12
13	0.9964	0.9929	0.9872	0.9784	0.9658	0.9486	0.9261	0.8981	0.8645	0.7813	0.6815	0.5730	0.4644	0.3632	13
14	0.9986	0.9970	0.9943	0.9897	0.9827	0.9726	0.9585	0.9400	0.9165	0.8540	0.7720	0.6751	0.5704	0.4657	14
15	0.9995	0.9988	0.9976	0.9954	0.9918	0.9862	0.9780	0.9665	0.9513	0.9074	0.8444	0.7636	0.6694	0.5681	15
16	0.9998	0.9996	0.9990	0.9980	0.9963	0.9934	0.9889	0.9823	0.9730	0.9441	0.8987	0.8355	0.7559	0.6641	16
17	0.9999	0.9998	0.9996	0.9992	0.9984	0.9970	0.9947	0.9911	0.9857	0.9678	0.9370	0.8905	0.8272	0.7489	17
18	1.0000	0.9999	0.9999	0.9997	0.9993	0.9987	0.9976	0.9957	0.9928	0.9823	0.9626	0.9302	0.8826	0.8195	18
19	1.0000	1.0000	1.0000	0.9999	0.9997	0.9995	0.9989	0.9980	0.9965	0.9907	0.9787	0.9573	0.9235	0.8752	19
20	1.0000	1.0000	1.0000	1.0000	0.9999	0.9998	0.9996	0.9991	0.9984	0.9953	0.9884	0.9750	0.9521	0.9170	20
21	1.0000	1.0000	1.0000	1.0000	1.0000	0.9999	0.9998	0.9996	0.9993	0.9977	0.9939	0.9859	0.9712	0.9469	21
22	1.0000	1.0000	1.0000	1.0000	1.0000	1.0000	0.9999	0.9999	0.9997	0.9990	0.9970	0.9924	0.9833	0.9673	22
23	1.0000	1.0000	1.0000	1.0000	1.0000	1.0000	1.0000	0.9999	0.9999	0.9995	0.9985	0.9960	0.9907	0.9805	23
24	1.0000	1.0000	1.0000	1.0000	1.0000	1.0000	1.0000	1.0000	1.0000	0.9998	0.9993	0.9980	0.9950	0.9888	24
25	1.0000	1.0000	1.0000	1.0000	1.0000	1.0000	1.0000	1.0000	1.0000	0.9999	0.9997	0.9990	0.9974	0.9938	25
26	1.0000	1.0000	1.0000	1.0000	1.0000	1.0000	1.0000	1.0000	1.0000	1.0000	0.9999	0.9995	0.9987	0.9967	26
27	1.0000	1.0000	1.0000	1.0000	1.0000	1.0000	1.0000	1.0000	1.0000	1.0000	0.9999	0.9998	0.9994	0.9983	27
28	1.0000	1.0000	1.0000	1.0000	1.0000	1.0000	1.0000	1.0000	1.0000	1.0000	1.0000	0.9999	0.9997	0.9991	28
29	1.0000	1.0000	1.0000	1.0000	1.0000	1.0000	1.0000	1.0000	1.0000	1.0000	1.0000	1.0000	0.9999	0.9996	29
30	1.0000	1.0000	1.0000	1.0000	1.0000	1.0000	1.0000	1.0000	1.0000	1.0000	1.0000	1.0000	0.9999	0.9998	30
31	1.0000	1.0000	1.0000	1.0000	1.0000	1.0000	1.0000	1.0000	1.0000	1.0000	1.0000	1.0000	1.0000	0.9999	31
32	1.0000	1.0000	1.0000	1.0000	1.0000	1.0000	1.0000	1.0000	1.0000	1.0000	1.0000	1.0000	1.0000	1.0000	32

TABLE 4   NORMAL DISTRIBUTION FUNCTION

The table gives the probability p that a normally distributed random
variable Z, with mean=0 and variance=1, is less than or equal to z.

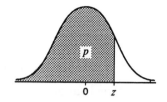

z	0.00	0.01	0.02	0.03	0.04	0.05	0.06	0.07	0.08	0.09	
0	0.50000	0.50399	0.50798	0.51197	0.51595	0.51994	0.52392	0.52790	0.53188	0.53586	0
0.1	0.53983	0.54380	0.54776	0.55172	0.55567	0.55962	0.56356	0.56749	0.57142	0.57535	0.1
0.2	0.57926	0.58317	0.58706	0.59095	0.59483	0.59871	0.60257	0.60642	0.61026	0.61409	0.2
0.3	0.61791	0.62172	0.62552	0.62930	0.63307	0.63683	0.64058	0.64431	0.64803	0.65173	0.3
0.4	0.65542	0.65910	0.66276	0.66640	0.67003	0.67364	0.67724	0.68082	0.68439	0.68793	0.4
0.5	0.69146	0.69497	0.69847	0.70194	0.70540	0.70884	0.71226	0.71566	0.71904	0.72240	0.5
0.6	0.72575	0.72907	0.73237	0.73565	0.73891	0.74215	0.74537	0.74857	0.75175	0.75490	0.6
0.7	0.75804	0.76115	0.76424	0.76730	0.77035	0.77337	0.77637	0.77935	0.78230	0.78524	0.7
0.8	0.78814	0.79103	0.79389	0.79673	0.79955	0.80234	0.80511	0.80785	0.81057	0.81327	0.8
0.9	0.81594	0.81859	0.82121	0.82381	0.82639	0.82894	0.83147	0.83398	0.83646	0.83891	0.9
1.0	0.84134	0.84375	0.84614	0.84849	0.85083	0.85314	0.85543	0.85769	0.85993	0.86214	1.0
1.1	0.86433	0.86650	0.86864	0.87076	0.87286	0.87493	0.87698	0.87900	0.88100	0.88298	1.1
1.2	0.88493	0.88686	0.88877	0.89065	0.89251	0.89435	0.89617	0.89796	0.89973	0.90147	1.2
1.3	0.90320	0.90490	0.90658	0.90824	0.90988	0.91149	0.91309	0.91466	0.91621	0.91774	1.3
1.4	0.91924	0.92073	0.92220	0.92364	0.92507	0.92647	0.92785	0.92922	0.93056	0.93189	1.4
1.5	0.93319	0.93448	0.93574	0.93699	0.93822	0.93943	0.94062	0.94179	0.94295	0.94408	1.5
1.6	0.94520	0.94630	0.94738	0.94845	0.94950	0.95053	0.95154	0.95254	0.95352	0.95449	1.6
1.7	0.95543	0.95637	0.95728	0.95818	0.95907	0.95994	0.96080	0.96164	0.96246	0.96327	1.7
1.8	0.96407	0.96485	0.96562	0.96638	0.96712	0.96784	0.96856	0.96926	0.96995	0.97062	1.8
1.9	0.97128	0.97193	0.97257	0.97320	0.97381	0.97441	0.97500	0.97558	0.97615	0.97670	1.9
2.0	0.97725	0.97778	0.97831	0.97882	0.97932	0.97982	0.98030	0.98077	0.98124	0.98169	2.0
2.1	0.98214	0.98257	0.98300	0.98341	0.98382	0.98422	0.98461	0.98500	0.98537	0.98574	2.1
2.2	0.98610	0.98645	0.98679	0.98713	0.98745	0.98778	0.98809	0.98840	0.98870	0.98899	2.2
2.3	0.98928	0.98956	0.98983	0.99010	0.99036	0.99061	0.99086	0.99111	0.99134	0.99158	2.3
2.4	0.99180	0.99202	0.99224	0.99245	0.99266	0.99286	0.99305	0.99324	0.99343	0.99361	2.4
2.5	0.99379	0.99396	0.99413	0.99430	0.99446	0.99461	0.99477	0.99492	0.99506	0.99520	2.5
2.6	0.99534	0.99547	0.99560	0.99573	0.99585	0.99598	0.99609	0.99621	0.99632	0.99643	2.6
2.7	0.99653	0.99664	0.99674	0.99683	0.99693	0.99702	0.99711	0.99720	0.99728	0.99736	2.7
2.8	0.99744	0.99752	0.99760	0.99767	0.99774	0.99781	0.99788	0.99795	0.99801	0.99807	2.8
2.9	0.99813	0.99819	0.99825	0.99831	0.99836	0.99841	0.99846	0.99851	0.99856	0.99861	2.9
3.0	0.99865	0.99869	0.99874	0.99878	0.99882	0.99886	0.99889	0.99893	0.99896	0.99900	3.0
3.1	0.99903	0.99906	0.99910	0.99913	0.99916	0.99918	0.99921	0.99924	0.99926	0.99929	3.1
3.2	0.99931	0.99934	0.99936	0.99938	0.99940	0.99942	0.99944	0.99946	0.99948	0.99950	3.2
3.3	0.99952	0.99953	0.99955	0.99957	0.99958	0.99960	0.99961	0.99962	0.99964	0.99965	3.3
3.4	0.99966	0.99968	0.99969	0.99970	0.99971	0.99972	0.99973	0.99974	0.99975	0.99976	3.4
3.5	0.99977	0.99978	0.99978	0.99979	0.99980	0.99981	0.99981	0.99982	0.99983	0.99983	3.5
3.6	0.99984	0.99985	0.99985	0.99986	0.99986	0.99987	0.99987	0.99988	0.99988	0.99989	3.6
3.7	0.99989	0.99990	0.99990	0.99990	0.99991	0.99991	0.99992	0.99992	0.99992	0.99992	3.7
3.8	0.99993	0.99993	0.99993	0.99994	0.99994	0.99994	0.99994	0.99995	0.99995	0.99995	3.8
3.9	0.99995	0.99995	0.99996	0.99996	0.99996	0.99996	0.99996	0.99996	0.99997	0.99997	3.9

TABLE 5 PERCENTAGE POINTS OF THE NORMAL DISTRIBUTION

The table gives the values of z satisfying $P(Z \le z) = p$, where Z is the normally distributed random variable with mean $= 0$ and variance $= 1$.

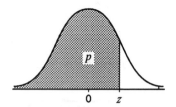

p	0.00	0.01	0.02	0.03	0.04	0.05	0.06	0.07	0.08	0.09	
0.5	0.0000	0.0251	0.0502	0.0753	0.1004	0.1257	0.1510	0.1764	0.2019	0.2275	**0.5**
0.6	0.2533	0.2793	0.3055	0.3319	0.3585	0.3853	0.4125	0.4399	0.4677	0.4958	**0.6**
0.7	0.5244	0.5534	0.5828	0.6128	0.6433	0.6745	0.7063	0.7388	0.7722	0.8064	**0.7**
0.8	0.8416	0.8779	0.9154	0.9542	0.9945	1.0364	1.0803	1.1264	1.1750	1.2265	**0.8**
0.9	1.2816	1.3408	1.4051	1.4758	1.5548	1.6449	1.7507	1.8808	2.0537	2.3263	**0.9**

p	0.000	0.001	0.002	0.003	0.004	0.005	0.006	0.007	0.008	0.009	
0.95	1.6449	1.6546	1.6646	1.6747	1.6849	1.6954	1.7060	1.7169	1.7279	1.7392	**0.9**
0.96	1.7507	1.7624	1.7744	1.7866	1.7991	1.8119	1.8250	1.8384	1.8522	1.8663	**0.9**
0.97	1.8808	1.8957	1.9110	1.9268	1.9431	1.9600	1.9774	1.9954	2.0141	2.0335	**0.9**
0.98	2.0537	2.0749	2.0969	2.1201	2.1444	2.1701	2.1973	2.2262	2.2571	2.2904	**0.9**
0.99	2.3263	2.3656	2.4089	2.4573	2.5121	2.5758	2.6521	2.7478	2.8782	3.0902	**0.9**

TABLE 6 χ^2 DISTRIBUTION FUNCTION

This table gives the values of x satisfying $P(X \leq x) = p$ where
X is χ^2 random variable with υ degrees of freedom.

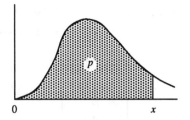

p	0.005	0.010	0.025	0.050	0.100	0.900	0.950	0.975	0.990	0.995	p
υ											υ
1	0.00004	0.0002	0.001	0.004	0.016	2.706	3.841	5.024	6.635	7.879	1
2	0.010	0.020	0.051	0.103	0.211	4.605	5.991	7.378	9.210	10.597	2
3	0.072	0.115	0.216	0.352	0.584	6.251	7.815	9.348	11.345	12.838	3
4	0.207	0.297	0.484	0.711	1.064	7.779	9.488	11.143	13.277	14.860	4
5	0.412	0.554	0.831	1.145	1.610	9.236	11.070	12.833	15.086	16.750	5
6	0.676	0.872	1.237	1.635	2.204	10.645	12.592	14.449	16.812	18.548	6
7	0.989	1.239	1.690	2.167	2.833	12.017	14.067	16.013	18.475	20.278	7
8	1.344	1.646	2.180	2.733	3.490	13.362	15.507	17.535	20.090	21.955	8
9	1.735	2.088	2.700	3.325	4.168	14.684	16.919	19.023	21.666	23.589	9
10	2.156	2.558	3.247	3.940	4.865	15.987	18.307	20.483	23.209	25.188	10
11	2.603	3.053	3.816	4.575	5.578	17.275	19.675	21.920	24.725	26.757	11
12	3.074	3.571	4.404	5.226	6.304	18.549	21.026	23.337	26.217	28.300	12
13	3.565	4.107	5.009	5.892	7.042	19.812	22.362	24.736	27.688	29.819	13
14	4.075	4.660	5.629	6.571	7.790	21.064	23.685	26.119	29.141	31.319	14
15	4.601	5.229	6.262	7.261	8.547	22.307	24.996	27.488	30.578	32.801	15
20	7.434	8.260	9.591	10.851	12.443	28.412	31.410	34.170	37.566	39.997	20
25	10.520	11.524	13.120	14.611	16.473	34.382	37.652	40.646	44.314	46.928	25
30	13.787	14.953	16.791	18.493	20.599	40.256	43.773	46.979	50.892	53.672	30
35	17.192	18.509	20.569	22.465	24.797	46.059	49.802	53.203	57.342	60.275	35
40	20.707	22.164	24.433	26.509	29.051	51.805	55.758	59.342	63.691	66.766	40
45	24.311	25.901	28.366	30.612	33.350	57.505	61.656	65.410	69.957	73.166	45
50	27.991	29.707	32.357	34.764	37.689	63.167	67.505	71.420	76.154	79.490	50

TABLE 7   CRITICAL VALUES OF THE PRODUCT MOMENT CORRELATION COEFFICIENT

| One tail | 10% | 5% | 2.5% | 1% | 0.5% | |
Two tail	20%	10%	5%	2%	1%	
n						
4	0.8000	0.9000	0.9500	0.9800	0.9900	4
5	0.6870	0.8054	0.8783	0.9343	0.9587	5
6	0.6084	0.7293	0.8114	0.8822	0.9172	6
7	0.5509	0.6694	0.7545	0.8329	0.8745	7
8	0.5067	0.6215	0.7067	0.7887	0.8343	8
9	0.4716	0.5822	0.6664	0.7498	0.7977	9
10	0.4428	0.5494	0.6319	0.7155	0.7646	10
11	0.4187	0.5214	0.6021	0.6851	0.7348	11
12	0.3981	0.4973	0.5760	0.6581	0.7079	12
13	0.3802	0.4762	0.5529	0.6339	0.6835	13
14	0.3646	0.4575	0.5324	0.6120	0.6614	14
15	0.3507	0.4409	0.5140	0.5923	0.6411	15
16	0.3383	0.4259	0.4973	0.5742	0.6226	16
17	0.3271	0.4124	0.4821	0.5577	0.6055	17
18	0.3170	0.4000	0.4683	0.5425	0.5897	18
19	0.3077	0.3887	0.4555	0.5285	0.5751	19
20	0.2992	0.3783	0.4438	0.5155	0.5614	20

TABLE 8　　CRITICAL VALUES OF SPEARMAN'S RANK CORRELATION COEFFICIENT

This table gives the critical values for different significance levels, of Spearman's rank correlation coefficient, r_s, for varying sample sizes, n.

One tail	10%	5%	2.5%	1%	0.5%	
Two tail	20%	10%	5%	2%	1%	
n						
4	1.0000	1.0000	1.0000	1.0000	1.0000	4
5	0.7000	0.9000	0.9000	1.0000	1.0000	5
6	0.6571	0.7714	0.8286	0.9429	0.9429	6
7	0.5714	0.6786	0.7857	0.8571	0.8929	7
8	0.5476	0.6429	0.7381	0.8095	0.8571	8
9	0.4833	0.6000	0.6833	0.7667	0.8167	9
10	0.4424	0.5636	0.6485	0.7333	0.7818	10
11	0.4182	0.5273	0.6091	0.7000	0.7545	11
12	0.3986	0.5035	0.5874	0.6713	0.7273	12
13	0.3791	0.4780	0.5604	0.6484	0.6978	13
14	0.3670	0.4593	0.5385	0.6220	0.6747	14
15	0.3500	0.4429	0.5179	0.6000	0.6536	15
16	0.3382	0.4265	0.5029	0.5824	0.6324	16
17	0.3271	0.4124	0.4821	0.5577	0.6055	17
18	0.3170	0.4000	0.4683	0.5425	0.5897	18
19	0.3077	0.3887	0.4555	0.5285	0.5751	19
20	0.2992	0.3783	0.4438	0.5155	0.5614	20

TABLE 9   PERCENTAGE POINTS OF THE STUDENT'S t-DISTRIBUTION

The table gives the values of x satisfying

$$P(X \leq x) = p$$

where X is a random variable having the Student's t-distribution with υ degrees of freedom.

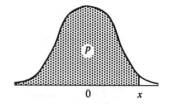

	0.900	0.950	0.975	0.990	0.995	
1	3.078	6.314	12.706	31.821	63.657	1
2	1.886	2.920	4.303	6.965	9.925	2
3	1.638	2.353	3.182	4.541	5.841	3
4	1.533	2.132	2.776	3.747	4.604	4
5	1.476	2.015	2.571	3.365	4.032	5
6	1.440	1.943	2.447	3.143	3.707	6
7	1.415	1.895	2.365	2.998	3.499	7
8	1.397	1.860	2.306	2.896	3.355	8
9	1.383	1.833	2.262	2.821	3.250	9
10	1.372	1.812	2.228	2.764	3.169	10
11	1.363	1.796	2.201	2.718	3.106	11
12	1.356	1.782	2.179	2.681	3.055	12
13	1.350	1.771	2.160	2.650	3.012	13
14	1.345	1.761	2.145	2.624	2.977	14
15	1.341	1.753	2.131	2.602	2.947	15
16	1.337	1.746	2.120	2.583	2.921	16
17	1.333	1.740	2.110	2.567	2.898	17
18	1.330	1.734	2.101	2.552	2.878	18
19	1.328	1.729	2.093	2.539	2.861	19
20	1.325	1.725	2.086	2.528	2.845	20
30	1.310	1.697	2.042	2.457	2.750	30
40	1.303	1.684	2.021	2.423	2.704	40
50	1.299	1.676	2.009	2.403	2.678	50
60	1.296	1.671	2.000	2.390	2.660	60
70	1.294	1.667	1.994	2.381	2.648	70
80	1.292	1.664	1.990	2.374	2.639	80
90	1.291	1.662	1.987	2.368	2.632	90
100	1.290	1.660	1.984	2.364	2.626	100

TABLE 10   PERCENTAGE POINTS OF THE F-DISTRIBUTION

The tables give the values of x satisfying

$$P(X \leq x) = p$$

where X is a random variable having the F-distribution with υ_1 degrees of freedom in the numerator and υ_2 degrees of freedom in the denominator.

F Distribution (p=0.995)

	1	2	3	4	5	6	7	8	9	10	11	12	15	20	25	30	40	50	100	∞	
1	16211	20000	21615	22500	23056	23437	23715	23925	24091	24224	24334	24426	24630	24836	24960	25044	25148	25211	25337	25464	1
2	198.5	199.0	199.2	199.2	199.3	199.3	199.4	199.4	199.4	199.4	199.4	199.4	199.4	199.4	199.5	199.5	199.5	199.5	199.5	199.5	2
3	55.55	49.80	47.47	46.19	45.39	44.84	44.43	44.13	43.88	43.69	43.52	43.39	43.08	42.78	42.59	42.47	42.31	42.21	42.02	41.83	3
4	31.33	26.28	24.26	23.15	22.46	21.97	21.62	21.35	21.14	20.97	20.82	20.70	20.44	20.17	20.00	19.89	19.75	19.67	19.50	19.32	4
5	22.78	18.31	16.53	15.56	14.94	14.51	14.20	13.96	13.77	13.62	13.49	13.38	13.15	12.90	12.78	12.66	12.53	12.45	12.30	12.14	5
6	18.635	14.544	12.917	12.028	11.464	11.073	10.786	10.566	10.391	10.250	10.133	10.034	9.814	9.589	9.451	9.358	9.241	9.170	9.026	8.879	6
7	16.236	12.404	10.882	10.050	9.522	9.155	8.885	8.678	8.514	8.380	8.270	8.176	7.968	7.754	7.623	7.534	7.422	7.354	7.217	7.076	7
8	14.688	11.042	9.596	8.805	8.302	7.952	7.694	7.496	7.339	7.211	7.104	7.015	6.814	6.608	6.482	6.396	6.288	6.222	6.088	5.951	8
9	13.614	10.107	8.717	7.956	7.471	7.134	6.885	6.693	6.541	6.417	6.314	6.227	6.032	5.832	5.708	5.625	5.519	5.454	5.322	5.188	9
10	12.826	9.427	8.081	7.343	6.872	6.545	6.302	6.116	5.968	5.847	5.746	5.661	5.471	5.274	5.153	5.071	4.966	4.902	4.772	4.639	10
11	12.226	8.912	7.600	6.881	6.422	6.102	5.865	5.682	5.537	5.418	5.320	5.236	5.049	4.855	4.736	4.654	4.551	4.488	4.359	4.226	11
12	11.754	8.510	7.226	6.521	6.071	5.757	5.525	5.345	5.202	5.085	4.988	4.906	4.721	4.530	4.412	4.331	4.228	4.165	4.037	3.904	12
15	10.798	7.701	6.476	5.803	5.372	5.071	4.847	4.674	4.536	4.424	4.329	4.250	4.070	3.883	3.766	3.687	3.585	3.523	3.394	3.260	15
20	9.944	6.986	5.818	5.174	4.762	4.472	4.257	4.090	3.956	3.847	3.756	3.678	3.502	3.318	3.203	3.123	3.022	2.959	2.828	2.690	20
25	9.475	6.598	5.462	4.835	4.433	4.150	3.939	3.778	3.645	3.537	3.447	3.370	3.196	3.013	2.898	2.819	2.716	2.652	2.519	2.377	25
30	9.180	6.355	5.239	4.623	4.228	3.949	3.742	3.580	3.450	3.344	3.255	3.179	3.006	2.823	2.708	2.628	2.524	2.459	2.323	2.176	30
40	8.828	6.066	4.976	4.374	3.986	3.713	3.509	3.350	3.222	3.117	3.028	2.953	2.781	2.598	2.482	2.401	2.296	2.230	2.088	1.932	40
50	8.626	5.902	4.826	4.232	3.849	3.579	3.376	3.219	3.092	2.988	2.900	2.825	2.653	2.470	2.353	2.272	2.164	2.097	1.951	1.786	50
100	8.241	5.589	4.542	3.963	3.589	3.325	3.127	2.972	2.847	2.744	2.657	2.583	2.411	2.227	2.108	2.024	1.912	1.840	1.681	1.485	100
∞	7.879	5.298	4.279	3.715	3.350	3.091	2.897	2.744	2.621	2.519	2.432	2.358	2.187	2.000	1.877	1.789	1.669	1.590	1.402	1.001	∞

F Distribution (p=0.99)

	1	2	3	4	5	6	7	8	9	10	11	12	15	20	25	30	40	50	100	∞	
1	4052	5000	5403	5625	5764	5859	5928	5981	6022	6056	6083	6106	6157	6209	6240	6261	6287	6303	6334	6366	1
2	98.50	99.00	99.17	99.25	99.30	99.33	99.36	99.37	99.39	99.40	99.41	99.42	99.43	99.45	99.46	99.47	99.47	99.48	99.49	99.50	2
3	34.12	30.82	29.46	28.71	28.24	27.91	27.67	27.49	27.35	27.23	27.13	27.05	26.87	26.69	26.58	26.50	26.41	26.35	26.24	26.13	3
4	21.20	18.00	16.69	15.98	15.52	15.21	14.98	14.80	14.66	14.55	14.45	14.37	14.20	14.02	13.91	13.84	13.75	13.69	13.58	13.46	4
5	16.26	13.27	12.06	11.39	10.97	10.67	10.46	10.29	10.16	10.05	9.96	9.89	9.72	9.55	9.45	9.38	9.29	9.24	9.13	9.02	5
6	13.745	10.925	9.780	9.148	8.746	8.466	8.260	8.102	7.976	7.874	7.790	7.718	7.559	7.396	7.296	7.229	7.143	7.091	6.987	6.880	6
7	12.246	9.547	8.451	7.847	7.460	7.191	6.993	6.840	6.719	6.620	6.538	6.469	6.314	6.155	6.058	5.992	5.908	5.858	5.755	5.650	7
8	11.259	8.649	7.591	7.006	6.632	6.371	6.178	6.029	5.911	5.814	5.734	5.667	5.515	5.359	5.263	5.198	5.116	5.065	4.963	4.859	8
9	10.561	8.022	6.992	6.422	6.057	5.802	5.613	5.467	5.351	5.257	5.178	5.111	4.962	4.808	4.713	4.649	4.567	4.517	4.415	4.311	9
10	10.044	7.559	6.552	5.994	5.636	5.386	5.200	5.057	4.942	4.849	4.772	4.706	4.558	4.405	4.311	4.247	4.165	4.115	4.014	3.909	10
11	9.646	7.206	6.217	5.668	5.316	5.069	4.886	4.744	4.632	4.539	4.462	4.397	4.251	4.099	4.005	3.941	3.860	3.810	3.708	3.602	11
12	9.330	6.927	5.953	5.412	5.064	4.821	4.640	4.499	4.388	4.296	4.220	4.155	4.010	3.858	3.765	3.701	3.619	3.569	3.467	3.361	12
15	8.683	6.359	5.417	4.893	4.556	4.318	4.142	4.004	3.895	3.805	3.730	3.666	3.522	3.372	3.278	3.214	3.132	3.081	2.977	2.868	15
20	8.096	5.849	4.938	4.431	4.103	3.871	3.699	3.564	3.457	3.368	3.294	3.231	3.088	2.938	2.843	2.778	2.695	2.643	2.535	2.421	20
25	7.770	5.568	4.675	4.177	3.855	3.627	3.457	3.324	3.217	3.129	3.056	2.993	2.850	2.699	2.604	2.538	2.453	2.400	2.289	2.169	25
30	7.562	5.390	4.510	4.018	3.699	3.473	3.304	3.173	3.067	2.979	2.906	2.843	2.700	2.549	2.453	2.386	2.299	2.245	2.131	2.006	30
40	7.314	5.179	4.313	3.828	3.514	3.291	3.124	2.993	2.888	2.801	2.727	2.665	2.522	2.369	2.271	2.203	2.114	2.058	1.938	1.805	40
50	7.171	5.057	4.199	3.720	3.408	3.186	3.020	2.890	2.785	2.698	2.625	2.562	2.419	2.265	2.167	2.098	2.007	1.949	1.825	1.683	50
100	6.895	4.824	3.984	3.513	3.206	2.988	2.823	2.694	2.590	2.503	2.430	2.368	2.223	2.067	1.965	1.893	1.797	1.735	1.598	1.427	100
∞	6.635	4.605	3.782	3.319	3.017	2.802	2.639	2.511	2.407	2.321	2.248	2.185	2.039	1.878	1.773	1.696	1.592	1.523	1.358	1.000	∞

F Distribution (p=0.975)

	1	2	3	4	5	6	7	8	9	10	11	12	15	20	25	30	40	50	100	∞	
1	647.8	799.5	864.2	899.6	921.8	937.1	948.2	956.7	963.3	968.6	973.0	976.7	984.9	993.1	998.1	1001.4	1005.6	1008.1	1013.2	1018.3	1
2	38.51	39.00	39.17	39.25	39.30	39.33	39.36	39.37	39.39	39.40	39.41	39.41	39.43	39.45	39.46	39.46	39.47	39.48	39.49	39.50	2
3	17.44	16.04	15.44	15.10	14.88	14.73	14.62	14.54	14.47	14.42	14.37	14.34	14.25	14.17	14.12	14.08	14.04	14.01	13.96	13.90	3
4	12.22	10.65	9.98	9.60	9.36	9.20	9.07	8.98	8.90	8.84	8.79	8.75	8.66	8.56	8.50	8.46	8.41	8.38	8.32	8.26	4
5	10.01	8.43	7.76	7.39	7.15	6.98	6.85	6.76	6.68	6.62	6.57	6.52	6.43	6.33	6.27	6.23	6.18	6.14	6.08	6.02	5
6	8.813	7.260	6.599	6.227	5.988	5.820	5.695	5.600	5.523	5.461	5.410	5.366	5.269	5.168	5.107	5.065	5.012	4.980	4.915	4.849	6
7	8.073	6.542	5.890	5.523	5.285	5.119	4.995	4.899	4.823	4.761	4.709	4.666	4.568	4.467	4.405	4.362	4.309	4.276	4.210	4.142	7
8	7.571	6.059	5.416	5.053	4.817	4.652	4.529	4.433	4.357	4.295	4.243	4.200	4.101	3.999	3.937	3.894	3.840	3.807	3.739	3.670	8
9	7.209	5.715	5.078	4.718	4.484	4.320	4.197	4.102	4.026	3.964	3.912	3.868	3.769	3.667	3.604	3.560	3.505	3.472	3.403	3.333	9
10	6.937	5.456	4.826	4.468	4.236	4.072	3.950	3.855	3.779	3.717	3.665	3.621	3.522	3.419	3.355	3.311	3.255	3.221	3.152	3.080	10
11	6.724	5.256	4.630	4.275	4.044	3.881	3.759	3.664	3.588	3.526	3.474	3.430	3.330	3.226	3.162	3.118	3.061	3.027	2.956	2.883	11
12	6.554	5.096	4.474	4.121	3.891	3.728	3.607	3.512	3.436	3.374	3.321	3.277	3.177	3.073	3.008	2.963	2.906	2.871	2.800	2.725	12
15	6.200	4.765	4.153	3.804	3.576	3.415	3.293	3.199	3.123	3.060	3.008	2.963	2.862	2.756	2.689	2.644	2.585	2.549	2.474	2.395	15
20	5.871	4.461	3.859	3.515	3.289	3.128	3.007	2.913	2.837	2.774	2.721	2.676	2.573	2.464	2.396	2.349	2.287	2.249	2.170	2.085	20
25	5.686	4.291	3.694	3.353	3.129	2.969	2.848	2.753	2.677	2.613	2.560	2.515	2.411	2.300	2.230	2.182	2.118	2.079	1.996	1.906	25
30	5.568	4.182	3.589	3.250	3.026	2.867	2.746	2.651	2.575	2.511	2.458	2.412	2.307	2.195	2.124	2.074	2.009	1.968	1.882	1.787	30
40	5.424	4.051	3.463	3.126	2.904	2.744	2.624	2.529	2.452	2.388	2.334	2.288	2.182	2.068	1.994	1.943	1.875	1.832	1.741	1.637	40
50	5.340	3.975	3.390	3.054	2.833	2.674	2.553	2.458	2.381	2.317	2.263	2.216	2.109	1.993	1.919	1.866	1.796	1.752	1.656	1.545	50
100	5.179	3.828	3.250	2.917	2.696	2.537	2.417	2.321	2.244	2.179	2.125	2.077	1.968	1.849	1.770	1.715	1.640	1.592	1.483	1.347	100
∞	5.024	3.689	3.116	2.786	2.567	2.408	2.288	2.192	2.114	2.048	1.993	1.945	1.833	1.708	1.626	1.566	1.484	1.428	1.296	1.000	∞

F Distribution (p=0.95)

	1	2	3	4	5	6	7	8	9	10	11	12	15	20	25	30	40	50	100	∞	
1	161.4	199.5	215.7	224.6	230.2	234.0	236.8	238.9	240.5	241.9	243.0	243.9	245.9	248.0	249.3	250.1	251.1	251.8	253.0	254.3	1
2	18.51	19.00	19.16	19.25	19.30	19.33	19.35	19.37	19.38	19.40	19.40	19.41	19.43	19.45	19.46	19.46	19.47	19.48	19.49	19.50	2
3	10.13	9.55	9.28	9.12	9.01	8.94	8.89	8.85	8.81	8.79	8.76	8.74	8.70	8.66	8.63	8.62	8.59	8.58	8.55	8.53	3
4	7.71	6.94	6.59	6.39	6.26	6.16	6.09	6.04	6.00	5.96	5.94	5.91	5.86	5.80	5.77	5.75	5.72	5.70	5.66	5.63	4
5	6.61	5.79	5.41	5.19	5.05	4.95	4.88	4.82	4.77	4.74	4.70	4.68	4.62	4.56	4.52	4.50	4.46	4.44	4.41	4.36	5
6	5.987	5.143	4.757	4.534	4.387	4.284	4.207	4.147	4.099	4.060	4.027	4.000	3.938	3.874	3.835	3.808	3.774	3.754	3.712	3.669	6
7	5.591	4.737	4.347	4.120	3.972	3.866	3.787	3.726	3.677	3.637	3.603	3.575	3.511	3.445	3.404	3.376	3.340	3.319	3.275	3.230	7
8	5.318	4.459	4.066	3.838	3.688	3.581	3.500	3.438	3.388	3.347	3.313	3.284	3.218	3.150	3.108	3.079	3.043	3.020	2.975	2.928	8
9	5.117	4.256	3.863	3.633	3.482	3.374	3.293	3.230	3.179	3.137	3.102	3.073	3.006	2.936	2.893	2.864	2.826	2.803	2.756	2.707	9
10	4.965	4.103	3.708	3.478	3.326	3.217	3.135	3.072	3.020	2.978	2.943	2.913	2.845	2.774	2.730	2.700	2.661	2.637	2.588	2.538	10
11	4.844	3.982	3.587	3.357	3.204	3.095	3.012	2.948	2.896	2.854	2.818	2.788	2.719	2.646	2.601	2.570	2.531	2.507	2.457	2.404	11
12	4.747	3.885	3.490	3.259	3.106	2.996	2.913	2.849	2.796	2.753	2.717	2.687	2.617	2.544	2.498	2.466	2.426	2.401	2.350	2.296	12
15	4.543	3.682	3.287	3.056	2.901	2.790	2.707	2.641	2.588	2.544	2.507	2.475	2.403	2.328	2.280	2.247	2.204	2.178	2.123	2.066	15
20	4.351	3.493	3.098	2.866	2.711	2.599	2.514	2.447	2.393	2.348	2.310	2.278	2.203	2.124	2.074	2.039	1.994	1.966	1.907	1.843	20
25	4.242	3.385	2.991	2.759	2.603	2.490	2.405	2.337	2.282	2.236	2.198	2.165	2.089	2.007	1.955	1.919	1.872	1.842	1.779	1.711	25
30	4.171	3.316	2.922	2.690	2.534	2.421	2.334	2.266	2.211	2.165	2.126	2.092	2.015	1.932	1.878	1.841	1.792	1.761	1.695	1.622	30
40	4.085	3.232	2.839	2.606	2.449	2.336	2.249	2.180	2.124	2.077	2.038	2.003	1.924	1.839	1.783	1.744	1.693	1.660	1.589	1.509	40
50	4.034	3.183	2.790	2.557	2.400	2.286	2.199	2.130	2.073	2.026	1.986	1.952	1.871	1.784	1.727	1.687	1.634	1.599	1.525	1.438	50
100	3.936	3.087	2.696	2.463	2.305	2.191	2.103	2.032	1.975	1.927	1.886	1.850	1.768	1.676	1.616	1.573	1.515	1.477	1.392	1.283	100
∞	3.841	2.996	2.605	2.372	2.214	2.099	2.010	1.938	1.880	1.831	1.789	1.752	1.666	1.571	1.506	1.459	1.394	1.350	1.243	1.000	∞

TABLE 11   CRITICAL VALUES OF THE WILCOXON SIGNED RANK STATISTIC

| One tail | 10% | 5% | 2.5% | 1% | 0.5% | |
Two tail	20%	10%	5%	2%	1%	
n						
3	5					**3**
4	9	10				**4**
5	12	14	15			**5**
6	17	18	20			**6**
7	22	24	26	28		**7**
8	27	30	32	35		**8**
9	33	36	39	42	44	**9**
10	40	44	47	50	53	**10**
11	47	52	55	59	62	**11**
12	55	60	64	69	72	**12**
13	64	69	74	79	82	**13**
14	73	79	84	90	94	**14**
15	83	89	95	101	105	**15**
16	93	100	106	113	118	**16**
17	104	111	118	126	131	**17**
18	115	123	131	139	145	**18**
19	127	136	144	153	159	**19**
20	139	149	157	167	174	**20**

TABLE 12

CONTROL CHARTS VARIABILITY

For range charts multiply σ by the appropriate value of D.

For standard deviation charts multiply σ by the appropriate value of E.

To obtain an estimate of σ multiply the mean range by the appropriate value of b.

Normal distribution is assumed.

Sample size	D 0.999	D 0.975	D 0.025	D 0.001	E 0.999	E 0.975	E 0.025	E 0.001	b
2			3.170	4.654			2.24	3.29	0.8862
3	0.060	0.303	3.682	5.063	0.03	0.16	1.92	2.63	0.5908
4	0.199	0.595	3.984	5.309	0.09	0.27	1.76	2.33	0.4857
5	0.367	0.850	4.197	5.484	0.15	0.35	1.67	2.15	0.4299
6	0.535	1.066	4.361	5.619	0.20	0.41	1.60	2.03	0.3946
7	0.691	1.251	4.494	5.730	0.25	0.45	1.55	1.93	0.3698
8	0.835	1.410	4.605	5.823	0.29	0.49	1.51	1.86	0.3512
10	1.085	1.674	4.784	5.973	0.36	0.55	1.45	1.76	0.3249
12	1.293	1.884	4.925	6.096	0.41	0.59	1.41	1.69	0.3069

ANSWERS

The answers to the questions set in the Exercises are given below. Answers to questions set in some of the Activities are also given where appropriate.

1 CONTINUOUS PROBABILITY DISTRIBUTIONS

Exercise 1A

1. $\frac{5}{6}$; 0.589

2. (b) $\frac{4}{3}$; $\frac{8}{9}$ (c) 0.943

3. (a) 0.148 (b) 0.1213
   (c) 0.2019 (d) 0.3297

Exercise 1B

1. (a) $N(950,800)$ (b) $N(25,1300)$

2. (a) $N(510,375)$; 0.788
   (b) 0.111

3. (a) (i) 0.092 (ii) 22.85 mins
   (b) 27.9 mins (c) 0.869 (d) Blue Star

Exercise 1C

1. (a) 0.248 (b) 0.424 (c) 0.202
   (d) 0.865

2. (a) 0.247 (b) 0.341 (c) 0.018
   (d) 0.148; 7.54 mins

3. (a) 0.148 (b) 0.121 (c) 0.202
   (d) 0.330

   250, 250; 250, $16\frac{2}{3}$; 0.274

Miscellaneous Exercises

1. (a) $\frac{a}{2}$; $\frac{a^2}{12}$ (b) $\frac{a}{2}$; $\frac{a^2}{12n}$

   (c) $\frac{a}{2}$, $\frac{a^2}{20}$

2. (a) 0.148 (b) 0.468 (c) 0.135 (d) 0.181, 0.223; 25 words

3. (a) 0.645 (b) 7.6 ; 0.3 (c) 0.3050
   (d) (i) 7.5 (ii) 8.545

4. (a) (i) 0.097 (ii) 0.941 (b) (470.7, 559.3)
   (c) 0.208

5. (a) 0.669 (b) 125.9 secs (c) 130 secs;
   9.8 secs (d) 0.425 (e) Lin Ying

6. (a) 0.7734 (b) 0.6285 (c) 2.8028
   (d) 0.9359 (e) $N(19.02, 0.36)$
   (f) (18, 20)

7. (a) 0.5987 (b) 11.921 (c) 0.8682
   (d) 0.243; 7

2 ESTIMATION

Exercise 2A

1. (235.06, 239.69)
2. (649.07, 687.18)
3. (a) (44.94, 73.29) (b) (38.49, 79.74)

Exercise 2B

1. (1.83, 5.65)
   (15.07, 46.34)
   (12.46, 35.33)
2. (0.0701, 0.1988); No
3. (0.2146, 1.0295); (0.0070, 0.0213); Yes

Exercise 2C

1. (0.072, 0.228)
2. (0.0119, 0.0261)
3. (0.241, 0.403)

Exercise 2D

1. (a) (183.46, 240.54) (b) (36.69, 48.11)
   (c) (75.22, 94.38) (d) (2094, 2994)

2. (5.1, 11.6)
3. (a) (25.27, 44.73)   (b) (0, 4.167)
   (c) (301.7, 398.3)   (a) (21.42, 39.58)
   (b) (0, 6.473)   (c) (259.9, 350.1)

Miscellaneous Exercises

1. (217.68, 245.46)
2. (a) (i) (96.55, 258.20) (ii) (85.09, 216.80)
3. (a) (0.017, 0.060)   (b) (i) (2431.7, 3001.6)
   (ii) $n = 98$
4. (a) (32.70, 90.73)
   (b) (i) (2347.5, 2399.36)
       (ii) (2329.6, 2417.2)
5. (a) (202.4, 207.4)   (b) (0.057, 0.343)
   (c) 0.00176
6. (b) (13.32, 37.78)   (c) (28.77, 53.23)
7. (a) (i) (24.52, 29.64)   (ii) (1.52, 5.98)
   (b) 38.43 kN   7.40 kN

3   HYPOTHESIS TESTING: ONE SAMPLE TESTS

Exercise 3A

1. Calculated $t = -0.53241$. Critical $t_{12} = \pm 2.179$. At the 5% significance level there is insufficient evidence to suggest that the population mean is not 50 cm.

2. Calculated $t = 1.433$. Critical $t_{11} = +1.796$. At the 5% significance level there is insufficient evidence to claim that the true population mean exceeds 25.0 kg.

3. Calculated $t = +2.7824$. Critical $t_{12} = +1.771$. At the 5% significance level there is evidence to support the claim that the true mean weekly milk yield for the herd is greater than 120 kg.

4. Calculated $t = -0.93686$. Critical $t_{14} = -1.761$. At the 5% significance level there is insufficient evidence to claim that the mean assembly time is less than 2 minutes.

5. Calculated $t = -2.361$. Critical $t_{10} = \pm 2.226$. At the 5% level of significance there is sufficient evidence to support the claim that the mean percentage extract differs from 95%.

6. Calculated $t = -2.455$. Critical $t_8 = -1.860$. At the 5% level of significance there is sufficient evidence to support the claim that the mean assembly time is less than 42 minutes.

Exercise 3B

1. Calculated $\chi^2 = 18.757$. From χ^2_{12} the critical region is < 4.404 or > 23.337. At the 5% level of significance there is not insufficient evidence to suggest that the population standard deviation is not 2.5 cm.

2. Calculated $\chi^2 = 17.152$. From χ^2_{11} the critical region is > 19.675. At the 5% significance level there is insuffient evidence to support the claim that the population standard deviation is greater than 2 kg.

3. Calculated $\chi^2 = 19.6358$. From χ^2_{13} the critical region is < 5.009 or > 24.736. At the 5% level of significance there is insufficient evidence to support the claim that the population standard deviation for the herd differs from 20 kg.

4. Calculated $\chi^2 = 5.7$. From χ^2_{14} the critical region is > 23.685. At the 5% level of significance there is insufficient evidence to suggest that the population variance exceeds 0.002 gm².

5. Calculated $\chi^2 = 2.998$. From χ^2_{10} the critical region is < 3.940. At the 5% significance level there is evidence to suggest that the population variance for percentage extract is less than 6.0.

6. Calculated $\chi^2 = 5.535$. From χ^2_8 the critical region is < 2.733. At the 5% level of significance there is insufficient evidence to support the manufacturers assumption.

Exercise 3C

1. One sided test. $P(X \geq 10 | p = 0.6) = 0.08344 > 0.05$
   At the 5% level of significance there is insufficient evidence to support the claim that p is greater than 0.6.

2. Two sided test.
   $P(X \geq 14 | p = 0.35) = 1 - 0.8737 = 0.1263 > 0.05$ and
   $P(X \leq 14 | p = 0.35) = 0.9348 > 0.05$. At the 10% level of significance there is insufficient evidence to dispute the claim that $p = 0.35$.

3. One sided test.
   $P(X \geq 21 | p = 0.5) = 1 - 0.9786 = 0.0214 < 0.05$. At the 5% significance level there is evidence to support the claim that more than half of all coffeee crinkers like the new brand of coffee.

4. One sided test. Poisson approximation with $\lambda = 12$. $P(X \leq 8 | \lambda = 12) = 0.1550 > 0.05$. At the 5% level of significance there is insufficient evidence to suggest that the true percentage of damaged tins is less than 2.

5. Two sided test. Normal approximation with $\mu = 200 \ \sigma^2 = 160$. Test statistic, $z = 1.818$. Critical value $= \pm 1.96$. At the 5% significance level there is insufficient evidence to suggest that the true population proportion of houses in Alverdale with some form of double glazing differs from 40%.

6. Two sided test. Normal approximation with $\mu = 60.75$, $\sigma^2 = 33.4125$. Test statistic, $z = 1.946$. Critical value $= \pm 1.96$. At the 5% significance level there is insufficient evidence to support the claim that the scoring ability differs from 0.45.

Exercise 3D

1. One sided test. $P(X \leq 2 | \lambda = 3.7) = 0.2854 > 0.05$. At the 5% level of significance there is insufficient evidence to support the claim that the average fault rate is less than 0.925 per 25 m^2.

2. Two sided test.
$P(X \geq 8 | \lambda = 12) = 1 - 0.0895 > 0.025$ and
$P(X \leq 8 | \lambda = 12) = 0.1550 > 0.025$. At the 5% significance level there is insufficient evidence to support the claim that the mean number of parasites per fish is not 4.

3. One sided test. Normal approximation to Poison distribution with $\mu = 450$, $\sigma^2 = 450$. Test statistic $z = -2.027$. Critical value $= -2.33$. At the 1% level of significance there is insufficient evidence to suggest that the average number of complaints is less than 3 per day.

4. Normal approximation to Poisson with $\mu = 8 \times 27 = 216$, $\sigma^2 = 216$. Test statistic, $z = -2.177$. Critical value $= -1.645$. At the 5% level of significance there is evidence to suggest that the mean number of breakages is less than 27 per week.

Exercise 3E

1. One sided test.
$P(X \geq 8 | p = 0.5) = 1 - 0.9453 = 0.0547 < 0.1$. At the 10% level of significance there is sufficient evidence to suggest that the median salary of all recent graduates exceeds £12,000.

2. One sided test.
$P(X \geq 8 | p = 0.5) = 1 - 0.9453 = 0.0547 > 0.05$. At the 5% level of significance there is insufficient evidence to support the claim that the median group is not C.

3. One sided test.
$P(X \geq 17 | p = 0.5, n = 20) = 1 - 0.9987 = 0.0023 < 0.05$
At the 5% significance level there is evidence to support the claim that more than 50% of all vehicles exceed the 30 mph speed limit.

4. One sided test. Using the normal approximation to the binomial distribution,
$P(X \geq 135 | n = 196, p = 0.5) < 0.05$. At the 5% significance level there is evidence to suggest that the median daily number of adjustments is not 1.

Miscellaneous Exercises

1. (a) Calculated $\chi^2 = 38.75$. From χ^2_{12} the critical region is < 4.404 and > 23.337. At the 5% significance level there is sufficient evidence to support the claim that the population variance is not 35 g^2.

   (b) Calculated $t = 1.299$. Critical $t_{10} = \pm 2.179$.

   At the 5% level of significance there is insufficient evidence to support the claim that the population mean differs from 60 g.

2. (a) Calculated $t = 0.9286$. Critical $t_{10} = \pm 1.812$. At the 10% significance level there is insufficient evidence to support the claim that the true mean differs from 40%.

   (b) Ones sided test.
   $P(X \geq 6 | p = 0.5, n = 10) = 1 - 0.6230 = 0.377 > 0.10$.
   At the 10% significance level there is insufficient evidence to support the claim that the median score for all candidates is not 40%.

3. (a) Total number of forecasts $= 400$ Total number of successes $= 190$. Using normal approximation to binomial distribution with $\mu = 200$ and $\sigma^2 = 100$ then calculated value $z = -0.1$. Critical value $= \pm 1.96$. At the 5% significance level there is insufficient evidence to support the claim that the probability of a true forecast is not 0.5. Probability of winning is estimated at $(0.5)^5 = 0.03125$ which can be compared with the pay out odds of 100 to 1.

4. Approximate the Poisson distribution with $\lambda = 30$ with the normal distribution with $\mu = 30$ and $\sigma^2 = 30$. Test statistic $= \dfrac{(40 - 30))}{\sqrt{30}} = +1.826$.

   Critical value $= +1.645$. At the 5% level of significance there is evidence to support the claim that the annual mean number of visits to general practitioners for employees of a particular nuclear power station is higher than 3 per year.

5. (a) Calculated $\chi^2 = 21.3244$. From χ_{17}^2 the critical region is defined by < 7.564 and > 30.191. At the 5% significance level there is insufficient evidence to support the claim that the population standard deviation is not 10 mm.

   (b) With $\sigma = 10$ mm the test statistic $z = -1.886$ $(t = -0.396)$. Critical value $z = \pm 1.96$, critical t_{17} value $= \pm 1.740$. At the 5% significance level there is insufficient evidence to support the claim that the population mean diastolic blood pressure is not 75mm.

6. Approximate the Poisson distribution with $\lambda = 4 \times 16 = 64$ with the normal distribution with mean $\mu = 64$ and $\sigma^2 = 64$. Test statistic
   $$z = \frac{(45 - 64)}{8} = -2.375.$$ Critical value $= -2.326$.
   At the 1% significance level there is sufficient evidence to support the claim that the true mean number of misprints per page in the Daily Planet is less than 16.

7. One sided test.
   $P(X \le 3 | p = 0.4, n = 20) = 0.0160 < 0.05$. At the 5% significance level there is evidence to support the claim that the new dietary treatment for severe allergy has a cure rate better than 60%.

8. Calculated t value $= -0.7209$ Critical $t_{14} = \pm 2.145$. At the 5% significance level there is insufficient evidence to support the claim that the population mean score for the new ice cream is not 14.

   One sided test.

   $P(X \le 5 | n = 15, p = 0.5) = 0.1509 > 0.05$. At the 5% significance level there is insufficient evidence to support the claim that the true population median for the new ice cream is not 13.

9. (a) Calculated $\chi^2 = 16.92$. From χ_9^2 critical region is < 2.70 and > 19.023. At the 5% significance level there is insufficient evidence to support the claim that the true population variance is not 0.005 cm^2.

   (b) Calculated $z = -1.3416$, (calculated $t = -0.978$). Critical region $= \pm 1.96$, (critical region $t_9 = \pm 1.833$). At the 5% significance level there is insufficient evidence to support the claim that the population mean external diameter is not 10 cm.

10. (a) Normal approximation to the binomial with $\mu = 56$ and $\sigma^2 = 16.8$. Test statistic $= 1.219$. Critical region $= \pm 1.96$. At the 5% significance level there is sufficient evidence to support the claim that the population proportion is 0.7.

   (b) Calculated t value $= -1.347$. Critical $t_{18} = \pm 1.734$. At the 10% significance level there is insufficient evidence to support the claim that the mean diameter is not 275 mm.

12. $n = 80 \times 5 = 400$ and $\hat{p} = \frac{272}{400} = 0.68$. Approximate the binomial distribution with a normal distribution with mean $\mu = 240$ and variance $\sigma^2 = 96$. Test statistic $z = 3.26598$. Critical value $= 1.645$. At the 5% significance level there is evidence to support the claim that more than 60% of cars contain a driver only.

13. Calculated $t = 1.4929$ Critical $t_7 = \pm 2.365$. At the 5% significance level there is insufficient evidence to support the claim that the population mean journey time is not 40 minutes.

14. (a) Two sided test under the assumption of normality. Calculated $\chi^2 = 14.045$. From χ_5^2 critical region is < 0.831 or > 12.833. At the 5% significance level there is sufficient evidence to support the claim that the population standard deviation is not £141.

   (b) Calculated t value $= 0.51999$. Critical $t_5 = \pm 2.571$. At the 5% significance level there is insufficient evidence to support the claim that the population mean bodywork claim is not £435.

15. (a) Calculated $t = -3.6181$. Critical $t_9 = -1.833$. At the 5% significance level there is sufficient evidence to support the claim that the mean operating time is less than 100 seconds.

   (b) Approximate the binomial distribution with the normal distribution with $\mu = 3500$ and $\sigma^2 = 2275$. Test value $z = 2.411$. Critical value $= 2.326$. At the 1% significance level there is sufficient evidence to support the claim that more than 35% of families buy this specific magazine.

16. (i) Calculated $\chi^2 = 39.18$. From χ_2^7 the critical region is defined by < 1.690 or > 16.013. At the 5% significance level there is sufficient evidence to support the claim that the population standard deviation is not 2.5 cm.

   (ii) Calculated $t = 2.570$. Critical $t_7 = \pm 2.365$. At the 5% significance level there is sufficient evidence to support the claim that the mean first year pine seedling growth is not 11.5 cm.

17. (a) Calculated $\chi^2 = 13.537$. From χ_2^7 critical region is < 1.69 or > 16.013. At the 5% significance level there is insufficient evidence to support the claim that the population standard deviation is not 10 seconds.

(b) Calculated value $z = -2.229$. Critical values $= \pm 1.96$. At the 5% significance level there is sufficient evidence to support the claim that the mean shaving time is not 240 seconds.

18. Calculated t value = 2.2979. Critical $t_{29} = 2.045$. At the 5% significance level there is sufficient evidence to support the claim that the population mean weight of packet filter coffee is not equal to 200 g.

19. (a) One sided test.

$P(X \geq 13 | \lambda = 7) = 1 - 0.9730 = 0.027 < 0.05$.

At the 5% significance level there is sufficient evidence to support the claim that there is an average of more than one accident per day.

(b) 150 house holders polled with 58 in favour and and 92 opposed. Two sided test. Approximate the binomial distribution with the normal distribution $\mu = 60$ and

$\sigma^2 = 36$. Test statistic $z = -\frac{1}{3}$. Critical

value $= \pm 1.96$. At the 5% significance level there is insufficient evidence to support the claim that the percentage of house holders in favour of the proposal is not 40.

20. Calculated $\chi^2 = 14.955$. From χ_6^2 critical region is < 1.237 or > 14.449. At the 5% significance level there is sufficient evidence to support the claim that the true standard deviation of the resistors is not 30 ohms.

Calculated $t = -1.48428$. Critical $t_6 = \pm 2.447$. At the 5% significance level there is insufficient evidence to support the claim that the mean resistance of the resistors is not 2400 ohms.

21. (a) One sided test.

$P(X \leq 2 | n = 8, p = 0.5) = 0.1445 > 0.05$. At the 5% significance level there is insufficient evidence to support the claim that the median is not 50.

22. Calculated $t = 1.013$. Critical $t_9 = 1.833$. At the 5% significance level there is insufficient evidence to support the claim that the mean survival time exceeds 400 days.

23. Calculated $\chi^2 = 6.46$. From χ_8^2 critical region is > 15.507. At the 5% significance level there is insufficient evidence to support the claim that the population standard deviation is in excess of 10 units.

Calculated t = -0.8902. Critical $t_8 = \pm 2.306$.

At the 5% significance level there is insufficient evidence to support the claim that the true population mean is not 20 units.

24. $P(X \leq 15 | n = 40, p = 0.4) = 0.4402 > 0.05$. At the 5% significance level there is insufficient evidence to support the claim that the percentage of employees requiring size 3 is not 40.

$P(X \leq 12 | n = 25, p = 0.5) = 0.5 > 0.05$. At the 5% significance level there is insufficient evidence to support the claim that the median size is not 3.

4 HYPOTHESIS TESTING: TWO SAMPLE TESTS

Exercise 4A

1. Calculated $F = 1.394$. Critical $F_{(12,8)} = 4.20$. At the 5% significance level there is insufficient evidence to support the claim that there is a difference in the variability of dust deposited.

2. Calculated $F = 4.2088$. Critical $F_{(11,9)} = 3.102$.

At the 5% significance level there is evidence to support the claim that an increase in variability has occurred.

3. Calculated $F = 1.478$. Critical $F_{(9,7)} = 3.677$. At the 10% significance level there is insufficient evidence to support the claim that these data have not come from normal populations with different variances.

4. Calculated $F = 3.299$. Critical $F_{(10,12)} = 2.753$.

At the 5% significance level there is evidence to suggest that variability in recognition times for librarians exceeds those for designers.

5. Calculated $F = 5.196$. Critical $F_{(6,5)} = 6.978$. At the 5% significance level there is insufficient evidence to support the claim that there is a difference in the variability of the two methods.

6. Calculated $F = 1.194$. Critical $F_{(3,7)} = 5.890$. At the 5% significance level there is insufficient evidence to support the claim that the population variances are unequal.

Exercise 4B

1. Calculated $z = 4.833$. Critical $z = \pm 1.96$. At the 5% significance level there is sufficient evidence to suggest that the mean mass of crisps delivered has changed.

2. Calculated $z = -1.2$. Critical $z = \pm1.9$. At the 5% significance level there is insufficient evidence to suggest that the two population means differ.

3. Calculated $z = 2.35$. Critical $z = \pm1.96$. At the 5% significance level there is insufficient evidence to support the claim that the two populations have the same mean.

4. Calculated $z = 1.679$. Critical $z = \pm1.96$. At the 5% significance level there is insufficient evidence to support the claim that the two population means differ.

5. (a) Calculated $z = -0.87712$. Critical $z = \pm1.96$. At the 5% significance level there is insufficient evidence to support the claim that the two population means differ.

   (b) Calculated $z = -2.056$. Critical $z = \pm1.96$. At the 5% significance level there is sufficient evidence to suggest that the two population means differ.

6. (a) Calculated $z = -1.92$. Critical $z = -1.645$. At the 5% significance level there is evidence to support the claim that the mean delivery time for James is less than that for Alsion.

Exercise 4C

1. Calculated $t = 2.338$. Critical $t_{12} = \pm2.178$. At the 5% significance level there is evidence to suggest that the two population mean times for making yogurt are different.

2. Calculated $t = 2.520$. Critical $t_{20} = \pm2.086$. At the 5% significance level there is evidence to suggest that the two population means (for the amount deposited) differ.

3. Calculated $t = -0.1943$. Critical $t_{20} = \pm2.086$. At the 5% significance level there is insufficient evidence to suggest that the two population means differ.

4. Calculated $t = 3.094$. Critical $t_{16} = 2.921$.

5. Calculated $t = 1.89$. Critical $t_{11} = \pm2.201$. At the 5% significance level there is insufficient evidence to suggest that there is a difference in the mean measurements for the two methods.

6. (a) Calculated $F = 1.202$. Critical $F_{(15,14)} = 2.949$. At the 5% significance level there is insufficient evidence to support the claim of differnt variability for the two processes.

   (b) Calculated $t = -0.7018$. Critical $t_{29} = \pm2.045$. At the 5% significance level there is insufficient evidence against the

claim $\mu_1 - \mu_2 = 5$ hours.

Exercise 4D

1. Calculated $t = -1.497$. Critical $t_{10} = \pm2.228$. At the 5% significance level there is insufficient evidence to support the claim that the two population means are different.

2. Calculated $t = -3.125$. Critical $t = -1.1812$. At the 5% significance level there is sufficient evidence to suggest that there has been an increase in the mean monthly sales.

3. Calculated $t = 3.277$. Critical $t_9 = 1.833$. At the 5% significance level there is insufficient evidence to support the claim that Crackshot shotgun is more accurate than Fastfire for clay pigeon shooting.

4. Calculated $t = 3.283$. Critical $t_4 = 2.776$. At the 5% significance level there is sufficient evidence to suggest that there has been a change in the mean score over two rounds.

5. Calculated $t = -1.198$. Critical $t_{11} = \pm2.201$. At the 5% significance level there is insufficient evidence to support the claim that the statement "$\mu_1 - \mu_2 = 5$" is not true.

6. Calculated $t = -2.538$. Critical $t_{10} = -1.812$. At the 5% significance level there is evidence to support the claim that the satellite sensors have average higher readings than ground thermometers.

Exercise 4E

1. $P(X \le 3 | n = 13, p = 0.5) = 0.0730 \ge 0.025$. At the 5% significance level there is insufficient evidence to support the claim of a difference in grades.

2. $P(X \le 4 | n = 11, p = 0.5) = 0.2744 \ge 0.025$. At the 5% significance level there is insufficient evidence to support the claim of a change in the marks.

3. $P(X \le 2 | n = 11, p = 0.5) = 0.0327 \le 0.05$. At the 5% significance level there is evidence to support the claim that there has been an increase in the mean monthly sales.

4. $P(X \le 3 | n = 10, p = 0.5) = 0.01719 > 0.05$. At the 5% significance level there is insufficient evidence to support the claim of a difference between pairs of scores.

5. $P(X \le 2|n=11, p=0.5)=0.0327 \ge 0.025$. At the 5% significance level there is insufficient evidence to support the claim that drug patients fare better than placebo patients.

6. $P(X \le 3|n=10, p=0.5)=0.1719 \ge 0.025$. At the 5% significance level there is insufficient evidence to support the claim of a difference in the B12 level in red blood cells under the two methods.

Exercise 4F

1. Calculated $T = 59.5$. Critical $T = 52$. At the 5% significance level there is evidence to support the claim that there has been an increase in mean monthly sales.

2. Calculated $T = 49$. Critical $T = 44$. At the 5% significance level there is evidence to support the claim that the Crackshot shotgun is more accurate than Fastfire for clay pigeon shooting.

3. Calculated $T = 57.5$. Critical $T = 52$. At the 5% significance level there is sufficient evidence to support the claim that drug treated patients fare better than placebo patients.

4. Calculated $T = 59$. Critical $T = 84$. At the 5% significance level there is insufficient evidence to support the claim that girls cannot accurately remember the frequency of the word "nice".

5. Calculated $T = 44$. Critical $T = 47$. At the 5% significance level there is insufficient evidence to support the claim that there is a difference in the B12 level in the blood cells under the two measurement methods.

6. Calculated $T = 74.5$. Critical $T = 74$. At the 5% significance level there is sufficient evidence to support the claim that the wear in the two leathers is not the same.

Miscellaneous Exercises

1. Calculated $F = 3.801$. Critical $F_{(4,7)} = 5.523$. At the 5% significance level there is insufficient evidence to suggest that the two population variances differ.

2. Calculated $z = 0.6418$. Critical $z = \pm 1.96$. At the 5% significance level there is insufficient evidence to suggest there is a diference in the population mean usages for exchanges X and Y.

3. (b) Calculated $t = 2.609$. Critical $t_{10} = 1.812$. At the 5% significance level there is sufficient evidence to suggest that the mean weekly provision cost in Southville is greater than than in Nortown.

4. Calculated $z = 1.94$. Critical $z = 2.326$. At the 5% significance level there is insufficient evidence to suggest that a high nitrate intake retards the mean percentage gain in mass of mice.

5. Calculated $t = 2.736$. Critical $t_9 = 1.833$. At the 5% significance level there is evidence to support the claim that alcohol intake reduces the useful consciousness time.

6. (a) (i) Calculated $F = 1.403$. Critical $F_{(7,5)} = 6.853$. At the 5% significance level there is insufficient evidence to suggest that there is a difference in variability in the usage time for the two systems.

 (b) (ii) Calculated $t = -0.6027$. Critical $t_{12} = \pm 2.179$. At the 5% significance level there is insufficient evidence to suggest that there is a difference in the population mean operating times.

7. (a) Calculated $t = 2.965$. Critical $t_9 = 2.262$.

 (b) Calculated $z = 1.97$. Critical $z = \pm 1.96$.

 At the 5% significance level there is evidence to suggest that the measured population mean is not 90.

8. Calculated $z = -2.490$. Critical $z = -1.645$. At the 5% significance level there is evidence to support that on the average examiner W awards more marks than examiner V.

9. (a) $P(X \le 5|n=14, p=0.5)=0.2120 \ge 0.05$. At the 5% significance level there is insufficient evidence to suggest that coursework marks are higher than examination marks.

 (b) Calculated $T = 60.5$. Critical $T = 52$. At the 5% significance level there is sufficient evidence to suggest that coursework marks are higher than examination marks (after disregarding those students who do not submit any coursework.)

10. Calculated $F = 1.750$. Critical $F_{(11,10)} = 3.665$. At the 5% significance level there is insufficient evidence to support the claim that the population variances are different.

 Calculated $t = -3.289$. Critical $t_{21} = \pm 2.080$. At the 5% significance level there is evidence to support the claim that the two population means differ.

11. $P(X \le 3|n=11, p=0.5)=0.113 > 0.05$. At the 5% significance level there is insufficient evidence to suggest that the new recipe is sweeter than the exisitng one.

 Critical $t = -3.319$. Critical $t_9 = \pm 3.250$. At the 5% significance level there is sufficient evidence to support the claim that there is a differnce in sweetness between the two recipes.

12. Calculated $F = 5.633$. Critical $F_{(7,5)} = 6.853$. At the 5% significance level there is insufficient evidence to support the claim of different variability in oxygen content.

Calculated $t = -3.342$. Critical $t_{12} = -1.782$. At the 5% significance level there is insufficient evidence to support the claim that the mean oxygen content "below" the factory is less than the "above" the factory.

13 (a) Calculated $t = 0.8729$. Critical $t_7 = \pm 2.365$. At the 5% significance level there is insufficient evidence to support the claim that the two trainees differ in their valuations.

(b) Calculated $T = 27$. Critical $T = 32$. At the 5% significance level there is insufficient evidence to support the claim that the two trainees differ in their valuations.

14. Calculated $F = 1.372$. Critical $F_{(7,5)} = 6.853$. At the 5% significance level there is insufficient evidence to support the claim that the two population variances are unequal.

Calculated $t = -0.6053$. Critical $t_{12} = \pm 2.179$. At the 5% significance level there is insufficient evidence to support the claim that the two population means are equal.

16. (a) (i) Calculated $F = 1.116$. Critical $F_{(9,9)} = 4.026$. At the 5% significance level there is insufficient evidence to support the claim that the two population variances are different.

(ii) Calculated $t = -0.898$. Critical $t_{18} = -1.734$. At the 5% significance level there is insufficient evidence to support the claim of an increase in mean weight.

17. (a) Calculated $T = 69.5$. Critical $T = 64$. At the 5% significance level there is sufficient evidence to support the claim of higher zinc concentration on the river bed than on the surface.

(b) Calculated $t = -3.233$. Critical $t_{11} = -1.796$. At the 5% significance level there is sufficient evidence to support the claim of higher zinc concentration on the river bed than on the surface.

18. (a) Calculated $t = 1.42$. Critical $t_3 = 2.353$. At the 5% significance level there is insufficient evidence to support the claim that the mean viscosity of paint A is more than 114.

(b) Calculated $F = 2.30$. Critical $F_{(5,3)} = 14.89$. At the 5% significance level there is insufficient evidence to support the claim of unequal variances.

(c) Calculated $t = -0.91$. Critical $t_8 = \pm 2.306$. At the 5% significance level there is insufficient evidence to support the claim of unequal means.

19. (b) Calculated $t = 2.225$. Critical $t_3 = \pm 3.182$. At the 5% significance level there is insufficient evidence to support the claim that there is a diference in the mean number of days to spoilage.

20. (a) Calculated $F = 1.334$. Critical $F_{(5,6)} = 5.988$.

(b) Calculated $t = 4.45$. Critical $t_{11} = \pm 2.201$. At the 5% significance level there is sufficient evidence to suggest that mean shaving times are different.

5 GOODNESS OF FIT TESTS

Exercise 5A

1. Calculated $\chi^2 = \dfrac{58}{17} \approx 3.412$.

From χ^2_3, critical region, > 7.815.

At the 5% significance level there is insufficient evidence to support the claim that the die is not fair.

2. Calculated $\chi^2 = 5.5$.

From χ^2_5, critical region, > 11.070.

At the 5% significance level there is insufficient evidence to support the claim that the die is biased.

3. Calculated $\chi^2 = 10.94$.

From χ^2_4, critical region, 9.488.

At the 5% significance level there is some evidence to support the claim that the number of absentees is dependent on the day of the week.

4. Calculated $\chi^2 = 13.2$.

From χ^2_6, critical region, > 12.592.

At the 5% significance level there is some evidence to support the claim that the number of accidents is dependent on the day of the week.

5. Calculated $\chi^2 = 8.86$.

From χ^2_3, critical region, > 7.815.

At the 5% significance level there is some evidence to support the claim that the doors do not have the same usage.

6. Calculated $\chi^2 = 3.246$.

From χ^2_3, critical region, > 7.815.

At the 5% significance level there is insufficient evidence to support the claim that blood type proportions are not the same as the rest of the country.

Exercise 5B

1. Calculated $\chi^2 = 4.859$.

From χ^2_5, critical region, > 11.070.

At the 5% significance level there is insufficient evidence to suggest that a binomial distribution with parameters, $n = 5$, $p = 0.5$, does not apply.

2. Calculated $\chi^2 = 0.9865$.

From χ^2_7, critical region, > 14.067.

At the 5% significance level there is insufficient evidence to suggest that a Poisson distribution with mean 4 does not apply.

3. Calculated $\chi^2 = 1.7317$.

From χ^2_3, critical region, > 6.251.

At the 10% significance level there is insufficient evidence to support the claim that a binomial distribution does not apply.

4. Calculated $\chi^2 = 1.668$.

From χ^2_3, critical region, > 6.251.

At the 10% significance level there is insufficient evidence to support the claim that a Poisson distribution does not apply.

Exercise 5C

1. Calculated $\chi^2 = 15.5977$.

From χ^2_7, critical region, > 14.067.

At the 5% significance level there is some evidence to suggest that an exponential distribution with mean 200 hours does not apply.

2. Calculated $\chi^2 = 25.038$.

From χ^2_7, critical region, > 14.067.

At the 5% significance level there is some evidence to suggest that an exponential distribution does not apply.

3. Calculated $\chi^2 = 19.556$.

From χ^2_4, critical region, > 9.488.

At the 5% significance level there is some evidence to support the claim that a normal distribution, with mean 35 seconds and standard deviation 10 seconds, does not apply.

4. Calculated $\chi^2 = 4.405$.

From χ^2_2, critical region, > 9.210.

At the 1% significance level there is insufficient evidence to support the claim that the data have not been sampled from a normal distribution.

Miscellaneous Exercises

1. Calculated $\chi^2 = 0.81061$.

From χ^2_2, critical region, > 5.991.

At the 5% significance level there is insufficient evidence to suggest that a binomial distribution does not apply.

2. (a) Calculated $\chi^2 = 108.737$.

From χ^2_3, critical region, > 11.345.

At the 1% significance level there is some evidence to support the claim that the data are not consistent with the Poisson distribution.

(c) Calculated $\chi^2 = 13.79$.

From χ^2_3, critical region, > 7.815.

At the 5% significance level there is some evidence to support the claim that breakdowns do not occur at an equal rate on each production line.

3. (a) Calculated $\chi^2 = 9.303$.

From χ^2_2, critical region, > 5.991.

(b) Calculated $\chi^2 = 3.23$.

From χ^2_1, critical region, > 3.841.

4. (a) Calculated $\chi^2 = 14.77$.

From χ^2_4, critical region, > 13.277.

At the 1% significance level there is some evidence to suggest that the number of books borrowed varies between the five days of the week.

(b) Calculated $\chi^2 = 5.147$.

From χ^2_2, critical region, > 5.991.

At the 5% significance level there is insufficient evidence to suggest that the data are not consistent with the postulated distribution.

5. (a) Calculated $\chi^2 = 9.37$.

   From χ_4^2, critical region, > 9.488.

   At the 5% significance level there is insufficient evidence to suggest that the data are not consistent with the uniform distribution.

   (b) Calculated $\chi^2 = 5.304$.

   From χ_6^2, critical region, > 12.592.

   At the 5% significance level there is insufficient evidence to support the claim that the data are not consistent with the exponential distribution with mean 20 000 hours

6. (a) Calculated $\chi^2 = 41.799$.

   From χ_6^2, critical region, > 12.592.

   At the 5% significance level there is some evidence to suggest that the Poisson distribution is not an adequate model for these data.

   (b) Calculated $\chi^2 = 3.492$.

   From χ_5^2, critical region, > 11.07.

   At the 5% significance level there is insufficient evidence to suggest that the Poisson distribution with mean 3 is not an adequate model for the data.

7. (a) $\bar{x} = 153.7169$, $\hat{\sigma} = 11.96012529$

   Calculated $\chi^2 = 102.151$.

   From χ_4^2, critical region, > 13.277.

   At the 1% significance level there is some evidence to suggest that a normal distribution is not an adequate model for the heights.

8.

0	1	2	3	4	5
7.6	35.1	64.8	59.8	27.6	5.1

   (a) 0.3893

   (b) 1.5228

9. (a) Calculated $\chi^2 = 4.236$.

   From χ_6^2, critical region, > 12.592.

   At the 5% significance level there is insufficient evidence to suggest that the Poisson distribution is not an adequate model for the data.

10. (a) Calculated $\chi^2 = 0.1438$.

   From χ_2^2, critical region, > 5.991.

   At the 5% significance level there is insufficient evidence to suggest that the binomial model is not an adequate model for the data.

(b) Calculated $\chi^2 = 0.4007$.

   From χ_3^2, critical region, > 7.815.

   At the 5% significance level there is insufficient evidence to suggest that the Poisson model is not an adequate model for the data.

7 ANALYSIS OF VARIANCE

Exercise 7A

1. Calculated $F = 4.48$. Critical $F_{(3, 16)} = 3.239$.

   At the 5% significance level there is some evidence to support the claim that the mean healing time is dependent upon treatment.

2. Calculated $F = 25.92$. Critical $F_{(2, 12)} = 3.885$.

   At the 5% significance level there is some evidence to support the claim that the mean lifetimes of the three brands of battery differ.

3. Calculated $F = 2.01$. Critical $F_{(2, 12)} = 3.885$.

   At the 5% significance level there is insufficient evidence to suggest that there is a difference in the mean operating times for the three brands of magnetron tubes.

4. Calculated $F = 3.07$. Critical $F_{(2, 12)} = 3.885$.

   At the 5% significance level there is insufficient evidence to support the claim that there are significant differences in the mean operating times of the three ovens.

5. Calculated $F = 12.78$. Critical $F_{(4, 14)} = 5.035$.

   At the 1% significance level there is some evidence to support the claim that the mean time spent in the intensive care unit is dependent on the hospital.

6. Calculated $F = 4.01$. Critical $F_{(4, 17)} = 2.965$.

   At the 5% significance level there is some evidence to support the claim that the mean weight gain in pigs is dependent on a particular diet.

Exercise 7B

1. For assessors, calculated $F = 4.18$.
   Critical $F_{(2, 6)} = 5.143$.

   At the 5% significance level there is insufficient evidence to suggest a difference between assessors' mean cost estimates.

2. For copper, calculated $F = 177.94$.
   Critical $F_{(3, 9)} = 3.863$.

For temperature, calculated $F = 19.13$.

Critical $F_{(3,9)} = 3.863$.

At the 5% significance level there is some evidence to support the claim that the mean amount of warping is dependent on both the copper levels and the temperature.

3. For site, calculated $F = 10.97$.

Critical $F_{(4,8)} = 7.006$.

For silkworms, calculated $F = 83.24$.

Critical $F_{(2,8)} = 8.649$.

At the 1% significance level there is some evidence to support the claim that the mean lengths of cocoon are dependent on the type of silkworm.

4. For solutions, calculated $F = 35.15$.

Critical $F_{(3,12)} = 3.490$.

At the 5% significance level there is some evidence to suggest that the retardation of bacterial growth is dependent on the solution.

For the blocking variable, calculated $F = 122.06$. Critical $F_{(4,12)} = 3.259$.

5. For training method, calculated $F = 1.212$.

Critical $F_{(3,6)} = 4.757$.

For occupation, calculated $F = 6.34$.

Critical $F_{(2,6)} = 5.143$.

At the 5% significance level there is some evidence to support the claim that the difference in mean times is explainable according to occupation.

6. For arrangement, calculated $F = 10.136$.

Critical $F_{(2,8)} = 4.459$.

For technician, calculated $F = 2.076$.

Critical $F_{(4,8)} = 3.838$.

At the 5% significance level there is some evidence to support the claim that there are no differences between technicians in their reaction times but there is a difference atrributable to the arrangements.

Miscellaneous Exercises

1. For document type, calculated $F = 6.903$.

Critical $F_{(4,12)} = 3.259$.

For people, calculated $F = 9.39$.

Critical $F_{(3,12)} = 3.490$.

At the 5% significance level there is some evidence to support the claim that differences in typing speed exist between people and between documents.

2. Calculated $F = 5.24$. Critical $F_{(2,11)} = 3.982$.

At the 5% significance level there is some evidence to support the claim that differences in the mean water content is attributable to the method of storage.

Method 3: 95% confidence interval is given by $(4.97, 6.43)$.

3. For cloths, calculated $F = 0.436$.

Critical $F_{(2,8)} = 4.459$.

For solutions, calculated $F = 9.01$.

Critical $F_{(4,8)} = 3.838$.

At the 5% significance level there is some evidence to support the claim that waterproofing is dependent on the solution strength and there is insufficient evidence to suggest that differences are attributable to using the three cloths.

4. (a) Calculated $F = 0.51$. Critical $F_{(2,9)} = 4.256$.

   At the 5% significance level there is insufficient evidence to support the claim that there are differences in the mean weight loss between tenderisers.

   (b) For tenderisers, calculated $F = 7.55$.

   Critical $F_{(2,4)} = 6.944$.

   For cooking time, calculated $F = 16.4$.

   Critical $F_{(2,4)} = 6.944$.

   At the 5% significance level there is some evidence to support the claim that there are differences in weight loss attributable to tenderisers and to cooking times.

5. Calculated $F = 0.55$. Critical $F_{(2,9)} = 4.256$.

At the 5% significance level there is insufficient evidence to suggest that the mean journey times differ according to mode of transport.

6. (a) Calculated $F = 4.512$.

   Critical $F_{(2,18)} = 3.555$.

   At the 5% significance level there is some evidence to support the claim that there are differences in the turning radius due to the springs.

   (b) For speed, calculated $F = 68.95$.

   Critical $F_{(1,5)} = 6.608$.

   At the 5% significance level there is some evidence to suggest that the turning radius is dependent on speed.

   For springs, calculated $F = 3.85$.

   Critical $F_{(2,5)} = 5.786$.

At the 5% significance level there is insufficient evidence to suggest that there is a difference in turning radius attributable to the spring type.

7. For fermenter, calculated $F = 2.88$.

Critical $F_{(3,6)} = 4.757$.

For salt type, calculated $F = 5.76$.

Critical $F_{(2,6)} = 5.143$.

At the 5% significance level there is some evidence to support the claim that the fermentation process is dependent on the type of salt.

8. For design, calculated $F = 8.89$.

Critical $F_{(7,6)} = 5.143$.

For employees, calculated $F = 50.32$.

Critical $F_{(3,6)} = 4.757$.

At the 5% significance level there is some evidence to support the claim that differences in mean assembly speeds are dependent on the design situation and on the employee.

9. Calculated $F = 15.17$. Critical $F_{(2,12)} = 6.927$.

At the 1% significance level there is some evidence to support the claim that differences in the mean milk quality is due to the method of transport.

8 STATISTICAL PROCESS CONTROL

Exercise 1A

1. (a) $\hat{\sigma} = 16.985$
   (b) Warning limits (735.1, 764.9)
       Action limits (726.5, 773.5)
       Target value 750
   (c) Warning limit 71.26
       Action limit 93.14
   (e) $\dfrac{1}{64}$

2. Warning limits for mean (12.852, 20.547)
   Action limits for mean (10.64, 22.77)
   Warning limit for standard deviation 6.528
   Action limit for standard deviation 8.942
   "Lower" warning limit for standard deviation 0.544
   "Upper" action limit for standard deviation 0.102.

3. (a) Warning limits for mean (981.39, 1018.61) $\equiv (31.39, 68.61)$ in coded data.
   (b) Action limits for mean (970.66, 1029.34) $\equiv (20.66, 79.34)$ in coded data.

   Warning limit for $\sigma = 33.4224$

   Action limit for $\sigma = 44.25$

   "Lower warning" limit for $\sigma = 5.1273$

   "Lower action" limit for $\sigma = 1.7091$.

   (c) $C_p = 1.23$

   (d) (i) 0.93;   (ii) 0.997

4. (a) $\hat{\sigma} = 5.1588$
   (b) (i) Warning limits for $\bar{x}$ (205.43, 214.57)

       Action limits for $\bar{x}$ (202.87, 217.13)

       (ii) Warning limit for $\hat{\sigma} = 8.6152$

       Action limit for $\hat{\sigma} = 11.09$

       ["Lower warning" for $\hat{\sigma} = 1.81$
       "Lower action" for $\hat{\sigma} = 0.774$]

   (e) $C_p = 0.646$

5. Warning limit (upper) ≈ 0.4453
   Action limit (upper) ≈ 0.5196

6. (a) Warning limit (upper) ≈ 0.02630 (≥ 16 or more)

   Action limit (upper) ≈ 0.3176 (≥ 19 or more)

   [Lower "warning" limit (upper) $\approx 0.074 \leq 4$.
   Lower "action" limit $\approx 0.019 \leq 1$]

9 ACCEPTANCE SAMPLING

Exercise 9A

2. (a) Required probabilities are, 0.9216, 0.5405, 0.1117 and 0.0142 respectively.
   (b) (i) 0.0001;

       (ii) $k = 25$ (to two significant figures)

       (iii) using $k = 25$, proportion not conforming = 0.124 and probability of acceptance is 0.044.

Exercise 9B

1. (i) 0.07405   (ii) 0.6030   (iii) 0.6331

2. (a) The comparable probabilities are 0.7604 and 0.7636.
   (b) 30, 32.96, 37.76, 36.83, 30 repsectively.

Miscellaneous Exercises

1. (a) Reject batch if more than two defects found in sample.

   (c) No

2. (a) Reject batch if more than 9 defects are found in sample.

   (b) (i) 0.2274   (ii) 22.97

3. Reject batch if 2 or more defects are found in sample.

4. Sample size, $n = 9$. If $\bar{x} \geq 1002.14$ accept batch, otherwise reject.

5. (a) 0.9868, 0.9235, 0.8129, 0.5371, 0.2537, 0.0982 respectively

   (i) Compare with 0.471

   (ii) Compare with 0.12148

   (b) Compare 0.0765 under first plan with 0.0748 under second plan.

   (c) Under first plan, 0.1204

   (d) 0.00691

6. (a) (i) 0.3743   (ii) 35.92

   (b) 4

   (c) 103.2 mm

   (d) Assuming independence,
   $$(1 - p_1)(1 - p_2)(1 - p_3)$$

INDEX